By WILLIAM A. EDSON
    Vacuum-Tube Oscillators

By ROBERT I. SARBACHER
    and WILLIAM A. EDSON

    Hyper and Ultrahigh
    Frequency Engineering

/

VACUUM-TUBE
OSCILLATORS

WILLIAM A. EDSON

Visiting Professor, Department of Electrical Engineering,
and Research Associate, Electronics Research Laboratory,
Stanford University

JOHN WILEY & SONS, INC., NEW YORK
CHAPMAN & HALL, LIMITED, LONDON
1953

Library of Congress Catalog Card Number: 52-13525

To
SARALOU
and
THE CHILDREN

PREFACE

At least one vacuum-tube oscillator is used in virtually every transmitter or receiver for radio, television, and radar. Oscillators are, therefore, of considerable economic as well as theoretical interest. Although they are discussed in many periodicals and books, there appears to be a genuine need for a connected discussion of the design and operation of these devices.

In this book I have attempted to present a systematic and reasonably complete treatment of the many factors which affect the behavior of vacuum-tube oscillators. The viewpoint of design is favored over that of analysis because it represents the basic purpose of engineering and because the ability to design is a priori proof of competence in analysis. It might appear that the subject is unreasonably specialized and that a lack of material would exist. Actually, just the reverse is true. The subject touches on a great variety of topics in electronics, circuit theory, and dynamics; and an extensive literature exists. In fact, the selection and the organization of this material have been the principal tasks in writing this book.

The execution of this project, which was conceived more than ten years ago, has been delayed by a number of events. Because the general understanding of the subject has been considerably advanced by many workers and because I have gained in experience, the treatment has profited considerably by the delay. Relatively little of the work here presented is original, and virtually all has been previously published. However, the material has been too scattered to be effectively available; and the viewpoints and notations used have been so divergent as to impede greatly the understanding of the work accomplished. I hope that the treatment in this book may overcome most of these difficulties by use of a uniform notation and several coordinated viewpoints developed in a logical sequence.

A clear and adequate exposition of the behavior of oscillators is the objective of my book, and mathematics has been employed freely where it is helpful. Wherever possible, relationships have been developed from fundamental considerations. In certain sections, however, the development has been omitted as impractically long or difficult, and the pertinent results are merely stated. The level of the treatment is directed toward the graduate of the usual four-year course in electrical engineering. It therefore appears that the book should be useful as a textbook for a senior or graduate course, as well as for the guidance of practicing engineers.

As far as practical, I have made the treatment of each chapter self-sufficient, so that the book may serve as a useful reference work and so that an instructor may adjust a course to the needs of his students and the time available. However, the subject is so interrelated that this objective has not been completely met; and in any event the first five chapters are needed as the basis for the following material. A reasonable familiarity with the characteristics of ordinary vacuum tubes is assumed, and little is said about this subject.

In the interest of keeping the length and cost of this book within reason it was necessary to omit much interesting and important material. Specifically, microwave oscillators are not discussed because they are already treated in several books.

A fairly extensive but by no means exhaustive bibliography is included as an aid to the worker who wishes a more detailed treatment than that offered here. I am aware that first-class work in numerous phases of this subject has been, and probably is being, done in every country of the world. However, nearly every important point has been competently discussed in English. Accordingly the bibliography contains a relatively small number of references to foreign periodicals, because language difficulties and library limitations make these unavailable to so many individuals.

The MKS system is used in all analytic work, although apparatus dimensions are sometimes given in inches and feet, in conformity to current practice. The abbreviations, symbols, network terminology, and graphical representations used conform to the Standards of the Institute of Radio Engineers. Consistent with that usage, the term phasor rather than vector is used to designate the complex quantities which represent sinusoidal voltages and currents. I have used the symbol ∞ to represent the value of by-pass condensers, and choke coils to indicate that the corresponding admittance or impedance is effectively infinite. The interpretation of schematic diagrams is considerably expedited by this notation, because attention can immediately be focused upon the elements which actually control the behavior of the system. With the same objective, I have, where practical, emphasized the frequency-controlling elements or resonator.

So many workers have contributed to the subject that it is quite impossible to make adequate acknowledgment. However, I am particularly indebted to Professor J. B. Russell of Columbia University for his constructive criticism of the manuscript. I have also been greatly aided by the works of J. R. Pierce and H. W. Bode and by discussions with my brother, J. O. Edson, all of the Bell Telephone Laboratories. Finally, I am indebted to the Georgia Institute of Technology for a policy which made it possible to do this work while there.

WILLIAM A. EDSON

Stanford, California
November, 1952

CONTENTS

SYMBOLS

Quantities which are independent of time are usually represented by capital letters. Quantities which vary with time are usually represented by small letters. Scalars are represented by light-face italic type. Phasors are represented by bold-face type.

1

INTRODUCTION

1.1 What an oscillator does

The vacuum-tube oscillator is an extremely versatile device for the production of alternating electric currents. The currents so produced are usually periodic, and often substantially sinusoidal. The useful power output and incidental losses are provided by a power input, which is ordinarily a direct current. The efficiency is commonly very low, in the order of a few per cent. In high-power applications, however, where efficiency is important it is possible to obtain values of efficiency well over 50 per cent.

The most important feature of the vacuum-tube oscillator is the great range of frequencies which may be produced. Frequencies as low as a hundredth of a cycle per second and as high as 50 billion cycles per second are now readily produced. Past experience indicates that both limits will be extended further.

In most applications a vacuum-tube oscillator serves primarily as a timing device. That is, the period or duration, T, of each cycle is of basic importance. Ordinarily this property is expressed in the inverse form as a frequency, f, in cycles per second according to the basic relationship

$$f = 1/T. \tag{1.1}$$

For purposes of analysis a related quantity, ω, is more convenient. This quantity, which is measured in radians per second, is given by the familiar equation

$$\omega = 2\pi f. \tag{1.2}$$

The quantity ω is often referred to as angular frequency, or simply as frequency when no misunderstanding is likely to occur.

In a great many applications it is important that the frequency be very nearly constant. The degree to which constant frequency is approached is referred to as frequency stability. Frequency stability

1

is ordinarily expressed by the statement that under specified conditions the frequency will not depart from a specified value by more than a certain fraction or per cent. For example, it is illegal for the carrier frequency of a commercial broadcast station to depart from its assigned value by more than 20 cycles.* The oscillator in a station whose assigned frequency is one megacycle must therefore have a frequency stability of 20 parts per million or two parts in 10^5 with respect to all causes, and for considerable intervals of time. Over a period of a few minutes the frequency of such an oscillator is likely to be constant to a few parts in 10^7. Oscillators exist which have a short-time stability of a few parts in 10^{10}.

Where the efficient generation of electric power from a prime mover is required, rotating machines such as the alternator are still the most desirable. However, the frequency range which is conveniently and efficiently generated in this way is quite limited. Frequencies of even a few kilocycles are now more efficiently generated by electronic than by machine methods.

1.2 Devices for producing oscillations

The high-vacuum tube is the only device now known for generating continuous waves at the higher frequencies, and it is the most flexible device for producing oscillations of a variety of wave forms and frequencies. High-vacuum tubes exist in a great variety of forms and employ a comparable variety of operating principles. Of these the triode is oldest and simplest, and remains one of the most useful. The tetrode has been largely superseded by the pentode, which is frequently useful in oscillators that must achieve great frequency stability or must simultaneously perform several functions.

Electrons produced by secondary emission have been employed in the dynatron and may prove to be useful in oscillators based upon electron multiplier schemes. To date, however, no form of secondary emission device has been found satisfactory in oscillator applications.

The motion of electrons in a high-vacuum tube can be controlled by means of a magnetic field instead of, or in conjunction with, electric fields. The split-anode cylindrical magnetron is an example of such a device, which, in connection with a suitable circuit, efficiently produces oscillations over a very wide band of frequencies. In the microwave magnetron, developed so intensively for military radar, the action of electric and magnetic fields is supplemented by the actual inertia or

---

* The terms cycles, kilocycles, etc., are used throughout this book as abbreviations for the longer terms cycles per second, kilocycles per second, etc. This is standard usage in the profession and is defended on the basis of expediency.

transit time of the electrons themselves. These transit-time magnetrons are highly efficient and powerful oscillators; but a particular tube is capable of operating over only a relatively narrow frequency band.

The effects of electron inertia are employed in almost all microwave oscillators. Tubes such as the klystron, which employ velocity modulation instead of magnetic fields, have been highly successful, especially as continuous wave generators at low power levels.

In addition to high-vacuum tubes there is a large and growing list of electronic devices which are useful as oscillators in certain circumstances. Of these, the gas-filled tube, such as the thyratron, is probably most important. (The oscillating arc, once widely used, is now virtually obsolete.) The transistor,[335, *] a semiconducting triode employing a germanium crystal,[20] appears very promising for the generation of oscillations in the low-power and medium-frequency region. Although they are not strictly vacuum tubes, these devices are included in the present treatment because they are closely related in operation, are useful, and in some cases serve to illustrate basic principles.

1.3 Types of oscillators

Oscillators may be divided into two broad classes, *harmonic* oscillators and *relaxation* oscillators. A majority of ordinary oscillators are harmonic oscillators, which are characterized by nearly sinusoidal wave forms and a relatively stable frequency of operation. They ordinarily employ a tuned circuit or other appropriate resonator.† Relaxation oscillators are characterized by wave forms which are markedly non-sinusoidal and by a relatively unstable frequency of operation. They usually have a period or frequency which is principally determined by a resistance-capacitance product.

Ordinarily, a particular oscillator can be readily assigned to one or the other class. In certain cases, however, the identification is not clear, because the performance and circuit configuration of the two classes merge smoothly together. In such cases the identification is best made in terms of the roots associated with the differential equation which describes the system.

Harmonic oscillators may be further classified as *linear* and *nonlinear*. Linear oscillators have the important property that all

---

* For all numbered references see the bibliography at the end of the book.

† The term resonator is used in a broad sense to include devices which have one or more natural frequencies. Tuned circuits of inductance and capacitance, sections of transmission lines, microwave cavity resonators, and piezoelectric crystals are important examples of electrical resonators.

voltages and currents in the oscillating circuit are very nearly sinusoidal. Such oscillators are desirable because the output is virtually free from harmonics and because the frequency of operation is quite stable. The mathematical analysis of linear oscillators is much simpler than that of nonlinear oscillators. Accordingly the study of such oscillators is an aid to understanding the more complex behavior of nonlinear systems.

The distinction between linear and nonlinear oscillators is not sharp. It will be shown that no oscillator can be absolutely linear; accordingly, the distinction is one of degree rather than of kind. In this book the term linear will be reserved for systems which are specifically designed to reduce harmonics; all other systems will be classed as nonlinear. Most practical oscillators are harmonic but nonlinear.

It is convenient to distinguish between *two-terminal* or *negative resistance* and *four-terminal* or *feedback* oscillators. Two-terminal oscillators are identified with electronic devices which produce a dynamic negative resistance between two accessible terminals. In a four-terminal oscillator the electronic device has three or more accessible terminals. Such a system may be drawn as an amplifier with its output connected to its input, as suggested by the term feedback.

Oscillators may also be classified on several other bases, including the frequency of operation, the circuit configuration, the type of electronic device used, and the type of resonator. These classifications are often convenient but are evidently not fundamental.

1.4 Fundamental principles of harmonic oscillators

A harmonic oscillator comprises two fundamental elements, the resonator and the driving system. To these a third element, the useful load system, is usually added. Because an actual oscillator consists of a number of components, a question of identifying components with functions arises. In general the resonator is readily identified. The remaining components, specifically including the electronic device, are identified with the driving system except for those which are assignable to a useful load. In most cases this identification is relatively straightforward.

In oscillators which must produce a very stable frequency the resonator must have a natural frequency which is sensibly constant with respect to temperature, the passage of time, etc. It is further necessary that the driving system and useful load shall not appreciably affect this frequency. The latter is facilitated if the resonator has inherently low losses or high selectivity, Q, and if the load absorbs very little power.

In oscillators such as those used in induction heating the efficiency of power conversion is of principal importance. In such devices the driving system and load must be so matched that a large fraction of the power supplied as direct current is delivered as alternating current in the load. The resonator function is now secondary and serves only to exercise reasonable control over the frequency. A large value of Q is still desirable, because it facilitates frequency control with a minimum loss of power. Great stability with respect to temperature, etc., is rarely needed in such apparatus.

1.5 Amplifier viewpoint

Many problems in connection with the behavior of oscillators are best treated by thinking of the system as a modified amplifier. A basic property of any amplifier is that the power output is greater than the

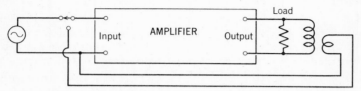

Fig. 1.1.   Oscillator represented as a self-energized amplifier.

input. Accordingly, it appears that we could obtain a considerable power output in the absence of any separately supplied input by substituting a suitable fraction of the output for this separate input. The situation is illustrated in Fig. 1.1.

This concept is fundamentally correct and, when suitably elaborated, is extremely useful. In the first place, it immediately points out that this sort of oscillator is representable as a closed ring, around which a signal is transmitted in one direction. Many of the difficulties in the study of oscillators arise from the fact that such a ring has no beginning or no end.

Most amplifiers have the property that the power output exceeds the power input over a considerable band of frequencies. Accordingly, this concept, based upon conservation of energy, is inadequate to account for the frequency of an oscillator, for it would suggest that a desired output frequency could be obtained by supplying and later removing it.

The situation is clarified by noting that the signal which is returned from the output to replace the original input must be of the correct phase as well as magnitude. In practical systems the phase varies rather rapidly with frequency. Therefore, a given system satisfies both phase and amplitude conditions at only one frequency (or occasionally several discrete frequencies). Subject to certain other restrictions which will be developed in later chapters, stable oscillations will occur at the frequency for which the returned signal is equal to and in phase with the original signal. The amplifier viewpoint is presented very lucidly by Horton.[144]

1.6 Functional diagram

The analysis of a feedback harmonic oscillator is extended and facilitated by the block diagram of Fig. 1.2. In this diagram the driving system has been further divided into an amplifier and a limiter. This division is desirable because it emphasizes two important properties which the driving system must have. It must be an amplifier or the

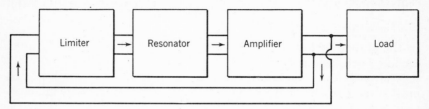

Fig. 1.2.   Functional diagram of feedback oscillator.

losses inherent in the other functions will bring the system to rest; and its amplification must decrease as the level of oscillation increases or the system will never reach an equilibrium. The four functions are basic, but the order in which they are performed is different in different practical systems.

In Fig. 1.2 the amplifier is assumed to be ideal in that its phase shift is zero and its amplification is independent of the frequency and level of the signal. The resonator is assumed to be linear and to have some definite natural frequency, with suitable associated variation of attenuation and phase shift with respect to frequency. (An ordinary bandpass filter has such properties.) The load is a simple linear impedance. The limiter is assumed to have zero phase shift and to have at all frequencies a loss which increases with increase of the voltage supplied to it. Although the limiter is fundamentally nonlinear, its losses may change so slowly with time that it produces little distortion of the wave which it transmits.

In most oscillators the vacuum tube functions both as amplifier and as limiter. The operation is substantially the same as that of a class C amplifier, so adjusted that the output is almost independent of the input. Such operation is characterized by relatively large harmonic currents. The resonator, in this case a simple tuned circuit or tank, discriminates against the harmonics so that the voltages are nearly sinusoidal.

In one class of linear oscillators the limiting action is produced by one or more thermally sensitive resistors called thermistors. A small tungsten-filament lamp is suitable for such application. In these circuits the lamp resistance, and hence the circuit loss, is a function of the effective current, as required for limiting. However, the thermal inertia of the filament is such that the resistance is almost constant over any one cycle so that little distortion of the wave form results.

In another class of linear oscillators the limiting action is provided by a slowly varying bias applied to a suitable electrode of the tube, as in an amplifier with automatic output control. A proper choice of elements and biases leads to adequate limiter action without distortion.

1.7 Equilibrium conditions

In the system of Fig. 1.2 it is clear that equilibrium can exist only if certain relationships exist between the gains and phase shifts of the several sections. The loss of the limiter plus the loss of the resonator must equal the gain of the amplifier, or the wave will change in amplitude until this condition is met. Similarly, the phase shift in the resonator must be zero since the limiter and amplifier have already been assumed to have zero phase shift. The frequency of operation will automatically adjust itself to meet this condition. The dual condition of zero net gain and zero phase shift is known as Barkhausen's condition for oscillation.

1.8 The negative resistance viewpoint

It is well known that a system of inductances and capacitances can oscillate if given an initial shock. However, in a passive system such oscillations rapidly disappear or decay with the passage of time because of the resistance which is present in all coils and to a lesser degree in all condensers. It is clear that this decay could be avoided if the positive resistance of the coil and condenser could be canceled by addition of a suitable negative resistance. This principle is employed in negative resistance oscillators, such as the dynatron, which use a type of vacuum tube approximating a single negative resistance to annul the losses of an associated coil and condenser and so produce continuous oscillations.

The negative resistance viewpoint is convenient in the mathematical study of oscillatory systems because the equation which describes the behavior of a resistance, positive or negative, is so simple. It is necessary to have this viewpoint in the study of all oscillators which are not representable as amplifiers. This includes all oscillators which employ true two-terminal negative resistance devices. Moreover, it is possible to have this viewpoint in the study of all types of oscillators, even those which are also representable as amplifiers.

A very simple negative resistance oscillator is represented by Fig. 1.3, which shows a passive series resonant circuit represented as L, R, and C in conjunction with a negative resistance device designated ρ. Any slight disturbance in the system, such as the closing of a switch or the thermal agitation of electrons in the conductors, will lead to oscillations which increase with time, provided ρ is negative and greater than R.

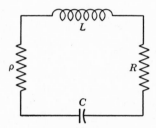

FIG. 1.3.   Oscillatory circuit.

Such a system will produce useful results only if the oscillations build up to and remain at some stable amplitude. As in the four-terminal oscillator already discussed, equilibrium can result from the action of nonlinearity. In the present example this limiting action must take place in the negative-resistance device. Moreover, it is clear that the effective negative resistance must become *smaller* as the level of oscillation increases if stable oscillation is to result. The property of negative resistance is possessed by the arc and other *current-controlled* negative-resistance devices. More is said of this matter in the chapters which follow.

1.9 The clock analogy

It has already been mentioned that the period or frequency of an oscillator is one of its most important properties. Therefore, an oscillator needs only the addition of a cycle-counting device to be a timekeeper. Briefly, an oscillator is the electronic counterpart of a mechanical clock. Moreover, an electronic clock employing a specially treated quartz plate as an electromechanical resonator in a suitable oscillator is, over a period of weeks, a better timekeeper than any mechanical clock.

It is profitable and enlightening to compare oscillators with clocks because the operation of a mechanical device is more familiar and is much more readily observed.   Furthermore, mechanical timekeepers have been carried to a very high state of development by the work of many skilled investigators over a period of more than two hundred years.

The heart of a mechanical timekeeper is the pendulum or balance wheel, which corresponds to the resonator in its electrical counterpart. Every effort is made to see that the period is constant, independent of aging, temperature, barometric pressure, etc.   In portable devices, such as watches and chronometers, where the restoring force must be provided by a spring, the balance wheel is used.   Greater accuracy is provided by the pendulum, whose period depends upon the length and the constant of gravity.   Maintaining the pendulum and associated parts at constant temperature ensures that the length is constant. Evacuating the system greatly reduces the energy loss of the swinging pendulum, and ensures that the operation will be independent of atmospheric pressure and humidity.

The driving system of a mechanical timekeeper also corresponds closely to that of an electrical oscillator.   In clocks, a constant prime driving force is provided by weights, which correspond to the B supply. Energy is delivered from the primary source to the resonator at appropriate intervals by means of the escapement or its analogue, the vacuum tube.

In both systems a counting mechanism must be added to indicate the total number of cycles which the resonator describes.   In mechanical systems this is conveniently incorporated in the gear train, which transforms the great force and short travel of the source into the delicate force over a great total distance required at the escapement. In electronic clocks the desired result must be achieved in a more complicated way, because the total charge drawn from the B battery is not a satisfactory measure of the number of cycles.   Moreover, since the period of electric oscillators is ordinarily very short compared to that of mechanical clocks, the counting process is substantially more difficult.   The customary procedure is to divide the frequency, that is, take groups of cycles, by successive small integral factors until the frequency is low enough to operate the synchronous motor of an ordinary type of electric clock, which in turn employs gears for the final reduction.

It has long been known that the period of a pendulum is not affected if a large force is applied for a very short interval when the pendulum is at the center of its swing.   Clock escapements are adjusted to meet this condition, which is known as Airy's* criterion, as nearly as possible. Moreover, in the most refined form of mechanical clocks (Shortt clocks) energy is supplied to the pendulum only once during thirty complete cycles.

It is seen that the escapement corresponds to extreme class C operation in an electrical oscillator. Careful consideration of the factors involved shows that the desired condition in the electrical case is for the pulse of plate current to flow at the instant when the alternating voltage is a maximum and the circulating current in the antiresonant circuit is zero.

It is worth noting that the tubes of the Meacham oscillator, most stable known timekeeper, operate in class A. Energy is thus delivered to the resonator smoothly throughout each cycle. No mechanism is known for achieving the mechanical analogue of this operation, but it is interesting to speculate upon the performance which might be achieved in this way.

Mention should also be made of the electronic system popularly referred to as the atomic clock. In this system a vacuum-tube oscillator has its frequency controlled by means of the molecular resonance of ammonia gas, which is maintained at reduced pressure in a wave guide system. The important property of this device is that resonant frequencies of this sort appear to be constants of nature, not subject to aging, and substantially independent of parasitic effects, such as temperature, pressure, and magnetic fields. Accordingly it appears that an absolute and highly accurate standard of time is within reach.

Although the atomic clock in its present form is extremely complicated and difficult to maintain, it appears that a reasonable amount of development should lead to a workable and reliable system. In conjunction with standards of length based upon spectral lines in the visible region it should offer a substantial improvement in the standards basic to all physical measurements.

1.10 Amplitude stability[4]

Ordinarily we wish an oscillator to deliver a wave of constant amplitude, frequency, and wave shape. Since all physical oscillators depart to some extent from this ideal, it is desirable to establish a measure of this departure for comparing the desirability of alternative oscillators.

The extent to which an oscillator approaches constancy of output in the face of various disturbances is referred to as *amplitude stability*. Ordinarily, the factors which influence the output amplitude are applied voltages, ambient temperature, tube condition, load imped-

* After Sir George Airy, who stated this principle in 1827.

ance, and assorted network parameters. In most practical oscillators the output is nearly proportional to one of the applied voltages, and is nearly independent of other parameters. In other oscillators the output depends upon the resistance of, and hence the temperature of, a thermally sensitive resistor. In these oscillators the output depends upon the ambient temperature and to a small extent upon other factors.

The equation which will be taken as defining amplitude stability, S_A, is

$$S_A = \frac{du/u}{dA/A},$$ (1.3)

where A represents the amplitude of oscillation, expressible in voltage or current at the output or other point, and u represents a circuit parameter or applied voltage. On this basis a large value of S_A for a specified du corresponds to a small value of dA and therefore represents the desirable situation of a high degree of stability.

1.11 Frequency stability

Most oscillator applications require only a very moderate degree of amplitude stability. The frequency requirement, on the other hand, is usually exacting and is often extremely severe. In fact, the search for frequency stability represents a great proportion of all the work which has gone into the development of vacuum-tube oscillators.

Virtually every parameter of the system has some effect on the operating frequency of an oscillator. In general, however, the frequency is principally controlled by a resonator or phase controlling unit, and depends only slightly upon other influences. It is therefore appropriate to define frequency stability, S_F, in terms of Fig. 1.2 by the equation

$$S_F = \frac{d\phi}{d\omega/\omega_0},$$ (1.4)

where ω_0 is the natural frequency, and $d\omega$ is the frequency change produced by a change of phase shift, $d\phi$, external to the resonator.

From this definition it is clear that frequency is referred to the natural frequency of the resonator, which is inferred to be absolutely stable. Accordingly, eq. 1.4 serves to measure the frequency stability of elements external to the resonator, that is, of the driving system. Changes in the natural frequency of the resonator are conveniently expressed by simple derivatives, such as

$$S_T = d\omega_0/dT,$$ (1.5)

where S_T represents the frequency coefficient of the resonator with respect to the ambient temperature T.

PROBLEMS

1.1. Which of the following have the general properties of an oscillator: (a) A vacuum windshield wiper, (b) a buzzer, (c) a gas turbine, (d) a V_1 "buzz bomb," (e) an air compressor, (f) a hydraulic ram, (g) an air hammer, (h) a steam whistle?

1.2. Of the above "oscillators," which are relaxation in character, which harmonic?

1.3. What basic condition must exist in a harmonic oscillator? Explain.

1.4. From the amplifier viewpoint, how must the gain vary with signal level if oscillations are to build up smoothly to a stable amplitude from some small disturbance? If stable oscillations result only from a large initial shock?

2

TRANSIENT BEHAVIOR OF
LINEAR SYSTEMS

This chapter is devoted to a review of the transient behavior of several simple linear systems; the inclusion of such familiar material is justified by the fact that it forms the foundation of several later sections. Particularly interesting, and perhaps less well understood, are the responses found when certain of the circuit elements take on negative values. The concept of a complex frequency is formulated and discussed; and suitable notations are introduced, to be extended and developed in subsequent chapters. Readers who wish additional information on the subject of transients, particularly the physical interpretation, are referred to the paper by Dudley.[79]

2.1 Resistance and capacitance

The simplest possible transient occurs when an initially charged condenser is allowed to discharge through a pure resistor. It is well known[179] that the charge q remaining in the condenser at any time t after the circuit is closed is represented by

$$q = q_0 e^{-t/RC}, \tag{2.1}$$

where q_0 is the initial charge, R is the resistance, and C is the capacitance of the circuit. This result evidently applies only for positive values of t because, prior to closing the circuit, $q = q_0$ by definition. One is ordinarily concerned only with positive values of R and C; however, eq. 2.1 is not so restricted, and it is instructive to plot it for positive and negative values of both R and t.

It will be noted from Fig. 2.1 that the graphs of q/q_0 versus t are symmetrical and that they extend smoothly into negative values of time. This feature corresponds to the physical fact that the circuit behavior at positive values of time would have been unaltered had the initial charge q_0 been appropriately changed and the switch closed at an earlier instant.

Inspection of eq. 2.1 shows that the charge will increase with positive increase of time if either (but not both) R or C is negative. Moreover, the behavior at negative values of t with both circuit elements positive is exactly the same as that at positive values of t with the resistive element negative. In this and subsequent discussions, emphasis is placed on negative values of R but not on negative values of C or L, since the latter do not appear in the physical systems of interest

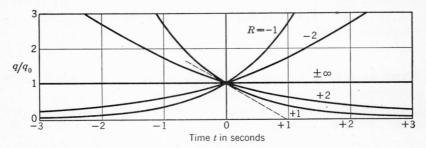

Fɪɢ. 2.1.   Variation of charge in resistance-capacitance circuit ($C = 1$).

and because equivalent results may be secured by use of positive reactances in conjunction with negative resistances, as proved by Verman,[332] and by Bode[34] on page 187 of his book.

2.2 Resistance, inductance, and capacitance

The resistance-capacitance system considered in Section 2.1 may be generalized by adding an inductance either in series or in parallel.

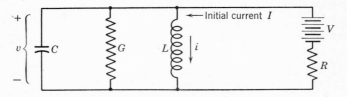

Fɪɢ. 2.2.   Parallel form of circuit.

The parallel form of connection is chosen in preference to the series arrangement because of closer conformity to actual oscillator systems.

The circuit of Fig. 2.2 is the dual* or inverse of the series RLC circuit treated in nearly every textbook on transients. Provided the switch has been closed for a long time, a current $I = V/R$ will be flowing

---

* The reader who is unfamiliar with the principle of duality is referred to Gardner and Barnes,[109] page 46, or Bode,[34] page 196. Useful related ideas are presented by Selgin.[277]

through the coil L, which is assumed to have zero resistance. On this basis, no voltage exists across C and G until the switch is opened.

At the instant $t = 0$ the switch is opened, and a transient is initiated. Following conventional methods of transient analysis, one may show that the current i at any later time is represented by the differential equation

$$LC \frac{d^2i}{dt^2} + GL \frac{di}{dt} + i = 0, \tag{2.2}$$

which has a solution of the form

$$i = K_1 e^{p_1 t} + K_2 e^{p_2 t}, \tag{2.3}$$

where K_1 and K_2 are constants which may be determined from the initial conditions,

$$p_1 = \alpha + j\omega, \tag{2.4}$$

and

$$p_2 = \alpha - j\omega. \tag{2.5}$$

Substitution of the network parameters yields

$$\alpha = -G/2C, \tag{2.6}$$

$$\omega_0 = \sqrt{1/LC}, \tag{2.7}$$

and

$$\omega = \sqrt{\frac{1}{LC} - \frac{G^2}{4C^2}} = \frac{\beta}{j}. \tag{2.8}$$

The quantities p_1 and p_2 are the roots of the algebraic auxiliary equation which has the same coefficients as eq. 2.2, the differential equation of the system. The real component, α, is called the decrement or damping factor; it expresses the rate at which the transient current increases or decreases with time. Because the transients in passive systems always decrease with time, α is negative in such systems. The imaginary component, ω, exists only if the conductance is sufficiently small; it represents the natural angular velocity or frequency of the system, and is reduced to ω_0, the undamped natural frequency if $G = 0$.

If the conductance is sufficiently small, that is,

$$G < 2\sqrt{C/L}, \tag{2.9}$$

the circuit is *oscillatory* or *underdamped*, and the current may be written

$$i = Ie^{-\alpha t}[\cos \omega t + (\alpha/\omega) \sin \omega t]. \tag{2.10}$$

If the conductance is large, corresponding to

$$G > 2 \sqrt{C/L}, \tag{2.11}$$

the circuit is *overdamped*, and the current is more conveniently represented by

$$i = Ie^{-\alpha t}[\cosh \beta t + (\alpha/\beta) \sinh \beta t]. \tag{2.12}$$

Finally, in the case of *critical damping* when

$$G = 2 \sqrt{C/L}, \tag{2.13}$$

the current is most readily calculated from the expression

$$i = Ie^{-\alpha t}[1 + \alpha t]. \tag{2.14}$$

The relationships represented by eqs. 2.10, 2.12, and 2.14 are most conveniently examined by letting $L = C = 1$, so that critical damping corresponds to $G = 2$. The behavior which results when G is assigned typical positive and negative values is shown in Fig. 2.3. As in Fig. 2.1, the extrapolation to negative values of time is interpreted as the behavior which *would have occurred* had the transient begun earlier and from different initial conditions. Moreover, the symmetry of the diagram is such that the value of i is unaffected if the signs of G and t are both reversed.

In the present connection, critical damping means that the current in the coil is extinguished at the most rapid possible rate. However, it should be noted that the common voltage v may be extinguished at an arbitrarily rapid rate by making G sufficiently *large*, and that a large value of G provides the most effective damping if the transient results from an initial charge in C rather than a current in L. Therefore, it is necessary to qualify the familiar statement that the critical damping resistance is one which brings a system to rest in the shortest possible time.

By analogy with the statement that the current in L is extinguished at the maximum possible rate by setting $G = 2$, one might anticipate that the current in the coil would increase at the greatest possible rate if $G = -2$. *This is not correct.* Corresponding to any fixed positive value of t, the values of both i and v can be made arbitrarily large by making the negative conductance sufficiently large. This behavior, which may be anticipated by inspection of the negative time extrapolation of passive systems, is explainable on both physical and mathematical bases.

From the physical standpoint, the condenser and negative conductance form an unstable combination (with time constant inversely

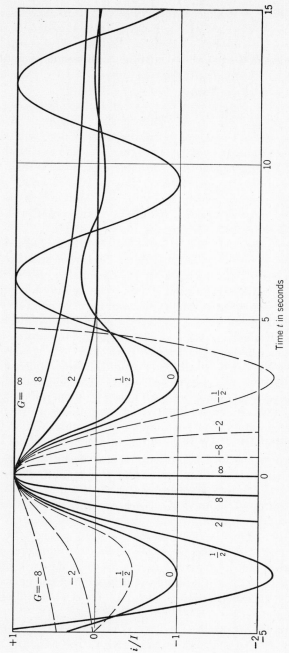

FIG. 2.3.   Variation of current in inductor of parallel *GCL* circuit ($L = 1$, $C = 1$).

proportional to G), initially held at rest by the low impedance of the external circuit. When the switch is opened, the unstable combination is released and is excited by the coil current. The resulting rapid increase of voltage across the condenser and negative conductance then overwhelms the coil, causing the current i to reverse and then rapidly increase without limit.

The mathematical viewpoint turns attention to the roots p_1 and p_2 of the algebraic auxiliary to the differential equation. When these roots are negative and real, the behavior of the network is ultimately governed by the smaller root because this root is associated with the more slowly decaying current or voltage. For positive real values of the roots (produced by negative G) the reverse is true. Here the behavior is governed primarily by the larger root, which corresponds to the more rapidly increasing quantity. This point will be made increasingly clear in the following section.

The curves of Fig. 2.3, like those of Fig. 2.1, have been plotted for negative as well as positive values of time. It is seen that the behavior for t less than zero is quite simple for the oscillatory cases, whether of the expanding or the contracting form. The behavior of nonoscillatory systems is somewhat more complex and requires careful treatment.

In all cases the behavior at positive values of time would be exactly duplicated by closing the switch at some negative instant provided the charge on C and the current through L at that instant were suitably chosen. However, for nonoscillatory conditions the required modification of the initial conditions is very great. Under all conditions the value of i is unaffected in eqs. 2.10, 2.12, and 2.14 when both α and t are reversed in sign.

2.3 Variation of the p roots

The system roots, p_1 and p_2, are important because they furnish a very good index to the behavior of the corresponding system. To

TABLE 2.1

p-Roots of GCL Equation for $L = C = 1$

Reference Point	G	p_1	p_2
1	∞	$-\infty + j0$	$0 + j0$
2	8	$-7.85 + j0$	$-0.15 + j0$
3	2	$-1 + j0$	$-1 + j0$
4	$\frac{1}{2}$	$-0.25 + j0.968$	$-0.25 - j0.968$
5	0	$0 + j1$	$0 - j1$
6	$-\frac{1}{2}$	$+0.25 + j0.968$	$+0.25 - j0.968$
7	-2	$+1 + j0$	$+1 + j0$
8	-8	$+0.15 + j0$	$+7.85 + j0$
9	$-\infty$	$0 + j0$	$+\infty + j0$

illustrate this point, the loci of p_1 and p_2 are plotted in Fig. 2.4, where the arrowheads indicate increasing G, and the circle has unit diameter because $C = L = 1$. To clarify the relation between the roots and the system behavior a number of points from Figs. 2.3 and 2.4 are given in Table 2.1. The nature of this relationship is further clarified by Table 2.2.

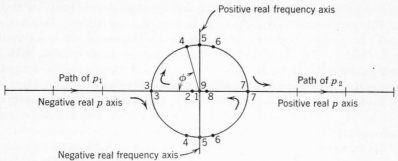

FIG. 2.4.   Variation of the p-roots in the complex plane as G is varied.

The four divisions of Table 2.2 include all simple oscillatory systems, electrical or otherwise. Regions I and II, passive systems, have been extensively studied and are not of principal interest here. Region

TABLE 2.2

RELATIONSHIP BETWEEN p-ROOTS AND GCL SYSTEM BEHAVIOR

Region No.	I	II	III	IV
Wave Form	Nonoscillatory decaying	Oscillatory decaying	Oscillatory expanding	Nonoscillatory expanding
ω	Imaginary	Real	Real	Imaginary
β	Real	Imaginary	Imaginary	Real
System Type	Passive		Active	
α	Negative		Positive	

III covers systems which generate expanding sine waves. It is therefore identified with *harmonic oscillators*, as discussed in Chapter 1, and serves to define the limits of that class.*   Region IV includes

* It will be recalled that the action of the limiter in physical systems serves to alter the average conductance as the level of oscillation increases, thereby avoiding the absurdity of unlimited amplitude. This consideration applies also to the nonoscillatory active systems of region IV.

systems which generate a nonreversing exponentially increasing wave. Such systems—characterized by the fact that the p-roots are (pure) real and positive—are known as *relaxation oscillators*.

2.4 Decrement and selectivity

At this juncture it is desirable to define and correlate a number of useful terms which apply to oscillatory or resonant systems.   Some of these definitions pertain to the free oscillation of a system and are most readily expressed in terms of the transient behavior.   Others apply to forced oscillations—that is, the a-c-steady state—and are best expressed in those terms.

Damping Factor or Time Decrement.   The quantity α, defined by eq. 2.6 and governing the time rate of change of amplitude in eq. 2.10, is known as the *damping factor*.   Evidently, in one second the system coordinate (current, voltage, etc.) will increase or decrease in amplitude by the factor

$$i_1/i_0 = e^{\alpha} \quad \text{or} \quad \alpha = \ln\,(i_1/i_0). \tag{2.15}$$

Since the natural logarithm of the ratio of two associated quantities is by definition their level difference in nepers, the time decrement α has the dimensions of *nepers per second*.

Logarithmic or Cyclic Decrement.   In many applications of oscillatory waves the decay per second is less important than that *per cycle*, which is represented by the *logarithmic decrement*

$$\delta = \ln\,(i_n/i_{n+1}) \text{ nepers per cycle}, \tag{2.16}$$

where i_n and i_{n+1} are the amplitudes of any two successive cycles. Because there are f cycles per second we see that

$$-\alpha = f\delta \text{ nepers per second}. \tag{2.17}$$

Selectivity or Quality Factor.   The selectivity Q of an oscillatory or resonant system is a widely used and important index of circuit behavior.   Because the loss in available condensers is much lower than that in available coils, there is a marked tendency to associate a quality factor with individual circuit elements—especially coils. In a strict sense, however, Q is a property of the complete resonant system.   Several definitions of Q are in general use.   All are equivalent when correctly applied, even in connection with heavily damped systems.   The following paragraphs are devoted to a comparison of these definitions.

A definition of Q, applicable to any simple oscillatory system, and particularly convenient in connection with cavity and electromechanical resonators, is

$$Q = 2\pi \frac{\text{Total energy stored in the system}}{\text{Energy lost per cycle from the system}}. \qquad (2.18)$$

Because Q is a constant, characteristic of the system, it is necessary that the energy losses and storage decrease similarly with time. In low-Q systems the rate of energy loss is not uniform, and the loss per cycle is comparable to the total stored energy. Nevertheless, as may be shown by direct integration, eq. 2.18 is applicable provided the numerator is taken as the *average* of the energy stored during the period of one full cycle.

The selectivity parameter Q is also useful in describing the steady-state behavior of a system. Under steady-state conditions the energy loss is supplied by an external source, and eq. 2.18 is applicable provided the denominator is interpreted as the energy supplied. Applying this definition to Fig. 2.2, we have

$$Q = 2\pi \frac{CV^2}{GV^2/f} = \omega C/G, \qquad (2.19)$$

where V is interpreted as the rms voltage and Q is assumed to be high. This expression is the dual of the familiar $\omega L/R$ of the series-tuned circuit. It is readily shown that Q as given by eq. 2.19 represents the ratio of the antiresonant natural frequency, ω_0, to the difference between the two frequencies at which the phase angle of admittance becomes $45°$.

Substituting eq. 2.6 to eliminate C/G yields the useful expression, which is correct for all values of Q and types of systems,

$$Q = -\omega/2\alpha. \qquad (2.20)$$

This definition is interpreted in Fig. 2.4, where the angle ϕ between the horizontal axis and one of the conjugate roots is

$$\phi = \tan^{-1}(-\omega/\alpha). \qquad (2.21)$$

In these terms

$$Q = \tfrac{1}{2} \tan \phi. \qquad (2.22)$$

Finally, the damping factor α may be eliminated between eqs. 2.17 and 2.20 to yield the useful relation

$$Q = (\omega/2f\delta) = \pi/\delta. \qquad (2.23)$$

Consistent with accepted conventions, the selectivity Q and the logarithmic decrement δ of a passive circuit are taken as positive, whereas the damping factor α is negative.   Conversely, Q is negative when α is positive.

2.5 Degrees of freedom

The number of degrees of freedom of a system—electrical, mechanical, or otherwise—is equal to the *least* number of variables which will uniquely specify the behavior of the system.[160] For example, knowledge of the charge as a function of time in any single-mesh electrical circuit permits specification of all currents, voltages, energies, and powers.   Therefore, any single-mesh[280] electrical system has a single degree of freedom, because its complete behavior can be described in terms of a single variable or coordinate.   Similarly, the behavior of a group of electrical elements connected in parallel between two junction points or *nodes*[124] is completely specified by the potential difference between these nodes as a function of time; therefore, such a parallel group possesses but a single degree of freedom.

In more complicated circuits the number of degrees of freedom is not immediately evident because it is necessary to use the *least* number of variables which will completely describe the system.   The conventional Kirchhoff equations, and the related mesh and nodal equations, ordinarily involve a number of equations and variables considerably in excess of the minimum.   Therefore, a comparison of the results obtained by the various methods of analysis becomes requisite in order to select the appropriate minimum number.   Fortunately, this requirement seldom presents serious difficulty in the study of oscillators.

2.6 Order of the differential equation

In general, the transient behavior of a system of any sort may be described by a set of differential equations, subject to the initial and boundary conditions corresponding to the original disturbance.   The minimum required number of these differential equations must evidently be equal to the number of degrees of freedom of the system, to conform with the definition given in the preceding section.

In a single-mesh system there can be at most a single equivalent inductance and a single equivalent capacitance; and in a system of n independent meshes there can be at most n distinct equivalent inductances and n equivalent capacitances.   In the single-mesh case it is clear, and in the n-mesh case it can readily be shown, that the order of each of the n differential equations which describe the behavior of the system cannot be greater than $2n$.

Starting from a single-mesh circuit, it is easy to see that the addition of a single distinct nonreducible inductance or capacitance increases by one the number of initial conditions which must be specified; hence the order of the differential equations must also increase by one. Repetition of this process shows that the order of each of the differential equations is equal to the total number of distinct inductances and capacitances present in the network. (For the present purposes, the effect of mutual inductance in physical transformers is most conveniently included by use of the equivalent T or Π configuration.)

The foregoing ideas are illustrated in Fig. 2.5, which shows a four-mesh circuit containing six reactive elements. This system evidently requires a differential equation of the sixth order to describe any of its currents or voltages. But there can be no more than four degrees of freedom, because the four mesh currents shown are sufficient to specify

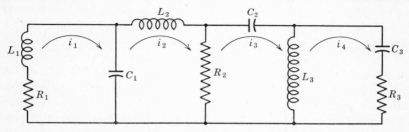

FIG. 2.5. Four-mesh, ladder-type network.

completely the behavior of the system. We might be led to the incorrect conclusion that the system requires a differential equation of the eighth order $(2n)$ from the fact that each of the meshes drawn contains both inductance and capacitance. However, it is possible to draw four independent meshes of which two involve only one type of reactance, so that the number six is correct in the present case.

Regardless of which of the currents (or voltages) is solved for, the same differential equation will be obtained. The auxiliary algebraic equation will be of the sixth degree and will have as solutions the six p-roots, which describe the properties of the system.

2.7 Modes of oscillation or motion

If an electrical (or mechanical) system is free from resistance (or friction) an initial direct or oscillating current continues undiminished with the passage of time. Such systems are sufficiently well approximated in practice by low-loss circuits that the results obtained from the idealized system are useful.

The basic idea of modes of oscillation is illustrated in Fig. 2.6. Foster's reactance theorem[101] indicates that there are two frequencies at

which an externally applied generator produces no line current.   One
of these is sufficiently lower than the natural frequency of L_2 and C_2 so
that the net inductive susceptance of the L_1C_1 combination equals the
capacitive susceptance of L_2C_2; the other is sufficiently higher than
the natural frequency of L_2 and C_2 to produce the converse effect.
If the free circuit is set into oscillation at either of these frequencies
there will be a unique relationship between the magnitude and phase
of the currents and voltages in various elements.   This combination
of effects is referred to as a *mode of oscillation*.   Because the system is
linear the two modes are independent and have no interaction.   However, if both modes are simultaneously excited the currents and voltages in the several elements will contain both frequencies superimposed, and beat effects will appear.   Thus the total energy of the
system may be transferred back and forth between the elements or
meshes, as shown by Howe.[145]

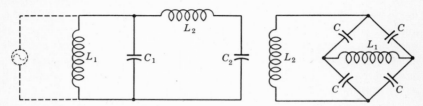

FIG. 2.6.   Two-mesh loss-free circuit.   FIG. 2.7.   Bridge circuit.

An additional useful idea is conveyed by Fig. 2.7, which represents
a bridge circuit of equal capacitances.   Under these circumstances
the elements L_1 and L_2 are *conjugate* because current flowing in one
produces no current in the other.   This system has two natural frequencies or modes of vibration which are *normal* or *orthogonal* in that
current can exist in L_1 without producing current in L_2, and vice
versa.

The concept of *normal modes* is particularly important in cavity and
quartz crystal resonators.   In these devices the term mode is used to
designate a particular pattern of electromagnetic fields or mechanical
motions in space.   Such modes are *normal* provided the existence of
one does not tend to excite the other.   Following Sokolnikoff,[291]
page 81, modes designated m and n are orthogonal provided that

$$\iiint U_m U_n \, dv = 0, \tag{2.24}$$

where U_m and U_n are functions which represent the field or motion;
and the integral is carried out throughout the volume of the resonator.
In simple symmetrical cavities all modes are normal.   In quartz

crystal resonators, however, modes are often *coupled* and therefore are not normal owing to the nature of the boundaries and the crystalline properties of the material.

Consistent with this concept, each distinct mode of oscillation has a distinct value of Q, most easily expressed in terms of the angular location of the p-roots. However, when coupling is present there is an interchange of energy accompanied by beats which make it difficult or impossible to apply any concept of Q. Normal modes are, by definition, free from this difficulty and therefore have uniquely defined values of Q. This is a very convenient and important property.

Because the order of the differential equation is equal to the number of independent reactive elements in an electric circuit, and because the number of modes of oscillation is equal to the number of pairs of reactive elements, it follows that the number of modes is equal to half the order of the equation, neglecting fractional remainders.

In many circuits resistance plays an important part and cannot be neglected. To such circuits the concept of modes of oscillation is greatly complicated by the fact that the number of complex roots may be considerably smaller than the number of independent reactive elements. Although we may still associate a mode of oscillation with each pair of conjugate roots, the mode concept rapidly becomes less exact and less useful as Q decreases.

2.8 A system with three p-roots

As shown by the foregoing discussion, an electrical system which contains three nonreducible reactive elements has an associated algebraic

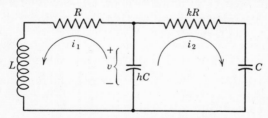

Fig. 2.8. Two-mesh dissipative circuit.

equation with three separate roots. No restriction exists as to whether reactive elements are inductive or capacitive. A simple system of this kind, which is capable of a very close physical approximation, is illustrated in Fig. 2.8. The equations which describe the transient behavior are conveniently written in terms of the differentiating operator

$$p \equiv d/dt. \qquad (2.25)$$

In this notation we have

$$v = (R + pL)i_1,\qquad(2.26)$$

$$v = (kR + 1/pC)i_2,\qquad(2.27)$$

and

$$i_1 + i_2 + (phC)v = 0.\qquad(2.28)$$

Elimination of the currents leads to:

$$\frac{v}{R + pL} + \frac{vpC}{1 + kRpC} + hpCv = 0,\qquad(2.29)$$

which becomes upon expansion

$$v[1 + p(kRC + hRC + RC) + p^2(LC + hLC + khR^2C^2)$$
$$+ p^3(khRLC^2)] = 0.\quad(2.30)$$

This differential equation in v will have a solution of exponential form, provided the exponents satisfy eq. 2.30, now regarded as an algebraic equation in p. It is known from the theory of algebraic equations that eq. 2.30 has three roots, at least one of which is real.[254] The other two roots are either real or a conjugate complex pair.

It is instructive to examine the circumstances under which eq. 2.30 has a pair of pure imaginary roots, because this situation corresponds to the condition of sustained oscillation in the physical circuit. To be consistent with previous work, all the reactive elements are assumed to be positive, so that L, C, and h are positive quantities. Physical consideration indicates that one resistance—and hence the factor k— must then be negative in order to maintain steady oscillations. The analysis is facilitated by assuming that the multiplier of v in eq. 2.30 is factorable in the form

$$(p - \alpha)(p + j\omega)(p - j\omega) = 0,\qquad(2.31)$$

where α and ω represent, respectively, the real and imaginary roots.

The expansion of eq. 2.31 yields a new third-degree equation in p:

$$p^3 - p^2\alpha + p\omega^2 - \alpha\omega^2 = 0.\qquad(2.32)$$

The corresponding coefficients in eqs. 2.30 and 2.32 must evidently be made equal, so that we have

$$\alpha = -\frac{L + hL + khR^2C}{khRLC},\qquad(2.33)$$

$$\omega = \sqrt{\frac{k + h + 1}{khLC}},\qquad(2.34)$$

and
$$\alpha\omega^2 = -1/khRLC^2. \tag{2.35}$$

The relationship which must exist between the resistances is found by equating eq. 2.35 to the product of eq. 2.33 and the square of eq. 2.34. Upon expanding the immediate result and collecting terms, a second-degree equation is obtained in k and R:

$$L + 2hL + h^2L + kL + khR^2C(1 + h + k) = 0. \tag{2.36}$$

Inspection shows that this equation can be satisfied only if k is negative, as was previously indicated from physical reasoning.

Because ω is assumed to be a real number, it follows from eq. 2.34 that

$$|k| > h + 1. \tag{2.37}$$

Finally, the additional requirement that the factor α is negative may be imposed. If this were not so, a simple exponential term expanding without limit as time went on would be present, and sustained oscillations would not exist in any practical sense. The condition $\alpha < 0$, when applied to eq. 2.35, shows that R must be negative, because k is negative. Physically, this condition indicates that an expanding transient will result if a negative resistance completes the mesh containing the two positive capacitances. It follows that sustained oscillations can exist only if the coil resistance R is negative and the condenser resistance kR is positive.

The interpretation of the results is simplified by making the further substitution

$$\omega L/R = Q, \tag{2.38}$$

which makes Q negative if R is negative. Multiplying eq. 2.36 by ω^2L, substituting eq. 2.38 and the square of eq. 2.34, we obtain

$$Q = \frac{1 + h + k}{\sqrt{-k-(1 + h)^2}}. \tag{2.39}$$

A still further restriction on k is now recognized, in that the denominator of eq. 2.39 can be real only if

$$|k| > (1 + h)^2. \tag{2.40}$$

The rapidity with which the undesired transient decays may now be expressed by substituting eq. 2.38 and 2.34 in eq. 2.35 to obtain a ratio between the magnitudes of the real and the imaginary roots,

$$\frac{\alpha}{\omega} = \frac{-1}{\omega^3hkRLC^2} = \frac{-Q}{\omega^4khL^2C^2}, \tag{2.41}$$

which reduces to

$$\frac{\alpha}{\omega} = \frac{-Qkh}{(k+h+1)^2} \text{ nepers per radian.} \tag{2.42}$$

In a system which is to produce sinusoidal waves it is ordinarily desirable to make the reactive terms large compared to the resistive terms. This corresponds to a large numerical value in eq. 2.39. Avoiding the degenerate case in which $h = 0$ and $k = -1$ by making h considerably larger than one, and satisfying eq. 2.40, we find that the numerator of eq. 2.39 is approximately proportional to k. Large values of Q are therefore to be secured by making k nearly equal to $-(1+h)^2$.

A numerical example serves to clarify the ideas involved. Let $h = 9$ and $k = -101$; whereupon, from eq. 2.39,

$$Q = -91 \tag{2.43}$$

From eq. 2.34,

$$\omega = \frac{1}{\sqrt{LC}} \cdot \sqrt{\frac{-91}{-909}} = 0.316 \frac{1}{\sqrt{LC}}. \tag{2.44}$$

The decay rate is, from eq. 2.42,

$$\frac{\alpha}{\omega} = \frac{-91 \times 101 \times 9}{(-91)^2} = -9.96 \text{ nepers per radian.} \tag{2.45}$$

That is, the simple transient decays through $2\pi \times 9.96 = 62.7$ nepers during the period of a single cycle of the desired oscillation. It should be noted that in the present case the ratio of α to ω expresses the behavior of two different signals, not the rate of decay of a sinusoid.

In practical oscillators a real root in addition to the desired pair of imaginary roots is often present. The foregoing discussion, therefore, has considerable interest. In actual circuits, however, it is seldom necessary or practical to make α/ω so large.

PROBLEMS

2.1. Derive eq. 2.1.

2.2. Derive the equation corresponding to eq. 2.1 for the transient in an RL network.

2.3. Sketch and interpret the curves corresponding to Fig. 2.1 for the RL network.

2.4. Set up and solve the differential equation for the current i in Fig 2.2.

2.5. Prove that eq. 2.18 is correct even if Q is low.

2.6. Express α and δ in decibel notation.

2.7. Prepare a table relating Q, bandwidth, α, δ, and the decibel equivalents of the latter.

3

NEGATIVE RESISTANCE
OSCILLATORS

Before proceeding further with purely analytical work it seems desirable to examine some physical problems. Such a procedure serves to justify the mathematical methods used, which might otherwise appear arbitrary and somewhat artificial. Moreover, the physical principles developed serve as a very useful guide in establishing and understanding the mathematical solutions.

3.1 Negative resistance

In a linear circuit the d-c resistance of any element or branch may be defined uniquely as the ratio of the terminal voltage to the current. This definition may be extended to include alternating currents by taking the resistance as the real part of the phasor ratio of the voltage to the current. Moreover, it is easy to show that this definition is equivalent to the ratio of the power dissipated to the square of the effective current, a definition which is sometimes more convenient in application.

In nonlinear systems an acceptable definition is far less simple. Some of the difficulties are apparent from inspection of Fig. 3.1, which shows an idealized volt-ampere characteristic similar to that of a glow discharge. The voltage is a single-valued function of the current, but not vice versa. It is therefore possible to show as additional single-valued functions of the current, the ratio e/i and the slope or derivative de/di. It is seen that the ratio e/i varies greatly with variation of the current but at least is always positive. The slope, on the other hand, is not only quite variable but is actually negative over a considerable range of current.

The quantity de/di, which has the dimensions of a resistance, is called the *dynamic resistance* and is very useful in oscillator theory and in all kinds of problems related to nonlinear resistances. Physically, it is the resistance which would be observed by superimposing a very small alternating current upon the direct current at the point in question. The simple ratio e/i is much less useful and will not be discussed further.

It should be noted that no mention of the time variable was made in the preceding discussion. Fortunately, the volt-ampere characteristics of vacuum tubes and other useful negative resistance devices are substantially independent of time. That is, the points of a curve such as that of Fig. 3.1 are traced out in exactly the same manner whether the current and voltage are varied rapidly or slowly. In fact, a nonlinear device is identified as a resistance by the fact that the

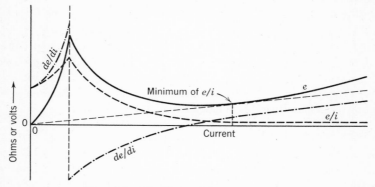

FIG. 3.1. Nonlinear volt-ampere curve.

voltage is a single-valued function of the current or vice versa.[44] A general nonlinear impedance, in contrast, does not have this property and comprises a linear or nonlinear resistance in conjunction with a linear or nonlinear reactance.

It should be recognized that no physical device constitutes a perfect nonlinear resistance, any more than a physical coil constitutes an ideal inductance.[46, 138, 257] In both cases parasitic effects are present and become important if the frequency is carried sufficiently high. These parasitic effects are quite complicated to analyze and are ignored whenever possible. They ordinarily set the upper limit on the frequency which a particular form of oscillator may produce, and are important only at frequencies near that limit.

Negative resistance characteristics fall into two distinct and important classes. When, as in Fig. 3.1, the voltage is a single-valued function of the current, the characteristic and the device which it represents are referred to as *current-controlled*. Devices in which the current is a single-valued function of the voltage are referred to as *voltage-*

controlled. No negative resistance device can possess a volt-ampere characteristic which satisfies both conditions, because this would require the slope to be negative over an unlimited range of current and voltage. Such a device would be capable of supplying infinite power to a suitable load, in obvious violation of the principle of conservation of energy.

No device is known which fails to fall into one of the two classes, but the existence of such a behavior is regarded as possible. A volt-ampere characteristic which is not single-valued with respect to either variable is shown in Fig. 3.2. It is interesting to note that the characteristic sketched is stable with respect to a constant voltage in series with a fixed resistance which lies in the range between the values corresponding to the dotted lines. Therefore, such a characteristic, if it

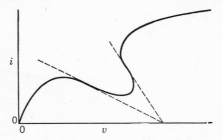

FIG. 3.2. Hypothetical characteristic.

existed, could actually be observed and plotted. It appears safe to predict that such a characteristic, even if available, would be of quite limited usefulness.

3.2 Negative resistance devices

A great variety of devices possess a region of negative slope in their volt-ampere characteristic; that is, they possess the property of dynamic negative resistance. Two of the more important of these are described in the following paragraphs.

The Transitron. A conventional pentode, when connected to produce a two-terminal negative resistance, is referred to as a transitron.[45, 219] A suitable arrangement and the corresponding characteristic are shown in Fig. 3.3. Because the operation is sufficiently similar to that for which tubes are designed, the governing tube parameters are normally held to reasonable tolerances in manufacture. Therefore, tubes of one type, at least from a given manufacturer, produce transitron characteristics which are quite similar.

The shape of the characteristic depends upon the action of the suppressor grid in diverting electrons from the plate to the screen. The behavior is conveniently explained by remembering that, provided $V < V_0$, no electrons can be captured by the suppressor; therefore, the total cathode current is equal to $I_1 + I$, and is governed almost entirely by the potentials of the control and screen grids as an equivalent triode.

For values of V substantially less than V_0, the suppressor grid is so negative with respect to the cathode that no electrons can reach the plate, and I_1 is zero. When $V = V_0$ the suppressor is at cathode potential, and the plate current I_1 is relatively large in comparison with I. In ordinary tubes the suppressor grid has considerably more

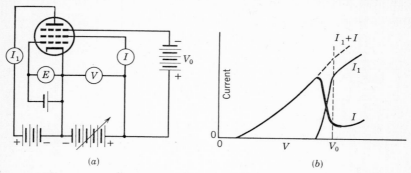

(a)   (b)

FIG. 3.3.   Pentode as a transitron: (a) circuit arrangement and (b) volt-ampere characteristic.

control over the plate current than does the screen, so there is a region in which increase of screen (and suppressor) potential results in a decrease of screen current. The resulting characteristic represents a voltage-controlled negative resistance as shown. The greatest (negative) slope corresponds to the minimum value of negative resistance, which lies in the range of 500 to 10,000 ohms for present-day tubes. For values of $V > V_0$ the suppressor is positive with respect to the cathode and draws current. This somewhat affects the shape of the characteristic curves in this region, as indicated in Fig. 3.3.

The coupling battery V_0 is inconvenient and undesirable in practical systems. It is replaced, without significantly modifying the action, by a coupling condenser from screen to suppressor and a grid leak from suppressor to cathode. A suitable negative bias is built up by rectification, exactly as at the control grid in more conventional circuits.

The Dynatron.   A vacuum tube which produces a negative resistance by the secondary emission of electrons from the plate is called a dynatron.[148] A tetrode connected as a dynatron is shown in Fig. 3.4. The shape of the characteristic curve depends upon the properties of secondary emission. For low values of the plate voltage v the energy with which electrons from the cathode strike the plate is insufficient to dislodge secondary electrons. Thus the plate retains essentially all the electrons which strike it, and the current increases approximately as the three-halves power of the voltage v, according to Child's law. At V_1, which is usually about 10 volts, the plate collects nearly all the electrons which pass through the screen grid.

When the plate voltage is increased beyond V_1, the velocity with which electrons strike the plate is also increased, and some of them are able to dislodge other *secondary* electrons, which are attracted from

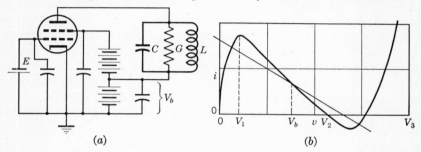

(a) (b)

Fig. 3.4. Dynatron oscillator: (a) circuit arrangement, and (b) nonlinear characteristic.

the plate to the more positive screen grid. These electrons serve to *decrease* the plate current, producing a corresponding increase of screen current. The number of secondary electrons steadily increases with increase of plate voltage until at V_2 it equals the number of primary electrons, and the net plate current is zero. For a range of plate voltages the plate current can actually become negative, with the screen current exceeding the cathode current. In practice, this situation may lead to difficulty with excessive heating of the screen, which is ordinarily designed to carry only a relatively small current.

As the voltage of the plate approaches the screen voltage V_3 there are still plenty of secondary electrons, but they are no longer able to reach the screen, and are forced to return to the plate. For plate voltages greater than V_3 the plate current and screen current approach constant values, as is desired in ordinary applications.

The control grid serves as a convenient means of controlling the total number of electrons which leave the cathode. The principal effect of the control grid voltage E is to change the current scale of the plate characteristic. The fact that it changes the slope of the curve without substantially changing the shape is useful in a number of applications.

3.3 The dynatron oscillator

A very simple and convenient oscillator results from the combination of a suitable antiresonant circuit with a vacuum tube operated as a dynatron.[108, 273] It is shown in Chapter 18 that sustained oscillations are produced only when an antiresonant circuit is associated with a voltage-controlled negative resistance device or when a resonant circuit is associated with a current-controlled negative resistance device. Figure 3.4a shows a complete dynatron oscillator with appropriate biasing batteries and by-pass condensers. The effects of unavoidable dissipation in the plate coil, together with any useful load, are accounted for by the shunt conductance G. The inductance and capacitance are thus represented as loss-free. A line having a slope which is the negative of G, commonly called the *load line*, is shown superimposed upon the associated volt-ampere characteristic. It is seen that the load line is less steep than the dynatron characteristic at the operating point, V_b. Therefore, the negative resistance of the tube is numerically smaller than the positive resistance of the tuned circuit or tank. Under these circumstances, as was shown in Chapter 2, oscillations, if once started, will build up or increase with the passage of time.

The final amplitude which will be reached by these oscillations and the exact frequency which will be produced depend upon both the shape of the volt-ampere curve and the element values in the resonant circuit. That is, both the final frequency and the amplitude depend upon the *nonlinearity* of the characteristic curve of the negative resistance device.

3.4 Intermodulation

The general nature of the problem of frequency departure in dynatron and other negative resistance oscillators may be understood by reference to well-known modulation theory. The explanation is most conveniently conducted in terms of successive approximations with reference to Fig. 3.5a, in which Z is a passive linear circuit and ρ is a nonlinear negative resistance.

A first approximation to the true condition of operation is that v is a sinusoidal voltage at the resonant frequency. A necessary consequence of this assumption is that the current wave i contains substantial components of harmonic frequency as well as of fundamental frequency, because ρ is nonlinear. A second approximation is now obtained by the knowledge that v must contain at least small harmonic voltages because of the harmonics in i which flow in the known imped-ance of the resonant circuit. Moreover, in the normal arrangement shown, the harmonic currents flow principally through the condenser so that the harmonic voltages are effectively in quadrature with the fundamental voltage.

The crucial step in the argument is based upon the modulating properties of a general nonlinear impedance subjected to two or more frequencies. It is well known that if a voltage containing a group of frequencies f_1, f_2, f_3, f_4, etc., is applied to a general nonlinear imped-

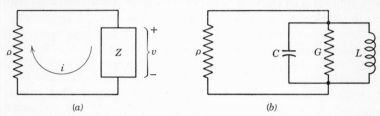

(a)   (b)

FIG. 3.5. Negative resistance oscillator: (a) general form and (b) specific arrangement.

ance the resulting current will contain, among the array of all possible harmonic and sum-and-difference terms, the following frequencies:

$$f_2 - f_1, f_3 - f_2, f_4 - f_3, f_2 - 3f_1, f_3 - 2f_2, f_4 - 3f_1, f_3 - 4f_1,$$
$$f_4 - 5f_1, \text{etc.}$$

In the present case, f_1 may be taken as the fundamental frequency, f_2 as the second harmonic, etc. Accordingly, all the terms enumerated above represent current of fundamental frequency contributed by the nonlinearity of the characteristic. Moreover, the phase of the har-monic voltages is such that these additional components of funda-mental current are in quadrature with the principal one. *Therefore, in a nonlinear resistance at the fundamental frequency the current and voltage are not in phase if harmonics are present.* That is, nonlinearity gives to a resistance the essential properties of a reactance. Excellent general discussions of this property have been given by Peterson[236] and by Espley.[87]

Returning to the negative-resistance oscillator, we see that the action of the harmonic voltages upon the nonlinear resistance will produce an effective phase shift between the fundamental components of v and i. Accordingly, the next approximation involves a change, in this case a lowering, of the frequency and a readjustment of the voltages and currents. With a sufficient number of trials, it is possible to determine a voltage wave of such frequency, amplitude, and harmonic content that the current which results from the application of this wave to the nonlinear negative resistance is equal and opposite to that which results when it is applied to the resonant circuit. The process for determining the amplitude and details for determining the frequency are presented in the following section.

3.5 Calculation of amplitude

It is clear that stable oscillations can exist only if the power supplied per cycle by the negative resistance ρ is equal to the power dissipated per cycle in the positive conductance G, and if the reactive currents in the coil and condenser are in equilibrium.[49] The conditions which lead to this balance are found by assuming an amplitude and phase of oscillation, determining the associated unbalance, and correcting the assumption in such a way as to obtain a better approximation. If, as is usually true, the Q of the resonant circuit is fairly high, it is appropriate to assume that the operating frequency is equal to the resonant frequency and that the voltage wave is sinusoidal. This assumption calls for a unique value of sinusoidal current in the resonant circuit and for a different and nonsinousoidal value of current in the negative resistance device. However, the circuit connections are such that these currents must be equal in the oscillating condition. Therefore, it is necessary to modify the assumed voltage wave to a slightly nonsinusoidal form to produce equilibrium. The procedure of successive approximations is used because of the difficulty of a direct analytical solution.

It is convenient to start the process by assuming various magnitudes of sinusoidal voltage at the resonant frequency and determining the current waves which result. An example of the process used is shown in Fig. 3.6. Horizontal and vertical time scales are drawn in conjunction with the volt-ampere characteristic, and a sinusoidal voltage wave of reasonable magnitude is assumed. The corresponding current wave is markedly distorted and has a prominent third harmonic. Choice of a somewhat larger voltage wave would have resulted in a much more distorted wave with even greater harmonic content. It is important to note that the magnitude of the fundamental component of the current wave *actually decreases* with increase of voltage, whereas the magnitude of the harmonic currents increases. In fact, there is some critical voltage amplitude for which the fundamental component of current actually vanishes; for still larger amplitudes the phase of the fundamental current reverses and the property of negative resistance is lost. Therefore, it is possible for the harmonic currents to be very large in comparison to the fundamental component. This fact, which has sometimes been overlooked, is important in explaining the behavior of negative-resistance oscillators. The variation of

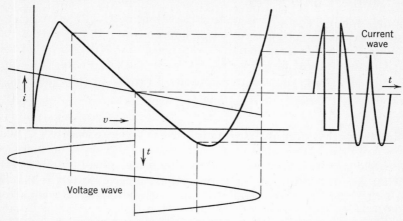

FIG. 3.6. Construction yielding the current wave corresponding to an assumed sinusoidal voltage.

fundamental current with voltage is shown in Fig. 3.7. It is seen that the tube current is substantially proportional to the voltage for small values, but rapidly decreases to zero as the voltage is further increased.

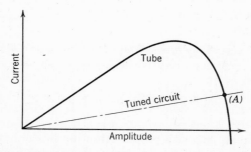

FIG. 3.7. Variation with amplitude of the real components of current at fundamental frequency.

The equilibrium amplitude is indicated by point A, where the real component of fundamental-frequency current is equal to that produced by the tube. This balance is not affected by harmonics produced in the tube or the resulting frequency shift unless the resonator presents an appreciable resistive component to the harmonic currents. Should this be true, the fundamental-frequency current produced by inter-modulation in the nonlinear device is not in quadrature with the basic term and the effective value of negative resistance changes.

3.6 Calculations of frequency

Several methods exist for calculating the extent to which the frequency is modified by the presence of harmonic currents.[14,19, 217] One of the simplest is due to Groszkowski,[121] who makes use of the fact that the negative resistance device is, by its basic nature, unable to store energy. This fact is represented in terms of Fig. 3.5 by the equation

$$\oint i \, dv = 0, \tag{3.1}$$

which states that over any closed cycle the net energy is zero. This is necessarily true if the current is a single-valued function of the voltage, and could be true in a special case for a multiple-valued function such as that shown in Fig. 3.2. The important thing, however, is that it must, by definition, be true for any voltage-controlled negative resistance.

The next step is to assume that the voltage and current waves are periodic and are expressible in the usual form of the Fourier series,

$$i = \sum_{a=1}^{\infty} I_a \sin (a\omega t + \phi_a) \tag{3.2}$$

and

$$v = \sum_{b=1}^{\infty} V_b \sin (b\omega t + \psi_b), \tag{3.3}$$

where ω is the actual operating frequency and ϕ and ψ represent phase displacements. A necessary consequence of eq. 3.3 is the equation

$$dv = \sum_{b=1}^{\infty} b\omega V_b \cos (b\omega t + \psi_b) \, dt. \tag{3.4}$$

Substitution in eq. 3.1 with proper attention to the limits yields

$$\oint i \, dv = 0 = \int_0^{2\pi/\omega} \sum_{a=1, b=1}^{\infty, \infty} b\omega I_a V_b \sin (a\omega t + \phi_a) \cos (b\omega t + \psi_b) \, dt, \tag{3.5}$$

where the double summation is taken to include all possible products. Because the series are known to be absolutely convergent for the functions of present interest it is possible to interchange the order of summation and integration and to apply a well-known trigonometric identity to obtain

$$0 = \sum_{a=1, b=1}^{\infty, \infty} \tfrac{1}{2} b \omega I_a V_b \int_0^{2\pi/\omega} \{\sin [(a + b)\omega t + \phi_a + \psi_b]$$
$$+ \sin [(a - b)\omega t + \phi_a - \psi_b]\} \, dt. \quad (3.6)$$

This integral is zero for all terms in which $a \neq b$, because the integral describes a discrete number of complete cycles in the range of interest and thus represents no net area. Therefore, terms in which $a \neq b$ are rejected, and the substitution of a for b is made to permit complete evaluation of the integral.

$$0 = \sum_{a=1}^{\infty} \tfrac{1}{2} a \omega I_a V_a \int_0^{2\pi/\omega} \{\sin [2a\omega t + \phi_a + \psi_a]$$
$$+ \sin [\phi_a - \psi_a]\} \, dt. \quad (3.7)$$

The time variable term again can make no contribution over a complete cycle, so the expression reduces to

$$0 = \sum_{a=1}^{\infty} \tfrac{1}{2} a \omega I_a V_a \{\sin (\phi_a - \psi_a)\} \frac{2\pi}{\omega}. \quad (3.8)$$

Division by the various quantities which are independent of a leads to an important result

$$0 = \sum_{a=1}^{\infty} a I_a V_a \sin (\phi_a - \psi_a). \quad (3.9)$$

Although the expression just derived does not give the operating frequency explicitly, it does permit calculation of this frequency for any particular circuit. The first step in this procedure is to substitute

$$\theta_a = \phi_a - \psi_a, \quad (3.10)$$

which represents the phase angle of the tuned circuit at the fundamental and harmonic frequencies. Moreover, reference to Fig. 3.5a shows that

$$V_a \sin \theta_a = I_a X_a, \quad (3.11)$$

where X_a is the reactance of the tuned circuit. Therefore eq. 3.9 reduces to

$$0 = \sum_{a=1}^{\infty} a I_a^2 X_a. \quad (3.12)$$

Alternatively, we may use the admittance form and write

$$I_a \sin \theta_a = V_a B_a, \tag{3.13}$$

which leads to

$$0 = \sum_{a=1}^{\infty} a V_a{}^2 B_a, \tag{3.14}$$

where B_a is the susceptance of the tuned circuit.

Equations 3.12 and 3.14 show that the presence of harmonics will always reduce the frequency in a simple tuned circuit. This is true because the impedance or admittance is capacitive at all harmonic frequencies. A summation to zero in eqs. 3.12 or 3.14 is therefore possible only if X or B has the opposite sign at the operating frequency, which must be below the resonant frequency.

3.7 Application to a simple circuit

The simple tuned circuit of Fig. 3.5b has an admittance of the form

$$\mathbf{Y} = G + j\omega C + \frac{1}{j\omega L}. \tag{3.15}$$

The susceptance or imaginary part is simply

$$B = \omega C - 1/\omega L. \tag{3.16}$$

The substitutions

$$\omega_0 = 1/LC, \tag{3.17}$$

$$\omega = a\xi\omega_0, \tag{3.18}$$

and

$$Q = \omega_0 C/G, \tag{3.19}$$

together with the fact that $\xi \doteq 1$, reduce the susceptance expression to

$$B_{(a)} = QG(a^2 - 1)/a \qquad (a \neq 1) \tag{3.20}$$

and

$$B_1 = QG(\xi - 1/\xi) \doteq 2QG(\xi - 1). \tag{3.21}$$

The additional substitution

$$m_a = V_a/V_1 \tag{3.22}$$

reduces eq. 3.14 to

$$1 - \xi = \tfrac{1}{2} \sum_{a=2}^{\infty} m_a{}^2(a^2 - 1). \tag{3.23}$$

As a numerical example, let the voltage wave contain only a third harmonic component, which is 5 per cent of the fundamental. Then by eq. 3.23

$$1 - \xi = 0.01. \tag{3.24}$$

That is, the operating frequency differs from the natural frequency by one per cent.

By a corresponding analysis based on impedances and currents we may obtain

$$1 - \xi = \frac{1}{2Q^2} \sum_{a=2}^{\infty} \frac{a^2 - n_a^2}{a^2 - 1} \tag{3.25}$$

where the new parameter is defined by

$$n_a = I_a/I_1. \tag{3.26}$$

Because the amplitude of oscillation, and hence the ratios of harmonics to the fundamental current, is established by the conductivity G and the negative resistance characteristic, we may interpret eq. 3.25 as showing that the frequency deviation due to nonlinearity varies inversely with the square of the resonator Q. This is a very important and general conclusion.

PROBLEMS

3.1. Show that the definitions of resistance in Section 3.1 are equivalent.

3.2. Consider a volt-ampere curve similar to that of Fig. 3.4b but having the shape of one full sinusoidal cycle. Evaluate e/i and de/di with respect to the center as an operating point.

3.3. Assuming that the above volt-ampere characteristic covers a total range of 100 volts and has a maximum negative conductance of 200 micromhos, and that the associated passive conductance is 100 micromhos, calculate the amplitude of oscillation by the method of Section 3.5.

3.4. Using eq. 3.25 and the current distribution associated with Prob. 3.3, calculate the fractional frequency shift which exists if the passive circuit has a Q of 50.

3.5. In a general way, show why a simple series-resonant circuit cannot produce stable oscillations if connected to a voltage-controlled negative resistance.

4

NONLINEAR OSCILLATIONS

In the foregoing chapters it has become clear that much may be learned about oscillators by suitable use of linear equations. It has also developed, however, that many important phenomena require nonlinear equations for their analysis. This chapter is devoted to a development of some of the simpler aspects of nonlinear behavior. The reader who wishes additional material on this extensive subject is referred to the books by Minorsky[211] and by Kryloff and Bogoliuboff.[177]

4.1 A nonlinear system

It is convenient to proceed by generalizing the system treated in Chapter 2 to include a single nonlinear negative resistance. Such a

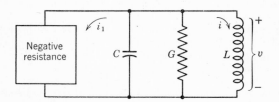

FIG. 4.1.   Nonlinear oscillatory circuit.

circuit is shown in Fig. 4.1.   The negative resistance may be identified with a dynatron or a pentode connected as a transitron, as described in the previous chapter.   All known negative resistance devices have the property of nonlinearity if the amplitude of oscillation is sufficiently large.   Otherwise, an indefinitely large amount of power could be drawn by a suitable load, a violation of the principle of conservation of energy.

The analysis begins with the characteristic of a typical negative resistance device, as shown in Fig. 4.2.   The curve, which may be obtained experimentally, is relatively complicated and is not representable by any simple equation.   For our present purposes it is sufficient to represent this characteristic symbolically as

$$i_1 = F(v), \tag{4.1}$$

where v represents the difference between the instantaneous potential and a bias voltage V_0. The other elements of Fig. 4.1 are readily identified with the passive linear tank circuit. All capacitances, including those of the tube, coil, and wiring, are lumped in C. All losses, including those of the coil, condenser, and any useful load, are

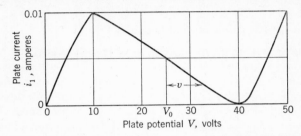

Fig. 4.2. Characteristic of a tetrode as a dynatron (idealized).

accounted for by the shunt conductance G. The inductance of the system is represented by L.

4.2 The differential equation

The differential equation which describes this system may be written in several forms. For present purposes, however, it is most convenient to use the form which results from application of Kirchhoff's current law

$$F(v) + C(dv/dt) + Gv + i = 0, \tag{4.2}$$

where i, the current through L, is related to the voltage across the system by the auxiliary equation

$$v = L(di/dt). \tag{4.3}$$

4.3 Solution by isoclines

The differential equations above involve both current and voltage, which vary with respect to time. Ordinarily we would eliminate either v or i between these equations and proceed to determine the variation of the other with respect to time. In the present case, however, the undefined function F greatly complicates this procedure. Accordingly, it is expedient to eliminate the time variable and study the relationship between v and i, following a method devised by Liénard[189] and explained very clearly by le Corbeiller.[186] The resulting plot is appropriately called a cyclogram.

The elimination of t is accomplished by use of the derivative identity

$$dv/dt = (dv/dx) \cdot (dx/dt), \qquad (4.4)$$

where x is any variable. In the present case it is convenient to use

$$x = i. \qquad (4.5)$$

In addition it is desirable to use a constant multiplier to change the voltage variable such that

$$v = k\upsilon. \qquad (4.6)$$

With these substitutions eq. 4.2 becomes

$$F(k\upsilon) + (k^2 C/L) \cdot (d\upsilon/di)\upsilon + Gk\upsilon + i = 0. \qquad (4.7)$$

By choosing

$$k = \sqrt{L/C} \qquad (4.8)$$

and

$$f(\upsilon) = F(k\upsilon) + Gk\upsilon, \qquad (4.9)$$

and transposing, we obtain

$$d\upsilon/di = -[i + f(\upsilon)]/\upsilon \qquad (4.10)$$

or

$$di/d\upsilon = -\upsilon/[i + f(\upsilon)]. \qquad (4.11)$$

In eq. 4.11 the slope $di/d\upsilon$ is determined as soon as the variables i and υ are specified. Moreover, the form is such that this slope may be determined very rapidly on a graphical basis.

The basic idea is simple and may be stated as follows: If the current and voltage at any instant assume values i and υ, then from eq. 4.11 we can readily calculate the slope $di/d\upsilon$ and hence the incrementally different values which i and υ will have some short time later. By sufficient repetition of this process and use of finite increments it is possible to determine completely the variation of i and υ from any assumed initial conditions.

In practice it is much more convenient to construct slope lines, called isoclines, from a large number of arbitrarily chosen starting points. Because these lines form a characteristic pattern, it is relatively easy to trace out the curve which will develop from any chosen starting point.

4.4 Isocline diagram

An isocline diagram having coordinates υ and i is shown in Fig. 4.3. The first step in the construction is to plot the negative quantity $-f(\upsilon)$ versus υ. This presents no basic difficulty because the constant

k is fixed by eq. 4.8, G is known, and $F(\text{ʋ})$ differs from the known $F(v)$ only by a change of abscissa. The resulting plot of $-f(\text{ʋ})$ in Fig. 4.3 is somewhat flatter than the original $F(v)$ because the positive conductance G partially annuls the negative conductance of the electronic device. Moreover, a change in the ordinate scale to conform to the new abscissa is necessary. The curve is translated so that the origin of Fig. 4.3 corresponds to V_0, which is usually chosen near the center of the negative slope region. The numerical values used in Fig. 4.3

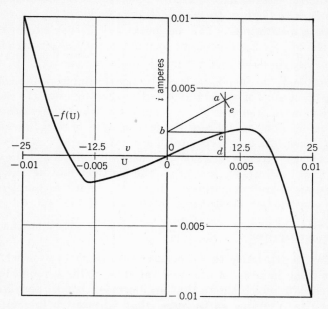

FIG. 4.3. Construction of isoclines.

correspond to those of Fig. 4.2 with the additional parameters $G = 2 \times 10^{-4}$ mho (5000 ohms), $L = 2.5 \times 10^{-3}$ henry, $C = 4 \times 10^{-10}$ farad, and $k = \sqrt{L/C} = 2500$. These parameters were chosen in conjunction with the negative resistance characteristic, which has a value of -2500 ohms at V_0, to correspond to reference point 6 of Figs. 2.3 and 2.4. The associated oscillation, although considerable distorted, is *harmonic* in character.

The point a anywhere on the plane is now chosen arbitrarily, and construction lines are drawn as shown. It is seen that the length of the line segments are given by

$$\overline{bc} = \text{ʋ}; \ \overline{ad} = i; \text{ and } \overline{ac} = i + f(\text{ʋ}). \tag{4.12}$$

From eq. 4.11 we know that the slope is given by

$$di/d\textsc{u} = -\overline{bc}/\overline{ac}. \tag{4.13}$$

Thus, the slope of the segment $\overline{ba}$ is the negative reciprocal of that called for in eq. 4.13. It is easily shown, by use of similar triangles or otherwise, that the slope of the segment $\overline{ae}$, which is perpendicular to $\overline{ba}$, is exactly $-\overline{bc}/\overline{ac}$ as required. *It should be noted that this construction is correct only if the coordinates are such that* $\textsc{u} = 1$ *and* $i = 1$ *occupy an equal distance.* The significant fact is that whenever i and $\textsc{u}$ have the values corresponding to point a the values are changing in such a way that the i vs. $\textsc{u}$ curve is tangent to $\overline{ae}$.

The isoclines, of which $\overline{ae}$ is only one example, are easily constructed by means of ruler and compasses as follows: (1) Select an arbitrary value of $\textsc{u}$ such as d. (2) Draw a vertical line corresponding to this value of $\textsc{u}$. (3) From the intersection of this line with the function curve, draw a horizontal line to the i axis. (4) Using this point, such as b, strike a series of short arcs which intersect the original vertical line. All these arcs cross the vertical line at the correct angle and are therefore isoclines. Figure 4.4 shows a complete set of isoclines constructed on the same coordinates as Fig. 4.3.

4.5 The cyclogram

It remains to determine the direction or sense of rotation which corresponds to an increase of the time variable. This is found by reference to eq. 4.3, which shows that an increase, that is, positive increment, in time requires an increase, that is, positive increment in i whenever v and, hence, $\textsc{u}$ is positive. This requires upward motion in the right half plane. Hence *counterclockwise rotation in Fig. 4.4 corresponds to increasing time.*

The entire performance of the system, including the build-up from arbitrary starting conditions and the steady state, is described by isoclines such as those of Fig. 4.4, which shows the behavior that follows from two different starting conditions. These curves are called *cyclograms.* Note in particular that the steady state corresponds to a closed curve which is nearly symmetrical and approximately circular. The closed curve is exactly symmetrical if the original $F(v)$ is symmetrical about the operating point. It approaches a circle as the function $-f(\textsc{u})$ approaches the horizontal axis. It will later be seen that a nearly circular cyclogram is associated with a quasilinear system in which k is relatively small.

4.6 Effect of parameters

Our previous investigation of linear systems showed that the behavior is greatly affected by the relative value of the circuit parameters. A corresponding situation exists in nonlinear systems, as shown by inspection of eqs 4.6, 4.8, and 4.11. The horizontal scale of Fig. 4.3, and hence the shape of the nonlinear curve and the distribution of the isoclines, is governed by the value of k, which in turn is governed by the L/C ratio, and is closely related to the damping factor α. In making these comparisons it should be further noted by eq. 4.3 that v and i are

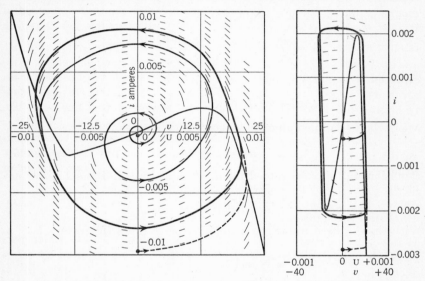

FIG. 4.4. Isocline diagram for harmonic oscillation. FIG. 4.5. Isocline diagram for relaxation oscillation.

related by the inductance L. Accordingly, variation of L and C leads to a number of changes in the circuit behavior.

To illustrate the effect of a significant change of parameters, let us preserve the conductance G and the characteristic of the electronic device. The choice of $L = 4 \times 10^{-2}$ henry and $C = 2.5 \times 10^{-11}$ farad yields $k = 40,000$ and leads to a considerably different behavior, as shown in Fig. 4.5. These parameters correspond to reference point 8 of Figs. 2.3 and 2.4, and therefore represent a case of relaxation oscillation.

Several marked differences exist between Figs. 4.4 and 4.5. Most conspicuous is the marked change in the scales of i, and v, with consequent emphasis of the ordinate scale. The actual voltage excursion is comparable in the two cases, but the coil current, which is magnified in the former, is much smaller in the latter. Finally, the cyclogram, which is approximately circular in the former, is almost rectangular in the latter.

4.7 Angular velocities

The question arises as to the time rate at which the cyclogram is described. This may be answered in part by defining the angle

$$\theta = \tan^{-1}(i/\upsilon). \tag{4.14}$$

The time derivative of this angle is

$$\omega = \frac{d\theta}{dt} = \frac{\upsilon(di/dt) - i(d\upsilon/dt)}{\upsilon^2 + i^2}. \tag{4.15}$$

Equations 4.3 and 4.8 yield

$$di/dt = k\upsilon/L = \sqrt{L/C} \cdot \upsilon/L = \omega_0\upsilon, \tag{4.16}$$

where the undamped angular velocity is defined as

$$\omega_0 = 1/\sqrt{LC}. \tag{4.17}$$

Equation 4.2 may be solved for $d\upsilon/dt$, and by suitable substitutions yields

$$d\upsilon/dt = -[i + f(\upsilon)]/kC = -\omega_0[i + f(\upsilon)]. \tag{4.18}$$

With these substitutions the angular velocity takes the form

$$\omega = \omega_0\left(1 + \frac{if(\upsilon)}{\upsilon^2 + i^2}\right). \tag{4.19}$$

In the quasilinear (high Q) case, the term $f(\upsilon)$ is always small compared to i, and the last term of eq. 4.19 is thus negligible. The corresponding cyclogram is nearly circular, and is traced out at a uniform angular velocity equal to ω_0.

In the heavily damped case, corresponding to relaxation oscillations, the situation is less simple. As we might anticipate from other experience, the angular velocity is nonuniform. Because the denominator of eq. 4.19 is approximately constant, the greatest angular velocity occurs in the regions where the product of i and $f(\upsilon)$ is a maximum. It should be noted that the angular velocity can be either larger or smaller than ω_0. Furthermore, ω equals ω_0 at the crossings of the axes, where i and $f(\upsilon)$ are respectively zero.

In summary, the method of isoclines yields a cyclogram for any possible negative-resistance oscillator. Equation 4.19 gives the time rate at which the cyclogram is described and thereby permits the current and voltage wave forms with respect to time to be constructed by integration. Although somewhat tedious and inelegant, this method has the merit of practicality in many cases.

4.8 Van der Pol's equation

Important contributions to the nonlinear theory of oscillations have been made by van der Pol.[322] His method is analytical rather than graphical, and accordingly is limited to negative-resistance characteristics which are capable of mathematical expression throughout the range of interest. Quite frequently, oscillators are operated near

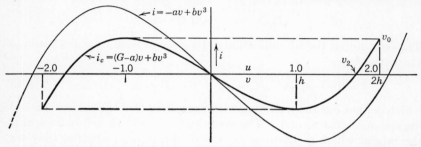

FIG. 4.6.   Cubic volt-ampere characteristic and related functions.

the middle of the negative-resistance region of the electronic device. In such cases a simple cubic equation of the form

$$i = F(v) = -av + bv^3 \qquad (4.20)$$

gives a fair approximation over the region of interest.   Such a characteristic is shown in Fig. 4.6.   The cubic representation is a very rough approximation to typical experimental curves such as that of Fig. 4.2, and results obtained thereby cannot be expected to explain all observed effects.   However, a great deal of useful information is obtained by the study of this particular case.   And the complexity of treating a more general case is such as to exclude it from this book.

The differential equation most suitable for this development is obtained directly from eq. 4.20 and Fig. 4.1:

$$-av + bv^3 + C(dv/dt) + Gv + (1/L) \int v \, dt = 0. \qquad (4.21)$$

Differentiating and multiplying by L gives

$$LC(d^2v/dt^2) + [L(G - a) + 3bLv^2](dv/dt) + v = 0. \qquad (4.22)$$

This differential equation is basic but involves coefficients which are inconveniently complicated.   By several successive changes of variables it is possible to obtain coefficients which are much simpler.   This procedure is desirable because it substantially reduces the difficulty of solving the differential equation.

The first step in this reduction is a change in the time variable accomplished by the substitutions

$$\tau = \omega_0 t, \tag{4.23}$$

where

$$\omega_0 = 1/\sqrt{LC}. \tag{4.24}$$

Introduction of this variable leads to*

$$\frac{d^2v}{d\tau^2} - \frac{(a - G)L}{\sqrt{LC}}\frac{dv}{d\tau} + \frac{3bL}{\sqrt{LC}}v^2\frac{dv}{d\tau} + v = 0. \tag{4.25}$$

The next step is the simplification of the second term by substitution of the variable

$$\epsilon = (a - G)\sqrt{L/C} = (a - G)\omega_0 L = (a - G)/\omega_0 C, \tag{4.26}$$

which defines ϵ as the reciprocal of the negative Q of the system, excluding the nonlinear term b.   The magnitude of ϵ will therefore determine the rate at which oscillations expand or shrink, and whether they will be harmonic or relaxation in character.   Substitution of ϵ yields

$$\frac{d^2v}{d\tau^2} - \epsilon\frac{dv}{d\tau} + 3b\sqrt{\frac{L}{C}}v^2\frac{dv}{d\tau} + v = 0. \tag{4.27}$$

The remaining step in the simplification involves a change in the dependent variable

$$v = hu, \tag{4.28}$$

where

$$h^2 = \frac{\epsilon}{3b\sqrt{L/C}} \quad \text{or} \quad h = \sqrt{(a - G)/3b}. \tag{4.29}$$

* This result may be obtained by a very general mathematical procedure. However, elementary methods serve to justify the present use.   Differentiating eq. 4.23 gives

$$\omega_0 dt = d\tau.$$

Combination with the differential of voltage yields

$$dv/dt = \omega_0(dv/d\tau).$$

Differentiation with respect to t gives

$$\frac{d^2v}{dt^2} = \omega_0\frac{d}{dt}\frac{dv}{d\tau} = \omega_0{}^2\frac{d}{d\tau}\frac{dv}{d\tau} = \omega_0{}^2\frac{d^2v}{d\tau^2}.$$

The resulting differential equation, generally referred to as van der Pol's equation, is fundamental, and describes a wide variety of systems

$$\frac{d^2u}{d\tau^2} - \epsilon(1 - u^2)\frac{du}{d\tau} + u = 0. \tag{4.30}$$

4.9 Solution of van der Pol's equation

Van der Pol in his original paper[322] offered two independent methods of solving eq. 4.30.   These are now generally referred to as the methods of *variation of parameters* and *equivalent linearization*.   A good discussion of available methods of solution is presented by Keller.[165]

The following paragraphs present a solution by the method of variation of parameters.   In this method it is assumed that the conductance term is equivalent to a linear conductance which depends upon the amplitude of oscillation.   The analysis involves separation of the original second-order differential equation into two distinct first-order differential equations, one of which determines the amplitude and the other the frequency of oscillation.   In the present case the analysis begins by assuming that the voltage across the antiresonant circuit of Fig. 4.1 may be expressed by the equation

$$v = hA(\tau) \cdot \cos \tau \quad \text{or} \quad u = A(\tau) \cdot \cos \tau, \tag{4.31}$$

where $A(\tau)$ represents an amplitude which varies relatively slowly with respect to time.   Specifically, the amplitude shall not vary appreciably during any one cycle.   This statement is expressed mathematically by the inequality

$$dA/d\tau \ll A. \tag{4.32}$$

To justify this assumption it is necessary to restrict the conductance parameter ϵ to small values by the additional inequality

$$\epsilon \ll 1. \tag{4.33}$$

This restriction is of great importance because it limits the study to systems which produce harmonic oscillations.   Such systems are referred to as *quasi-linear* because the nonlinear conductance or resistance terms are small compared to the associated susceptance (or reactance) terms, even though the conductance (or resistance) characteristic itself is quite curved in the region of interest.   Alternatively, we may say that a quasi-linear system is also a high-Q system because the stored energy is large compared to the energy gain or loss per cycle.

The analysis proceeds by noting that the solution assumed in eq.

4.31 leads as a necessary consequence to the equality

$$u^3 = A^3 \cos^3 \tau = A^3 \left(\tfrac{3}{4} \cos \tau + \tfrac{1}{4} \cos 3\tau\right). \qquad (4.34)$$

Furthermore, differentiation of eq. 4.31 with appropriate neglect of higher order derivatives of A yields

$$\frac{du}{d\tau} = -A \sin \tau + \frac{dA}{d\tau} \cos \tau \qquad (4.35)$$

and

$$\frac{d^2u}{d\tau^2} = -A \cos \tau - 2 \frac{dA}{d\tau} \sin \tau. \qquad (4.36)$$

An additional relationship which will be needed in testing the solution is obtained by differentiating eq. 4.34 and neglecting a number of small terms to obtain

$$\frac{d(u^3)}{d\tau} = -\tfrac{3}{4} A^3 \sin \tau. \qquad (4.37)$$

Equating this to the formal derivative $3u^2 \, du/d\tau$ leads to the desired relation

$$u^2 \frac{du}{d\tau} = -\tfrac{1}{4} A^3 \sin \tau. \qquad (4.38)$$

The neglect in eq. 4.37 of terms which are only moderately small is justified by the fact that eq. 4.38 will in turn be multiplied by a factor, ϵ, which is itself small. Substitution of eq. 4.35, 4.36, and 4.38 into 4.30 yields

$$\left(-A \cos \tau - 2 \frac{dA}{d\tau} \sin \tau\right) - \epsilon \left(-A \sin \tau + \frac{dA}{d\tau} \cos \tau + \tfrac{1}{4} A^3 \sin \tau\right)$$
$$+ (A \cos \tau) = 0. \quad (4.39)$$

The first and last terms cancel, which indicates that, to the present approximation, the frequency is equal to the natural frequency of the resonator. Furthermore, the term $\epsilon(dA/d\tau) \cos \tau$ is negligible compared to the remaining terms. Multiplication by A and division by $\sin \tau$ permits writing the equation

$$\frac{d}{d\tau} (A^2) - \epsilon (A^2 - \tfrac{1}{4} A^4) = 0, \qquad (4.40)$$

which represents the variation of the amplitude A with respect to time. Solution of this equation is facilitated by the temporary substitution

$$A^2 = 1/x \qquad (4.41)$$

which leads to the simple differential equation

$$\frac{dx}{d\tau} + \epsilon \left(x - \tfrac{1}{4} \right) = 0. \tag{4.42}$$

The solution of this equation, as found by ordinary methods, is

$$x = \tfrac{1}{4} [1 + e^{-\epsilon(\tau - \tau_0)}], \tag{4.43}$$

where τ_0 is the constant of integration, which depends upon the initial conditions, and e is the base of natural logarithms. Elimination of x leads to

$$A^2 = \frac{4}{1 + e^{-\epsilon(\tau - \tau_0)}} \tag{4.44}$$

and

$$u = \frac{2 \cos \tau}{\sqrt{1 + e^{-\epsilon(\tau - \tau_0)}}}, \tag{4.45}$$

which describe the complete process of build-up and steady state of oscillation.

If, as is usually the case, oscillations start from a small amplitude it is necessary to assign τ_0 a large positive magnitude. The denominator then has a large initial magnitude, which decreases with time to a final value of unity. During the period of small amplitude the exponential term is large compared to one, and the oscillation takes the approximate form

$$u = 2[e^{-\epsilon \tau_0 / 2}][e^{\epsilon \tau / 2}] \cos \tau. \tag{4.46}$$

The significant factor in this equation is the exponent $\epsilon \tau / 2$ which gives the rate at which the oscillations expand with respect to time. The correctness of this result is readily verified directly from eq. 4.30, since in the interval in question u^2 is negligible compared to one.

Substitution of the original variables leads to the final result

$$v = \sqrt{\frac{4}{3} \left(\frac{a - G}{b} \right)} \cdot \frac{\cos (\omega_0 t + \phi_0)}{\sqrt{1 + e^{-(t - t_0)(a - G)/c}}}, \tag{4.47}$$

where the parameter ϕ_0 takes account of the oscillation phase at the initial instant specified by t_0. In terms of the original parameters, the final peak amplitude v_0 is given by

$$v_0 = hA_0 = 2h = \sqrt{\frac{4}{3} (a - G)/b}. \tag{4.48}$$

Until the amplitude v reaches the value $v_2 = \sqrt{(a - G)/b}$, the net resistance is negative throughout the cycle. For amplitudes larger than v_2 the net resistance is positive at each peak, and the rate of expansion is checked. The initial rate of build-up, consistent with eq. 4.46, is governed by the exponent

$$\frac{\epsilon\tau}{2} = -\frac{(a - G)L}{2\sqrt{LC}} \cdot \frac{t}{\sqrt{LC}} = \frac{(a - G)}{2C}\, t, \qquad (4.49)$$

which is recognized as the result achieved by linear analysis in Chapter 2. The oscillation envelope, as given by eq. 4.47, is plotted in Fig. 4.7. It is seen that the choice of the time variable is such that the oscillation reaches 0.707 of its maximum value at the instant $t = t_0$.

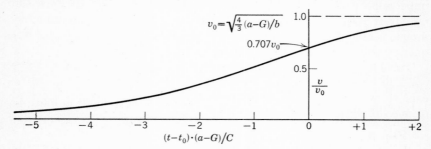

FIG. 4.7. Envelope of oscillation.

It is interesting to determine the point of zero slope of the characteristic $i = F(v) - Gv$. From eq. 4.20 we may write for the total conduction current

$$i_c = (G - a)v - bv^3. \qquad (4.50a)$$

Setting the derivative equal to zero gives

$$di_c/dv = 0 = a - G = 3bv^2, \qquad (4.50b)$$

which yields as the point of zero slope in Fig. 4.6

$$v = \sqrt{(a - G)/3b} = h \quad \text{or} \quad u = 1. \qquad (4.50c)$$

4.10 Method of equivalent linearization[177]

The current which flows when a nonlinear resistance is subjected to a sinusoidal voltage may be resolved by means of Fourier's series into a fundamental term which has the same frequency as the voltage, plus harmonic terms in which the frequency is an integral multiple of the fundamental. The fundamental current is in phase with the voltage and has a magnitude which depends upon the voltage. *Therefore, in terms of the fundamental frequency the nonlinear resistance may be replaced by a linear resistance, provided the magnitude is suitably chosen for the voltage in question.* This is the basic idea of the method of equivalent linearization. To apply this idea to oscillators it is necessary to generalize it to include the effect of a nonsinusoidal voltage wave, which consists of fundamental and harmonic terms. Again the current wave contains terms of fundamental and harmonic frequencies. However, as shown in Chapter 3, the current and voltage of fundamental frequency are no longer in phase. Accordingly, the nonlinear resistance now requires a reactance as well as a resistance for its complete representation. Nevertheless, for any specified combination of fundamental and harmonic voltages, there is a linear impedance which draws the same fundamental current as does the nonlinear resistance. This impedance may be used as an undetermined coefficient, subject to final evaluation, to determine the frequency and amplitude of the steady state of oscillation.

This method as given by van der Pol[322] will now be applied to solve eq. 4.30 for the steady-state oscillation. The first step is to multiply each term by $u \, d\tau$ and to integrate over the not-yet-determined period of one full cycle:

$$\int_0^\theta u \frac{d^2 u}{d\tau^2} \, d\tau - \int_0^\theta \epsilon u \frac{du}{d\tau} \, d\tau + \int_0^\theta \epsilon u^3 \frac{du}{d\tau} \, d\tau + \int_0^\theta u^2 \, d\tau = 0, \quad (4.51)$$

where θ is an angle nearly equal to 2π which corresponds to one full period. The second and third terms vanish, as is easily shown by noting that

$$u \, du = \tfrac{1}{2} \, d(u^2), \qquad\qquad\qquad (4.52a)$$

$$u^3 \, du = \tfrac{1}{4} \, d(u^4), \qquad\qquad\qquad (4.52b)$$

and by definition u has the same value at the beginning and end of any period.

The trial solution

$$u = A \cos \tau \qquad\qquad\qquad (4.53)$$

identically satisfies the remaining terms of eq. 4.51, without restriction on A save that it be constant. Therefore, to the order of approximation that the voltage wave is cosinusoidal, the operating frequency is equal to the natural frequency of the resonator.

The amplitude is determined by multiplying each term of eq. 4.30 by the quantity $(du/d\tau)d\tau$ and integrating over the cycle

$$\int_0^\theta \frac{du}{d\tau} \frac{d^2u}{d\tau^2} \, d\tau - \int_0^\theta \epsilon \left(\frac{du}{d\tau}\right)^2 d\tau + \int_0^\theta \epsilon u^2 \left(\frac{du}{d\tau}\right)^2 d\tau$$

$$+ \int_0^\theta u \frac{du}{d\tau} \, d\tau = 0. \quad (4.54)$$

The last definite integral vanishes by direct integration to the form $u^2/2$ as in eq. 4.51. The first integral is evaluated by use of the identity

$$\frac{1}{2} \frac{d}{d\tau} \left(\frac{du}{d\tau}\right)^2 = \frac{du}{d\tau} \frac{d^2u}{d\tau^2}, \quad (4.55)$$

which reduces the integral to that of an exact derivative. Integration leads to

$$\frac{1}{2} \left(\frac{du}{d\tau}\right)^2 \Big]_0^\theta = 0, \quad (4.56)$$

which is zero by periodicity. The two remaining integrals are evaluated by substitution of eq. 4.53,

$$\int_0^\theta A^2 \sin^2 \tau \, d\tau = \int_0^\theta A^4 \cos^2 \tau \sin^2 \tau \, d\tau. \quad (4.57)$$

The evaluation of the left integral is well known. Since by eq. 4.53, $\theta \doteq 2\pi$, the equation reduces to

$$\pi = A^2 \left\{ \pi - \int_0^{2\pi} \sin^4 \tau \, d\tau \right\}. \quad (4.58)$$

Integration by means of Peirce's[235] formula 483 reduces the last term to $3\pi/4$ so that the amplitude becomes

$$A^2 = 4 \quad \text{or} \quad A = 2, \quad (4.59)$$

which is consistent with the steady-state value given by eq. 4.44.

4.11 Frequency correction

The method of equivalent linearization next introduces a correction of the frequency term by a variant of the method presented in the previous chapter. Integrating the first term of eq. 4.51 by parts yields

$$\int_0^\theta u \frac{d^2u}{d\tau^2} \, d\tau = \int_0^\theta ud\left(\frac{du}{d\tau}\right) = u \frac{du}{d\tau}\Big]_{\tau=0}^{\tau=\theta} - \int_{\tau=0}^{\tau=\theta} \frac{du}{d\tau} \, du. \quad (4.60)$$

Because $du/d\tau$ must be periodic with the same period as u, it follows that the integrated term is zero, so that eq. 4.51 reduces to

$$\int_{\tau=0}^{\tau=\theta} \frac{du}{d\tau} \, du = \int_{\tau=0}^{\tau=\theta} \left(\frac{du}{d\tau}\right)^2 d\tau = \int_{\tau=0}^{\tau=\theta} u^2 \, d\tau. \quad (4.61)$$

Use of the relation $\tau = \omega_0 t$, transforms this expression to

$$\int_{\omega t = 0}^{\omega t = 2\pi} \frac{1}{\omega_0^2} \left(\frac{du}{dt}\right)^2 \omega_0 \, dt = \int_{\omega t = 0}^{\omega t = 2\pi} u^2 \omega_0 \, dt. \qquad (4.62)$$

The next step is to assume that the voltage wave is represented by the Fourier series

$$u = \sum_{a=1}^{a=\infty} A_a \cos (a\omega t + \phi_a), \qquad (4.63)$$

whose derivative is

$$\frac{du}{dt} = - \sum_{a=1}^{a=\infty} a\omega A_a \sin (a\omega t + \phi_a). \qquad (4.64)$$

Substitution in eq. 4.62 and integration yields

$$\frac{\pi}{\omega_0} \sum_{a=1}^{a=\infty} a^2 \omega^2 A_a^2 = \pi \omega_0 \sum_{a=1}^{a=\infty} A_a^2, \qquad (4.65)$$

which leads to the compact and important expression

$$\frac{\omega^2}{\omega_0^2} = \frac{\displaystyle\sum_{a=1}^{a=\infty} A_a^2}{\displaystyle\sum_{a=1}^{a=\infty} a^2 A_a^2}. \qquad (4.66)$$

Consistent with the notation of Chapter 3, let

$$\omega = \xi \omega_0. \qquad (4.67)$$

Forming $1 - \omega^2/\omega_0^2$ and using eq. 4.67, we have

$$1 - \xi^2 = \frac{\displaystyle\sum_{a=1}^{a=\infty} (a^2 - 1) A_a^2}{\displaystyle\sum_{a=1}^{a=\infty} a^2 A_a^2}, \qquad (4.68)$$

where the combination of infinite sums is justified on the basis of absolute convergence from physical considerations. Although this result was derived on the basis of a cubic characteristic, it is correct for a single-valued characteristic of any shape. With the notation

$$m_a = A_a/A_1, \qquad (4.69)$$

eq. 4.68 reduces to

$$1 - \xi^2 = \frac{\sum\limits_{a=2}^{a=\infty} m_a{}^2(a^2 - 1)}{1 + \sum\limits_{a=2}^{a=\infty} a^2 m_a{}^2}. \tag{4.70}$$

Because the assumed system is quasi-linear, the harmonics in the voltage wave are small. For this reason the infinite sum in the denominator is negligible compared to unity, and eq. 4.70 reduces to eq. 3.23, of the previous chapter, as it should.

The frequency correction may also be expressed in terms of the Q of the system and the magnitude of the curvature of the original cubic function. It is known from eq. 4.47 that the voltage is given approximately by

$$v = v_0 \cos \omega_0 \tau = \sqrt{\tfrac{4}{3}(a - G)/b} \, \cos \omega_0 \tau. \tag{4.71}$$

On this basis, the current wave through the nonlinear resistance is, by eq. 4.20,

$$i = -av_0 \cos \omega_0 t + bv_0{}^3 \cos^3 \omega_0 t, \tag{4.72}$$

which reduces to

$$i = (\tfrac{3}{4}bv_0{}^3 - av_0) \cos \omega_0 t - \tfrac{1}{4}bv_0{}^3 \cos 3\omega_0 t. \tag{4.73}$$

In terms of eq. 3.26,

$$n_3 = i_3/i_1 = -bv_0{}^2/(3bv_0{}^2 - 4a) = -\tfrac{1}{3}(a - G)/G. \tag{4.74}$$

Thus,

$$1 - \xi = (a - G)^2/(16QG^2), \tag{4.75}$$

where

$$Q = \omega_0 C/G = (1/G)\sqrt{C/L} \tag{4.76}$$

is a property of the passive elements only, and

$$a - G = \epsilon\sqrt{C/L}. \tag{4.77}$$

Combining yields

$$1 - \xi = \epsilon^2/16, \tag{4.78}$$

which is in agreement with a result given by Kryloff and Bogoliuboff[177] on page 40 of their book. Because ϵ is the reciprocal of the small-signal selectivity Q, it is clear that Q should be kept high if good frequency stability is required.

4.12 Relaxation oscillations

In Chapter 2 it was shown that critical damping in the parallel circuit of G, C, and L occurs when the total conductance satisfies the equation

$$G = 2 \sqrt{C/L}. \tag{4.79}$$

The boundary between harmonic and relaxation oscillations was defined as the negative of this value. In the present case the total conductance at small signals is given by $(G - a)$. Consistent with eq. 4.77, relaxation oscillations* will occur if and only if

$$\epsilon > 2. \tag{4.80}$$

Specifically, if condition 4.80 is satisfied a small disturbance will increase without reversal until its magnitude is sufficient to involve the nonlinearity of the characteristic. If $\epsilon \gg 2$, the first cycle is almost identical with all the following cycles. Experimental data showing the variation of oscillator behavior as ϵ is varied and a very clear discussion of the effects involved are given by Appleton and van der Pol.[13]

Unfortunately, the mathematics of relaxation oscillations is in a most unsatisfactory state of development. For reasons that are not obvious, the methods just outlined, and all other known methods, fail to yield useful solutions. From practical experience, as well as from the cyclogram method, it is known that the solution is periodic, and that a Fourier series containing only a few terms gives a good approximation to the wave shape which is generated. However, the period does not depend in any simple way upon the circuit parameters, and no practical analytic means has been found for evaluating either the period or the relative amplitude and phase of the components.

The wave form produced by a typical relaxation oscillator is shown in Fig. 4.8. It is seen to be characterized by regions of small slope alternating with regions of large slope. This property forms the basis of a partial mathematical solution, which gives a certain amount of insight into the behavior. Because the region designated I in Fig. 4.8 is nearly straight, the second derivative (curvature) term is small, and the behavior is governed principally by the second and third terms of eq. 4.30. Neglecting the first term of eq. 4.30 for treatment

---

* Van der Pol in a basic paper[320] gives an excellent discussion of the fundamental properties of relaxation oscillators. Cyclograms and an analytic treatment similar to that given here are presented. However, it is inferred that $\epsilon = 1$ is the boundary condition; and the apparently erroneous statement is made that a finite value of inductance is required for *any* form of oscillation.

of region I leads to

$$\epsilon(1 - u^2)(du/d\tau) = u \quad \text{or} \quad (1 - u^2)(du/u) = d\tau/\epsilon. \quad (4.81)$$

Direct integration of this equation gives

$$\ln u - u^2/2 = \tau/\epsilon + K \quad \text{or} \quad \ln u^2 - u^2 = 2\tau/\epsilon + 2K, \quad (4.82)$$

where K, the constant of integration, involves the displacement of the time scale. It is convenient to set $K = 0$ for a sample calculation.

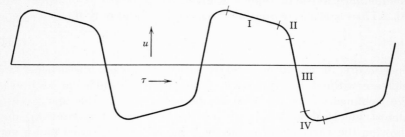

FIG. 4.8. Relaxation oscillation.

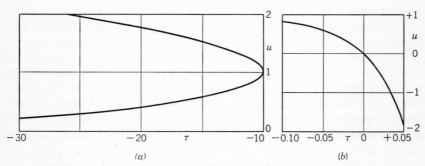

FIG. 4.9. Plot of: (a) $20 \ln u - 10u^2 = \tau$; and (b) $u = 1 - e^{20\tau}$.

The additional arbitrary choice $\epsilon = 20$ (ten times the critical value) leads to the curve of Fig. 4.9a. It is seen that eq. 4.82 gives a good fit to the curve of Fig. 4.8, not only through region I, but also by accident through region II. This close fit arises because under the chosen assumptions the derivative term must pass from positive to negative through infinity as u passes through one.

In region III the function itself is relatively small, and is negligible compared to the slope and curvature terms, which are both large. To explore this region use eq. 4.30 with the last term omitted. The resulting equation

$$d^2u/d\tau^2 = \epsilon(du/d\tau) - \epsilon u^2(du/d\tau), \quad (4.83)$$

integrates directly to

$$du/d\tau = \epsilon(u + K_1) - \epsilon(u^3/3).$$ (4.84)

This expression is not readily integrated, but is capable of useful interpretation. In particular it shows that the slope $du/d\tau$ must be zero for

$$u + K_1 = u^3/3.$$ (4.85)

Making the additional arbitrary assumption that $K_1 = -1$ reduces this expression to

$$3u - 3 = u^3,$$ (4.86)

which is satisfied approximately by

$$u = -2.104.$$ (4.87)

Near the middle of region III, u^2 is small compared to one; and it is possible to simplify eq. 4.84 by omission of the last term. The remaining equation is readily integrated to yield

$$u = K_2 e^{\epsilon\tau} - K_1.$$ (4.88)

The new constant, K_2, gives a choice of sign or direction but is otherwise not important because it is interchangeable with a shift of the τ axis.

The plot of this equation for $K_2 = -1$, $\epsilon = 20$, and $K_1 = -1$ as before is shown in Fig. 4.9b. The marked change in abscissa scale with respect to Fig. 4.9a is especially noteworthy because it indicates the extent to which different terms of the original equation vary in importance during the oscillation cycle. In the range $-\frac{1}{2} < u < \frac{1}{2}$, corresponding to region III of Fig. 4.8, eq. 4.88 is a relatively good approximation to the actual behavior of the system.

Figure 4.10 shows the results of a point-by-point calculation of eq. 4.84. It is, of course, indistinguishable from Fig. 4.9b in the central region, and satisfies the condition of eq. 4.87. Superimposed upon this figure are the data of Fig. 4.9a, adjusted to the same abscissa scale and arbitrarily made to coincide at $u = 1$. It is seen that the several curves which have been calculated can be fitted together to describe substantially the entire cycle of Fig. 4.8.

Additional insight into the situation is gained by reference to Fig. 4.6. It is seen that, for $|u| > 1$, the dynamic resistance of the total system is positive. In this region, therefore, the system is semistable; and the process of decay or relaxation occurs at a relatively slow rate. as $|u|$ decreases toward unity, the dynamic resistance increases toward infinity; that is, the decay current becomes independent of the voltage. At $|u| = 1$ a marked change occurs, corresponding to the transition between the curves of Fig. 4.10. When $|u|$ becomes slightly less than one, the behavior is governed almost entirely by the interaction of the condenser and negative resistance (Fig. 4.1). The condenser voltage changes at a very rapid rate, which would be exponential except for the effects of the curvature of the characteristic. This behavior has already been presented mathematically in eqs. 4.83 and 4.84.

It is interesting to note from Fig. 4.6 that the value of i is the same for $u = -1$ and $u = +2$. This fact, together with eq. 4.87, strongly suggests that the rapid voltage excursion just described actually does

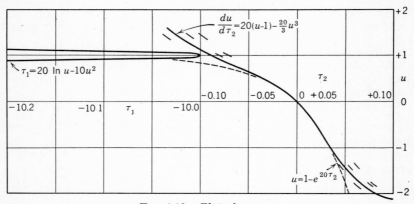

FIG. 4.10. Plot of u vs. τ.

take place between the limits -1 and $+2$ or, alternatively, $+1$ and -2. In the region $1 < |u| < 2$ the behavior is, as previously noted, governed principally by the inductance and resistance. The charge on the capacitance decreases relatively slowly by a factor of two.

The total (normalized) period may be calculated approximately by use of the information already tabulated. From Fig. 4.9a it is clear that a period $\tau_1 = 16.1$ is required for u to decay from 2.0 to 1.0. The period required for u to reverse from $+1.0$ to -2.0 is approximately $\tau_2 = 0.2$ from the isocline plot of Fig. 4.10. Adding and doubling these figures yields $\tau_0 = 32.6$ for the total period. That is, for $\epsilon = 20$ the total period is approximately $32.6/2\pi$ or 5.2 times the period of the resonant circuit itself. This result agrees to within about 20 per cent with other theoretical and experimental results.

4.13 Summary

In this chapter we have explored some of the simpler aspects of the mathematics of nonlinear systems. In spite of the numerous simplifying assumptions made, the relationships are complicated. The treatment of relaxation oscillations is even less satisfactory, because no single expression is adequate to describe the entire cycle of the generated wave.

In later chapters the same general methods will be used to explore the behavior of other systems, such as those with more than one resonant frequency, and those which oscillate at an integral fraction of an externally applied voltage. It is hoped that the mathematical methods now available will sometime be refined to facilitate a more complete analysis of these important practical systems.

PROBLEMS

4.1. Substituting $i = 0.01 \sin 50v$ in eq. 4.1 and letting $G = 10^{-4}$, $L = 10^{-3}$, and $C = 10^{-10}$, calculate isoclines and a cyclogram like those of Fig. 4.4.

4.2. Repeat Prob. 1, changing only $L = 10^{-1}$, and $C = 10^{-12}$.

4.3. Evaluate the angular velocity at $45°$ intervals in Prob. 4.1.

4.4. Verify eq. 4.35.

4.5. Verify eq. 4.37.

4.6. Verify eq. 4.50b.

4.7. Verify eq. 4.58.

4.8. Repeat the derivation of eq. 4.66, justifying the procedure.

4.9. Evaluate ϵ in Problems 4.1 and 4.2.

4.10. Following the method of Section 4.11, derive the wave form associated with $a = 11 \times 10^{-5}$, $b = 1 \times 10^{-9}$, $G = 1 \times 10^{-5}$, $L = 1$, and $C = 10^{-11}$.

5

FEEDBACK SYSTEMS AND
STABILITY CRITERIA

This chapter is devoted to an outline of existing feedback theory with particular emphasis upon the way it affects oscillators. This material is included for two reasons. (1) Negative feedback is applied directly in a number of oscillator circuits in the interest of stability. (2) Existing theory is highly developed and is sufficiently general to include cases of positive as well as negative feedback.

5.1 Nature of the problem

It is well known that vacuum tubes are neither as linear nor as stable as might be desired for many applications. In amplifiers, nonlinearity leads to nonlinear distortion and intermodulation effects; whereas changes of the parameters lead to variation of gain, impedance, and frequency response. Corresponding difficulties appear in oscillators and other devices which employ vacuum tubes. Because it has not proved feasible to construct vacuum tubes which are substantially free from these defects, much work has been done to develop circuits in which the important properties are insensitive to the variations of the parameters of the tubes employed.

In amplifiers it is possible to secure a remarkable reduction in the degree of nonlinear distortion by properly returning a portion of the output signal to the input terminals. The advantages of this arrangement, which is referred to as inverse or negative feedback, appear first to have been recognized by H. S. Black.[33] The mathematics of feedback systems has been extensively studied by H. Nyquist,[228] H. W. Bode,[34] and others.[208, 237]

A relatively large amount of feedback must be applied to an amplifier if a significant improvement in stability and linearity is to be secured. It then becomes difficult to avoid oscillations, which would seriously interfere with the operation of the circuit as an amplifier.

Much of the work which has gone into the analysis of feedback systems has been directed toward overcoming this tendency toward uncontrolled oscillation. Fortunately, the analysis is sufficiently general to be a substantial aid when oscillation is desired as well as when it is to be avoided.

In amplifiers, as well as in oscillators, it is necessary to define the system under consideration with considerable care before we can make exact statements about it. For instance, the output load impedance may or may not be considered a portion of the amplifier, depending upon the conditions. As an example, consider a phonograph amplifier, which receives a small signal from the pickup device and delivers a much larger signal to the loudspeaker; here it would appear that neither pickup nor loudspeaker was part of the amplifier. However, the performance of the loudspeaker will depend upon the internal impedance of the device which drives it. Therefore, we must consider both pickup and amplifier in determining this impedance. Also, the behavior of the pickup depends upon the impedance into which it works. Therefore, the loudspeaker as a load must be considered as part of the amplifier in so far as it affects the input impedance.

When feedback is used the input and output impedances are likely to depend upon the associated load and source impedances, respectively. Moreover, the behavior of the amplifier itself may be considerably affected by these impedances. For example, an amplifier which operates quite satisfactorily under normal conditions may oscillate if the load or the source is disconnected. Therefore, in defining the amount of feedback and other properties, it is usually necessary to consider the entire amplifier system.

5.2 Effects of feedback

The various aspects of feedback are conveniently discussed with reference to Fig. 5.1, which shows a conventional amplifier in which feedback is produced by the relatively high impedance Z_5. This arrangement is referred to as *shunt* or *voltage* feedback because the feedback path is connected in shunt with both input and output circuits and because the feedback action depends upon voltage rather than current.

The analysis assumes that the system is substantially linear for a sufficiently small input voltage V_3. If the system is stable, this assumption is justifiable; if unstable, the analysis serves only to indicate that fact. To simplify the analysis it is further assumed that Z_1 is very large.

The amplification or *gain without feedback*, μ, is readily determined by assuming $Z_5 = \infty$. By consideration of the output circuit as a potentiometer, we see that

$$\mu = V_2/V_3 = kZ_4/(Z_2 + Z_4), \tag{5.1}$$

where k is the intrinsic amplification factor. In typical situations the voltage amplification is large ($V_2 \gg V_1$), and Z_5 is large compared to all other impedances in the system (except perhaps Z_1).

The magnitude of the voltage returned or fed back is measured by the parameter

$$\beta = Z_3/Z_5, \tag{5.2}$$

which is seen to be the fraction of the output voltage which is applied to the input circuit.

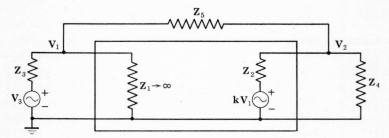

FIG. 5.1. Amplifier with shunt feedback.

The amplification μ' which exists when feedback is present is obtained from the two relations

$$V_2/V_1 = kZ_4/(Z_2 + Z_4) \tag{5.3}$$

and

$$V_1 = V_3 + \beta V_2. \tag{5.4}$$

Eliminating V_1 and using eq. 5.1, we have

$$\mu' = V_2/V_3 = \mu/(1 - \mu\beta). \tag{5.5}$$

It is seen that μ' becomes infinite when the product $\mu\beta$ is equal to unity; this special condition corresponds to oscillation, because a finite output exists in the absence of an input.

The product $\mu\beta$ represents the *loop transmission* of the system and is a very important quantity. For reasons presented later, it often provides a more convenient criterion of stability than does the position of the system roots. The nature of this product is clarified by inquiry as to how it could be measured. From Fig. 5.1 it is seen that if the grid lead of the input vacuum tube were cut and a signal V_0 applied to this grid, a voltage μV_0 would be produced at the output terminals, and a voltage $\beta \mu V_0$ would be developed at the point where the cut was made. Moreover, it is seen that the ratio of returned to supplied signal would be the same and equal to $\mu \beta$ if the circuit had been opened at some other point.

It should be pointed out that Fig. 5.1 represents a *single-loop* feedback system in which the loop transmission is zero if Z_5 is open or if any of the vacuum tubes is disabled. Conversely, a *multiple-loop* feedback system is one in which feedback may occur through two or more distinct paths. Multiple-loop systems are quite complicated and are discussed further only in the final section of this chapter.

A single-loop system is absolutely stable if the feedback loop is opened at any point; therefore, $\mu \beta$ is a measure of the behavior which will result when the loop is closed.

5.3 Increase of stability

In the absence of feedback the overall amplification of an amplifier depends directly upon the condition of the tubes and the various related elements. Where several tubes are used in tandem, the amplification may vary rather drastically because all the tubes are likely to respond in the same way to such effects as heater voltage, plate voltage, or aging; and the overall amplification involves these separate effects as a product. This is represented mathematically by eq. 5.1 in which the amplification μ involves **k** as a direct factor.

One of the most important properties of feedback is its ability to improve stability. The truth of this statement can be seen in a general way by rewriting eq. 5.5 in the form

$$\mu' = \frac{1}{(1/\mu) - \beta}. \tag{5.6}$$

It is practical to establish the condition $\beta \gg 1/\mu$, in which case the amplification with feedback, μ' is substantially equal to $(-1/\beta)$ and hence is nearly independent of the condition of the tubes and in fact of everything except β, which involves only Z_3 and Z_5.

The improvement in stability is determined quantitatively by comparing the differential fractions $d\mu/\mu$ and $d\mu'/\mu'$. The fractional form of the differential is appropriate because we are interested in the ratio rather than in the absolute amount by which amplification is reduced. Differentiating eq. 5.5 leads to

$$d\mu' = \frac{(1 - \mu\beta)d\mu + \mu\beta \, d\mu}{(1 - \mu\beta)^2}, \tag{5.7}$$

which, when divided by eq. 5.5, yields

$$\frac{d\mu'}{\mu'} = \frac{1}{1 - \mu\beta} \cdot \frac{d\mu}{\mu}. \tag{5.8}$$

This is an important relationship because it shows that feedback has improved the stability, or reduced the variation of the amplification due to any cause, by exactly the same factor that it reduced the amplification itself.   The improvement results from the fact that, with feedback present, the overall amplification depends principally upon *passive* elements, Z_3 and Z_5 in the present example, which can be made much more stable than vacuum tubes.

In practice, the improvement of stability and other benefits of feedback are secured by first designing an amplifier which has an amplification considerably in excess of that actually desired.   The excess amplification is then exchanged for improved stability, linearity, etc., by application of suitable negative feedback, based upon *stable linear* elements.   However, there are grave practical difficulties in securing large amounts of negative feedback, especially across wide intervals of frequency, so that we should not enter lightly into such an undertaking.

5.4 Reduction of noise, hum, and distortion

Feedback may be employed to reduce the voltages which appear in the output due to distortion, hum, and certain forms of noise.   We can prove this statement by referring to Fig. 5.1 and assuming that the output contains an undesired term, V_5, in addition to the desired signal, kV_1.   In the absence of feedback the output voltage is given by

$$V_2 = (V_5 + kV_1) \, Z_4/(Z_2 + Z_4). \tag{5.9}$$

When feedback is applied the output of both desired and undesired voltages is divided by the factor $(1 - \mu\beta)$ as shown by insertion of V_5 in the equations which lead to eq. 5.5.

The useful signal output may now be restored to the value which would have existed in the absence of feedback either by increasing the input signal or by adding at the input a low level amplifier *which is free from distortion, hum, and noise.*

In practice, this increase of amplification is usually incorporated within the feedback path so that the pertinent comparison is between two amplifiers which have equal overall amplification and differ in the presence or absence of feedback.   Because the added amplification system operates at a small signal level, it is relatively easy to meet the requirement of negligible distortion.   Therefore it is quite practical by use of feedback to reduce distortion to the extent of the factor $(1 - \mu\beta)$, which may be made large.

Feedback is equally effective in reducing harmonic distortion or intermodulation effects which result from the simultaneous presence of signals, whether the distortion arises in the output tube or in any other tube of the amplifier.   Such reduction is of considerable importance, especially if none of the tubes is driven to the overload point and if several signals are present, as in telephone repeater amplifiers. If, however, some tube is overloaded, so that a violent curvature in the operating characteristic is involved, the action of feedback may produce objectionable intermodulation effects and harmonic distortion terms which would not otherwise be produced.

The conduction of vacuum tubes results from the motion of electrons in the space between the cathode and the anode.   Because electrons carry a finite charge and are emitted in a random manner, the current flow is not perfectly smooth, but fluctuates in an irregular manner about some average value.   This phenomenon, which is referred to as tube noise, is discussed more fully in Chapter 15.   It sets a lower limit on the magnitude of signals which may be amplified by means of vacuum tubes.   Ordinarily, the limit is established in the first tube where the signal is smallest.

We may readily show that feedback is unable to reduce noise produced in the first tube by comparing a feedback amplifier with one which does not employ feedback.   We assume that both have equal amplification, that both employ the same input circuit and tube, and that all the noise is produced by the first tube of each amplifier. Because of the equality of amplification, both amplifiers produce the same output from a given input signal.   And both produce equal noise outputs because the intrinsically higher amplification factor of the feedback system leads to a proportionally higher noise value. When both the amplification and the noise values are divided by the factor $(1 - \mu\beta)$ they correspond exactly to those of the nonfeedback amplifier.   Thus we conclude that *feedback is of no help in reducing noise produced in the input stage.*

5.5 Modification of input and output impedances

Feedback has a profound influence upon the effective input and output impedances of an amplifier.   We may show that this is true by reference to Fig. 5.1.   In the absence of feedback, the output impedance is simply Z_2.   That is, a current V_2/Z_2 will flow as a consequence of applying a voltage V_2 to the output terminals when V_3 is zero.   When feedback is present, however, the application of V_2 results in a voltage,

$$V_1 = \beta V_2 \tag{5.10}$$

at the input terminals.   The voltage effective in producing current in Z_2 is now $V_2 - k\beta V_2$, and the effective output impedance is

$$Z_0 = Z_2/(1 - k\beta). \tag{5.11}$$

Because the product $k\beta$, which is closely related to $\mu\beta$, is negative and large compared to unity, the output impedance is greatly reduced.

Analysis of other feedback systems shows that in general the shunt connection at input or output decreases the associated impedance whereas the series connection increases the impedance.   Moreover, bridge or hybrid-coil arrangements lead to finite impedances of convenient magnitude which are almost independent of the condition of the associated vacuum tubes.

5.6 Positive and negative feedback combined

Oscillators are sometimes designed and analyzed from the viewpoint that a positive feedback path sufficient to produce oscillation is added to an amplifier system stabilized by means of negative feedback.[46] It is argued that the negative feedback amplifier, taken as a unit, is highly stable and linear.   Therefore, the positive feedback path need have a transmission only slightly in excess of some minimum value in order to ensure that oscillation will persist even if the performance of the tubes is considerably degraded by age or substitution.   At this point there is a great temptation to conclude that the resulting oscillations will be substantially linear because of the action of negative feedback.   This is *not true* unless the feedback paths include a thermistor or similar device suitable for producing linear oscillations.   The difficulty lies in the fact that overload must produce a very large reduction of tube performance before the gain of a stabilized amplifier is appreciably reduced.

Assuming that two feedback paths are effectively in parallel, and consist only of *linear* elements, as is usually the case, we can see that these paths are equivalent to a single more complicated linear circuit. Ordinarily, the total feedback path constitutes a bridge circuit in which a considerable increase in the effective selectivity is produced as the balanced condition is approached.   Usually, it is much easier to obtain a correct interpretation of the operation of such systems by treating the *entire* feedback system as one unit and the unstabilized amplifier as another.   This viewpoint has been ably presented by Post and Pit.[242]

When the negative feedback path is not effectively in parallel with the positive one the combination constitutes a multiple-loop feedback system. The general treatment of such systems is quite complicated, but practical cases are ordinarily sufficiently simple to permit solution by a slight extension of the methods already presented. The most common example of such a simpler system is a linear oscillator in which the cathode resistor is not by-passed and so constitutes a negative-feedback element.

In any event it is necessary to use considerable care in the analysis of feedback systems, particularly those in which several paths exist. The following sections, which are devoted to a study of the stability of feedback systems, illustrate some useful techniques for the analysis of such problems.

5.7 Conditions for oscillation

It was shown in Chapter 2 that a system will generate spontaneous oscillations if and only if the characteristic equation has roots in the right half plane. Unfortunately, this criterion of stability is not a convenient one for use in the design and analysis of regenerative arrangements because a very large amount of work is required to calculate the roots of typical systems and because the position of the roots offers little or no guide for improving the performance if unsatisfactory.[36]

It has been found that the loop transmission $\mu\beta$ provides a far more satisfactory criterion for the design of feedback devices. Compared to the system roots, $\mu\beta$ has the advantage that it can be measured directly, so that the existence of any unintentional coupling effects may be detected if present, and that the effect of a given parameter change may be readily predicted. The first accurate statement of the relation between stability and loop transmission is due to H. Nyquist.[228] However, a simpler proof and useful extensions of his results have been developed by Bode.[34] The boundary between oscillation and nonoscillation is of interest in connection with both amplifiers and oscillators. However, in amplifiers a large scalar magnitude of $(\mu\beta)$ is necessary, whereas in oscillators a smaller feedback is often adequate.

5.8 The $(\mu\beta)$ diagram

The preceding sections have shown that a feedback system is unstable (that is, it may produce an output with no input) if

$$\mu\beta = 1. \tag{5.12}$$

Moreover, ordinary experience would predict expanding oscillations if $(\mu\beta)$ were real and greater than unity; this prediction is ordinarily but not always correct.   The exact situation is expressed in terms of a Nyquist plot such as that of Fig. 5.2, which shows in polar form the locus of the loop transmission ($\mu\beta$) as the real frequency ω is varied from $-\infty$ to $+\infty$.*

It is seen that the loop transmission is real and exceeds unity at both a positive and a negative frequency near 1.5 ω_0.   Therefore, it is correctly anticipated that oscillation will occur at about this frequency.

A significantly different and more complicated situation is shown in Fig. 5.3a.   Although there are two positive (and two negative) frequencies at which the loop transmission is real and greater than unity, the system is actually stable!   That is, there are no roots in the right

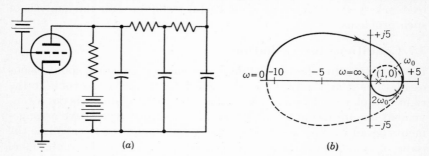

FIG. 5.2.   A resistance-capacitance oscillator: (a) circuit, and (b) Nyquist plot with approximate frequency scale in arbitrary units.

half of the complex plane, and small oscillations decrease rather than increase with time.

5.9 Nyquist's criterion

The results of the foregoing discussion are compactly stated as follows: *A single-loop feedback system is stable if and only if the Nyquist plot of the loop transmission ($\mu\beta$), in the frequency range $-\infty < \omega < \infty$, does not encircle the point $(1, 0)$.*

It is apparent that a system having a Nyquist plot such as that of Fig. 5.3b must be absolutely stable, because there is no frequency at which ($\mu\beta$) is real and as large as unity.   And it is clear that a system such as that of Fig. 5.2 is unstable, that is, will oscillate.   A slight

---

* In this and other Nyquist diagrams a dotted line indicates negative frequencies. The inclusion of negative frequencies is required only in systems such as that of Fig. 5.2, in which finite transmission exists at zero frequency, and it is necessary to close the curve in order to establish whether or not the critical point is encircled. In all cases the diagram is symmetrical about the horizontal axis, and negative frequencies are physically indistinguishable from positive frequencies, so that no additional effort is required.

difficulty may arise with the conditional case of Fig. 5.3a but, as the point $(1, 0)$ is *not* encircled, the system is actually stable! This stability is, however, only conditional because the plot will encircle the critical point if the loop amplification is reduced by a factor of about two. Moreover, in many systems of this kind sustained oscillations will result if the system is given an initial disturbance large enough to introduce nonlinearity through overloading.

The fact that small signals decrease rather than increase in a conditionally stable system may be traced to the behavior of expanding sinusoidal waves. The reversed curvature of the Nyquist plot of Fig. 5.3a in the region of $2\omega_0$ is associated with a circuit behavior which

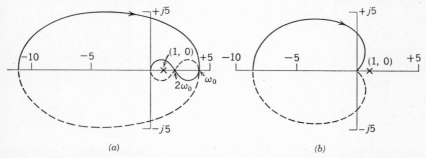

(a)   (b)

FIG. 5.3. Nyquist plots: (a) conditionally stable system and (b) absolutely stable system.

tends to damp out rather than enlarge an oscillation near that frequency. In this connection it should be noted that sustained oscillations which result from a reduction of $(\mu\beta)$ will occur at a frequency near ω_0 whereas the inner crossover of Fig. 5.3a is at a frequency near $2\omega_0$. The discussion of oscillation build-up in Chapter 18 will help to clarify this behavior.

5.10 Basis of the criterion

The rigorous proof of Nyquist's criterion requires extensive manipulation of complex variables and a familiarity with the theory of contour integration which is beyond the scope of this book. The interested reader should refer to Bode[34] for this material. It is, however, possible to explain the ideas involved and to give the results a degree of plausibility.

Nyquist's criterion depends upon a relationship between the phasor plot of $(\mu\beta)$ at various real sinusoidal frequencies and the location of the system roots in the complex frequency plane as discussed in Chapter 2. In fact, the Nyquist plot is a transformation of the points on the vertical (real frequency) axis of the p plane. Somewhat less obviously, the point $(1, 0)$ in the Nyquist plot is identified with the roots of the equation representing the loop transmission.

The situation is clarified by reference to Fig. 5.4, which shows a complex frequency plane and associated Nyquist plot. Traversing the Nyquist plot with increasing frequency we find that the critical point is constantly on the right until infinite frequency is reached. Correspondingly, the root is constantly on the right as the real frequency axis of Fig. 5.4b is traversed (upward) with increasing frequency. If, on the other hand, the roots had existed in the left half

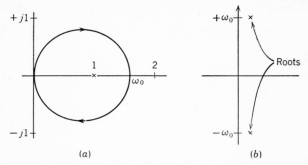

(a)　　　　　　　　　　　　(b)

FIG. 5.4. Example of Nyquist's criterion for an unstable system: (a) Nyquist plot and (b) complex frequency plane. Arrow heads indicate increasing frequency.

of the p plane there could have been no encirclement of the critical point in Fig. 5.4a.

5.11 Correlation between the Nyquist plot and root position

The proof of Nyquist's criterion shows that there must be a relationship between the Nyquist plot and the position of the roots in the complex plane. As stated, the criterion tells only whether or not there are roots with positive real parts, on the basis of encirclement of the point $(1, 0)$. Because it is often desirable to know the location or value of the roots of the system, it would be very convenient if the Nyquist plot could be made to yield this information. Experience indicates that, although this is possible on a rough basis, it is impractical to obtain any very exact information in this way.

The problem, which has been studied by Vazsonyi[330] from a somewhat different viewpoint, may be approached by reference to the tuned plate oscillator shown in Fig. 5.5. This particular circuit is chosen because of its simplicity and the symmetry of the associated equations. It is assumed that the grid is negatively biased so as to draw no current, and that tests are made at a sufficiently low level to justify the assumption of linearity. With these restrictions it is clear that the grid voltage is a fraction M/L of the plate voltage, and that the system is correctly represented in Fig. 5.5b, where r_p is the plate resistance and g_m is the transconductance. Because the same current would be drawn by a suitable negative resistance, it is possible to simplify the equivalent circuit still further to the form of Fig. 5.6.

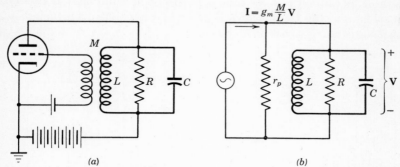

FIG. 5.5. Tuned plate oscillator: (a) circuit diagram and (b) equivalent circuit.

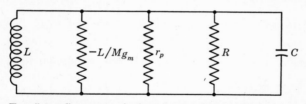

FIG. 5.6. System equivalent to tuned plate oscillator.

Inspection of this figure shows that the roots are pure imaginary if the total conductance vanishes, that is, if

$$1/r_p + 1/R - Mg_m/L = 0. \qquad (5.13)$$

As shown in Chapter 2, the roots will be complex with negative real part if

$$2\sqrt{C/L} > (1/r_p + 1/R - Mg_m/L) > 0 \qquad (5.14)$$

and complex with positive real part if

$$-2\sqrt{C/L} < (1/r_p + 1/R - Mg_m/L) < 0. \qquad (5.15)$$

Harmonic oscillations, therefore, correspond to transconductance values lying between the limits

$$L(1/r_p + 1/R + 2\sqrt{C/L}) > Mg_m > L(1/r_p + 1/R). \qquad (5.16)$$

The ratio n, of the upper to the lower limit of g_m, is

$$n = 1 + \frac{2\sqrt{C/L}}{1/r_p + 1/R}. \tag{5.17}$$

This ratio may be made relatively large by choosing a tuned circuit with a high Q, and a tube with a high plate resistance. This choice is desirable, because it ensures that the wave form will remain reasonably sinusoidal and the frequency will be nearly constant even though the transconductance varies appreciably.

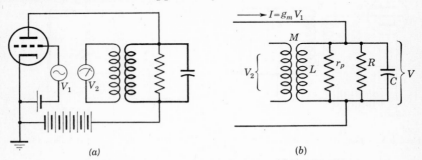

FIG. 5.7.   Arrangement for evaluation of loop transmission: (a) actual and (b) equivalent.

The roots of the system of Fig. 5.6 are, as shown in Chapter 2,

$$p_1 = \alpha + j\omega = Mg_m/2LC - 1/2RC - 1/2r_pC$$
$$+ j\sqrt{1/LC - (Mg_m/2LC - 1/2RC - 1/2r_pC)^2} \tag{5.18}$$

and

$$p_2 = \alpha - j\omega = Mg_m/2LC - 1/2RC - 1/2r_pC$$
$$- j\sqrt{1/LC - (Mg_m/2LC - 1/2RC - 1/2r_pC)^2}. \tag{5.19}$$

The loop transmission of Fig. 5.5 is calculated with reference to the equivalent circuit of Fig. 5.7. It is readily shown that the loop transmission is

$$(\mu\beta) = \frac{V_2}{V_1} = \frac{Mg_m}{L(1/r_p + 1/R + j\omega C + 1/j\omega L)}. \tag{5.20}$$

Inspection of this equation shows that the magnitude is directly proportional to g_m, that the phase angle is zero if $\omega C = 1/\omega L$, and that the phase angle is $\pm 45°$ if $\omega C - 1/\omega L = \pm(1/r_p + 1/R)$. Moreover, it is easy to show that the Nyquist plot has the form of a circle.

For this particular system it is possible to calculate a relatively simple relationship between the frequency scale on the Nyquist plot and the location of the complex roots. The procedure is facilitated by use of the substitutions

$$\omega_0 = 1/\sqrt{LC}, \tag{5.21}$$

$$\omega = \omega_0(1 - \xi), \tag{5.22}$$

$$G = 1/r_p + 1/R, \tag{5.23}$$

and

$$Q = 1/G\omega_0 L. \tag{5.24}$$

With these substitutions the roots become

$$\alpha \pm j\omega = \tfrac{1}{2}(Mg_m\omega_0{}^2 - G/C) \pm j\sqrt{\omega_0{}^2 - \tfrac{1}{4}(Mg_m\omega_0{}^2 - G/C)^2}. \tag{5.25}$$

Because, for any prescribed ω_0, the roots vary along the arc of a circle, it is sufficient to specify α. Eliminating Mg_m between eqs. 5.20 and 5.25 yields

$$(\mu\beta) = \frac{2\alpha/\omega_0 + G/\omega_0 C}{\omega_0 L(G + j\omega C + 1/j\omega L)}. \tag{5.26}$$

Elimination of C with introduction of eqs. 5.22 and 5.24 leads to

$$\begin{aligned}
(\mu\beta) &= \frac{2\alpha/\omega_0 + 1/Q}{\omega_0 L[G + j(1 - \xi)/\omega_0 L) + 1/j(1 - \xi)\omega_0 L]} \\
&= \frac{1 + 2Q\alpha/\omega_0}{1 + jQ(1 - \xi) - jQ/(1 - \xi)}, \quad (5.27)
\end{aligned}$$

which shows that the Nyquist plot is uniquely expressed in terms of the angular position of the root, the Q of the passive portion of the circuit and the frequency variable ξ.

The desired relationship is most conveniently expressed by assigning a fixed small value to ξ and exploring the contour described. If ξ is restricted to small values we may use the approximate relation

$$1 + \xi \doteq 1/(1 - \xi) \tag{5.28}$$

to obtain

$$(\mu\beta) = \frac{1 + 2Q\alpha/\omega_0}{1 - j2Q\xi}. \tag{5.29}$$

Converting to rectangular coordinates by use of

$$(\mu\beta) = x + jy, \tag{5.30}$$

we may expand eq. 5.29 to obtain

$$x + jy - j2Q\xi x + 2Q\xi y = 1 + 2Q\alpha/\omega_0. \tag{5.31}$$

The relation

$$y/x = 2Q\xi, \tag{5.32}$$

which results when the imaginary terms are equated may be used to eliminate Q in eq. 5.31. With this substitution we have

$$x + y^2/x = 1 + \alpha y/\xi x \omega_0 \tag{5.33}$$

or

$$\alpha/\omega_0 = \xi(x^2/y + y - x/y). \tag{5.34}$$

The location of roots is illustrated in Fig. 5.8, which shows an arbitrarily chosen Nyquist plot of the circular shape required by eq. 5.20.

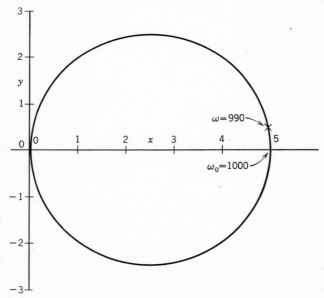

FIG. 5.8.   Determination of roots from Nyquist plot.

In this example $x = 5$, $y = \frac{1}{2}$, $\omega_0 = 1000$, $\omega = 990$, and $\xi = 0.010$. Consistent with eq. 5.34, $\alpha/\omega_0 = 0.40$, and the system roots are $400 \pm j1000$. An oscillator having these properties would have relatively poor performance as to wave form and frequency stability, but would exhibit a very rapid rate of build-up at the beginning of oscillation.

It is emphasized that the foregoing analysis is accurate only under the assumed conditions. However, it yields useful qualitative information under any conditions in which the Nyquist plot resembles the circular form of Fig. 5.8.

5.12 Frequency and amplitude stability

The Nyquist diagram for a system is very helpful in calculating, or at least estimating, the frequency stability. The calculations are exact if the system is linear, and give an excellent approximation in quasi-linear, that is, high-Q nonlinear systems.

As a first step toward the determination of frequency stability, we must note that the shape of the Nyquist plot may change in two basically different ways as the loop gain is reduced by the action of the limiter. If the limiter is independent of the resonator the diagram

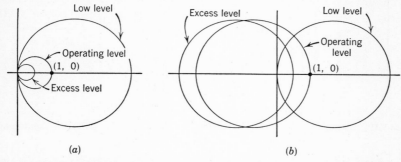

(a)   (b)

FIG. 5.9. Nyquist plots at various levels: (a) limiter isolated and (b) limiter and resonator combined in bridge.

simply shrinks, as shown in Fig. 5.9a. If, however, the limiter and the resonator are combined, as in the Meacham or Wien bridge circuits, the diagram is displaced laterally without appreciably changing its size, as shown in Fig. 5.9b. If we know the behavior of the Nyquist diagram with changes in amplitude, we may find the frequency stability from the diagram which corresponds to a very low amplitude level. Otherwise, we must use the diagram which corresponds to the desired operating level, and therefore passes through the critical point (1, 0).

The construction is shown in Fig. 5.10a. The frequencies ω_0 and $\omega_0 + \delta\omega$ corresponding respectively to the critical point (1, 0) and to a point displaced by a small angle $\delta\phi$ are observed. Then, from the basic formula given in Chapter 1, the frequency stability with respect to phase shifts external to the resonator is

$$S_F = \frac{\delta\phi}{\delta\omega/\omega_0} \tag{5.35}$$

provided $\delta\phi$ is taken sufficiently small.   In practice, this approximation is entirely satisfactory, and the frequency stability of a system is
readily predicted by inspection of the frequency scale of the Nyquist
plot.   A high degree of frequency stability is seen to correspond to a
Nyquist plot in which the frequency scale is very open.

The amplitude stability is determined in a somewhat different manner, for it depends upon the rate at which the plot in the region of
(1, 0), shrinks with increase of amplitude.   The curves corresponding
to two slightly different known amplitudes of signal are drawn, as in

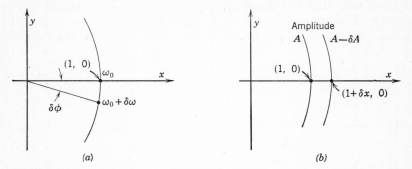

Fig. 5.10.   Determination of stability factors from Nyquist plot: (a) frequency
stability and (b) amplitude stability.

Fig. 5.10b, and the difference δx between the horizontal intercepts is
noted.   The amplitude stability is then given by

$$S_A = \frac{\delta x}{\delta A / A}. \tag{5.36}$$

A high degree of amplitude stability is seen to correspond to a system
of Nyquist plots which for small differences of signal level are widely
separated in the region of (1, 0).

Because it is quite tedious to obtain data for Nyquist plots at
various amplitude levels, the amplitude relationship is less generally
useful than the frequency relationship.   Fortunately, frequency
stability is ordinarily more important than amplitude stability, so this
is not a matter of grave importance.

5.13 Llewellyn's criterion

An additional criterion which is sometimes convenient for testing
the stability of linear systems was stated intuitively by Llewellyn and
has since been verified by Bode[34] on page 165 of his book and by
Chu.[62] It is applicable to linear systems of all classes, but is most

useful in connection with two-terminal oscillators, to which Nyquist's criterion is not applicable.

The conditions for applying the test in its first form are shown in Fig. 5.11a. The network is opened at some point a, as indicated, and the impedance between the opened points is observed as a function of frequency. *If the polar plot of impedance, for all frequencies from − ∞ to + ∞ does not encircle the origin and if the system is stable with the terminals open, then it is also stable with the terminals short circuited.*

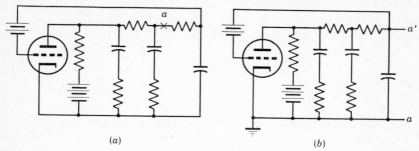

FIG. 5.11. Llewellyn's criterion: (a) direct test; and (b) modified test.

In the alternative form the *admittance* between two points in the network, as shown in Fig. 5.11b, is measured as a function of frequency. Then *if the polar plot of admittance for all frequencies from − ∞ to + ∞ does not encircle the origin and if the system is stable with the terminals short circuited, then it is also stable with the terminals open circuited.*

We see that Llewellyn's criterion is closely related to Nyquist's. Therefore, it should be possible to relate the shape of the Llewellyn plot to the position of the complex roots and to the amplitude and frequency stability of the system. These relationships are not developed here because they are not used in the following sections.

Taken together, the relationships developed in this chapter provide a very powerful means for the analysis and the design of feedback systems, whether the objective is a stable amplifier or a reliable oscillator. These relationships are used and extended to treat multiply-resonant systems in Chapter 18.

PROBLEMS

5 1. Show how to measure the loop transmission of a feedback amplifier.

5.2. Sketch a single-loop and a multiple-loop feedback system.

5.3. Explain why fractional derivatives are used in eq. 5.8

5.4. Verify the argument of Section 5.4 that distortion is reduced in the ratio $(1 − \mu\beta)$.

5.5. Discuss the use of feedback in connection with tube noise in the input stage.

5.6. Discuss the significance of negative frequencies in conjunction with the Nyquist diagram.

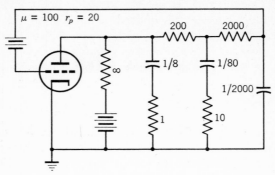

PROBLEM 5.7

5.7. Calculate the system roots for the circuit shown, assuming for convenience that the impedance of each RC section is high compared to that of the adjacent one.

5.8. Calculate the Nyquist diagram for the above system under the same assumptions.

5.9. Calculate the Llewellyn plot for the above system at the terminals of the grid condenser.

6

RESONATORS

Resistance-capacitance oscillators, although important, are not capable of extreme frequency stability; all other oscillators use some form of resonator. As stated in Chapter 1, a complete oscillator consists of a resonator and an associated driving system. This chapter is devoted to a discussion of resonators which are suitable for oscillators. The features which would characterize an ideal resonator are enumerated as a basis for evaluating realizable units.

The most flexible and generally useful resonator is composed of a condenser and coil. By varying the size, shape, and number of turns in conjunction with the permeability of the core it is possible to construct useful coils over a remarkable range of inductance. Similarly, variations in the construction of condensers lead to a wide range of useful capacitance. Inductance-capacitance resonators may, therefore, be constructed for operation over a very wide range of impedances and frequencies. Where extreme frequency stability is required the mechanical vibrations of a quartz plate are profitably employed. In the microwave region electrical cavity resonators or molecular resonance devices are most suitable. Considerations which govern the choice of a resonator are developed in the following sections.

6.1 General properties of resonators

The properties of resonators are conveniently discussed in terms of the circuit of Fig. 6.1, which shows the series combination of an inductance and a capacitance. The losses, which are always present to some degree, and are usually due mainly to the coil, are represented by the resistance. The properties of this circuit are, of course, completely specified when the three element values are given. In particular, the value of Q and the resonant frequency are known from the formulas of Chapter 2. As noted there, the transient oscillations of the free circuit have a frequency which is slightly different from that at which the largest steady-state response occurs. Moreover, the value of Q

may be thought of either in terms of the energy loss per cycle of the free oscillation or the energy which must be supplied per cycle in the steady state.

The latter viewpoint is the more profitable for our present purpose in that it establishes on a general basis the desirability of a high Q. *Because a high Q resonator requires less driving power than a corresponding low Q resonator, its frequency is less affected by a given fractional change in the driving system.* However, the frequency stability of a given system is seldom appreciably improved by an improvement of the resonator alone unless the driving system is readjusted to take advantage of the decreased losses.

These ideas are interpreted in terms of Fig. 6.2, which was analyzed in Chapter 4. Corresponding to prescribed values of L, R, and C,

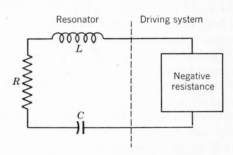

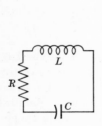

Fig. 6.1. Series resonance.   Fig. 6.2.   Negative resistance oscillator.

sustained oscillations will occur only if the negative resistance device, which is inherently nonlinear, has an incremental negative resistance larger than R. The operating frequency differs somewhat from the natural frequency of L and C because of intermodulation effects, and therefore changes with variations of the nonlinear characteristics.

If the resonator Q is increased by reducing R without making any other change, the frequency stability is not greatly improved and may actually be degraded, because the relationship of the reactances to the driving system is unchanged. If, however, the resonator Q is increased by increasing both of the reactances, leaving R unchanged, the frequency stability is improved proportionally.

From the foregoing discussion we may draw this important conclusion: *The essential properties of a resonator are its natural frequency f, its selectivity Q, and its characteristic impedance Z.* The natural frequency is the frequency which would result if the driving system were nonreactive; the selectivity controls the extent to which the frequency is affected by a given imperfection of the driving system;

and the characteristic impedance determines the impedance level which the driving system should have.

As shown in the preceding example, a reduction of the losses of a given resonator ordinarily affects the impedance level as well as the Q because the reactances tend to remain constant. Therefore, as previously shown, it is ordinarily necessary either to modify the driving system or to provide an impedance transformer in order to take advantage of a loss reduction in a resonator. Failure to observe this principle is responsible for many experimental observations in which frequency stability is not improved by reduction of resonator losses.[136] The characteristic impedance of a resonator is its resistance at the operating frequency. Series resonant systems usually have characteristic impedances much lower than those of antiresonant systems.

At any one instant a given resonator has only the three properties just enumerated. However, the engineering need is for frequencies which remain constant over considerable intervals of time and in spite of various disturbing influences. We must, therefore, determine the extent to which such changes affect the natural frequency of resonators.

To a greater or lesser extent the natural frequency, as well as the selectivity and impedance, of a given resonator is affected by every feature of its environment. However, the requirements on constancy of frequency are so much more severe than those on selectivity and impedance that a resonator which has satisfactory frequency stability rarely fails to meet other stability requirements. Principal factors affecting frequency are the ambient temperature, atmospheric pressure, and relative humidity. Other factors include electric and magnetic fields, various forms of radiation, gravitational attraction, amplitude of oscillation, and the passage of time. These several variables affect different resonators in different ways and to different extents. They are discussed in the following paragraphs. It should be noted that a high-Q resonator may be greatly affected by temperature or other influences and that a low-Q resonator may be quite stable. That is, the two properties are essentially independent.

6.2 The ideal resonator

In the previous section it was shown that the selectivity of a resonator determines the ease with which it may be driven, and that the impedance level must be suitably matched to the driving circuit for best results, that is, best frequency stability. A high Q is therefore desirable in the interest of making the frequency insensitive to variations in the driving system. To maintain constancy, the natural frequency must not be affected by the passage of time or variations such as temperature and humidity.   To ensure that operation will occur at the natural frequency and that the response will be simple and symmetrical the resonator must have only one principal response in the region of interest.

We may therefore conclude that the ideal resonator is characterized by the following:

(1) A natural frequency which is appropriate.

(2) A value of Q approaching infinity.

(3) An impedance level suitable to available driving circuits.

(4) A natural frequency which does not change with time, temperature, or other uncontrolled variables.

(5) Freedom from additional resonances which would affect the behavior at the desired frequency.

6.3 Thermal and secular effects

The ambient temperature affects the frequency of every known form of resonator, but the extent of this influence varies enormously.   In a poorly constructed LC circuit the effect may be as large as forty parts per million per degree centigrade,* whereas in a GT cut quartz crystal operating in the region of 40°C the effect may well be some 10,000 times smaller.

The behavior of a more or less typical LC resonator is shown in Fig. 6.3.   It is seen that the frequency is not a single-valued function of the temperature, but depends in a rather complicated way upon the previous history as well.   In fact, the frequency is ordinarily a function of the present temperature, of all past temperatures, and the present time rate of change of temperature.   It is therefore difficult to speak in precise terms about temperature stability.

However, it is possible to construct resonators in which these parasitic effects are quite small; and it is highly desirable to do so because of the superior performance obtained.   In such resonators the frequency is, at least effectively, a single-valued function of temperature, so that a definite slope or temperature coefficient exists at each temperature.   Such behavior, which is referred to as cyclic, is shown in Fig. 6.4.   In this case the frequency varies in a parabolic manner, while its slope or coefficient varies linearly with the temperature T. Clearly it is absurd to speak of the temperature coefficient of this resonator without also specifying the temperature in question.   In the

---

* The abbreviation ppm will be used to represent parts per million, and all temperatures will be given in degrees centigrade throughout this book, except in a few cases where the corresponding absolute scale, °K, is more appropriate.

present case the behavior is correctly described by the equation

$$\frac{d}{dT}\left(\frac{df}{dT}\right) = \frac{d^2f}{dT^2} = \text{constant.} \qquad (6.1)$$

Because resonators rarely behave so simply, it is ordinarily necessary to refer to the actual response curve when precise statements are to be made. The measurement of such small frequency changes is difficult, but adequate methods have been developed.[188]

Resonators which are insensitive to temperature are desirable because it is difficult to prevent temperature changes in operating appara-

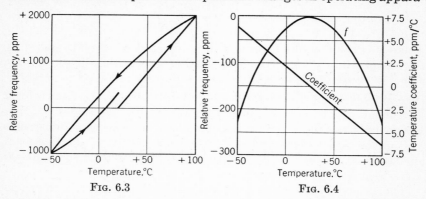

Fig. 6.3   Fig. 6.4

Fig. 6.3. Variation of the frequency of an *LC* resonator with slow changes of temperature.

Fig. 6.4. Temperature variation of the frequency of a *BT* cut quartz crystal resonator.

tus. In spite of important advances in the construction of constant-temperature ovens, they are still too bulky and expensive for use in ordinary apparatus.

In most resonators the natural (and thus operating) frequency changes with the passage of time, even if the temperature and other conditions are maintained constant. This secular or time variation is often referred to as aging or drift. It is present to a greater or lesser extent in all known resonators, but may be held to a minimum by the choice of materials which are inherently stable. Quartz, ceramics, and most metals have good secular stability, whereas most plastics do not.

6.4 Humidity and other effects

The conductivity, dielectric constant, and dielectric strength of air are affected by its pressure and humidity. Therefore, the resonant frequency of air dielectric LC or cavity resonators is a function of these variables. Moreover, the mechanical dimensions of coil forms and condenser supports are often affected by humidity. Precise control of frequency is therefore possible only if suitable precautions are taken in the construction of the elements. Vacuum impregnation and hermetic sealing are two widely-used methods.

The dielectric constant of dry air at 0°C and normal atmospheric pressure is 1.000583. It varies with the density, composition, and relative humidity.[86] For dry air the dielectric constant ϵ_r is given by the equation

$$\epsilon_r = 1 + \frac{0.00021P}{T + 273}, \tag{6.2}$$

where P is the pressure expressed in millimeters of mercury and T is the temperature (°C). Humidity further affects the dielectric constant, as shown in Table 6.1. Superposition may be used to combine the effects of pressure, temperature, and humidity.

TABLE 6.1

EFFECT OF HUMIDITY AND TEMPERATURE UPON THE RELATIVE DIELECTRIC CONSTANT OF AIR AT STANDARD PRESSURE

($\epsilon_r = 1 + h \times 10^{-6}$, where h is the tabulated value)

Temp., °C	Relative Humidity											δh
	0%	10%	20%	30%	40%	50%	60%	70%	80%	90%	100%	
−40	682	682	682	682	682	682	682	682.	682	682	682	0
−30	655	655.1	655.2	655.2	655.3	655.4	655.5	655.6	655.6	655.7	655.8	0.08
−20	629	629.2	629.5	629.7	629.9	630.2	630.4	630.6	630.9	631.1	631.3	0.23
−10	605	605.6	606.1	606.7	607.2	607.8	608.4	608.9	609.5	610	610.6	0.56
0	583	584.3	585.5	586.8	588.1	589.3	590.6	591.9	593.2	594.4	595.7	1.27
+10	562	564.5	566.9	569.4	571.8	574.3	576.8	579.2	581.7	584.1	586.6	2.46
+20	543	547.6	552.1	556.6	561.1	565.6	570.2	574.7	579.2	585.8	588.3	4.53
+30	525	532.9	540.9	548.8	556.8	564.7	572.7	580.6	588.6	596.5	604.5	7.95
+40	508	521.4	534.8	548.2	561.6	575	588.4	601.8	615.2	628.6	642	13.4
+50	493	514.7	536.4	558.1	579.8	601.5	623.2	644.9	666.6	688.3	710	21.7
+60	478	512	546	580	614	648	682	716	750	784	818	34.0
+70	464	515.5	567.0	618.5	670	721.5	773	824.5	876	927.5	979	51.5

Composition is important principally because dry ice is sometimes used in tests to produce the low temperatures required to simulate field conditions. This procedure may lead to serious error in frequency, because at normal atmospheric pressure and temperature the dielectric constant increases approximately 375 ppm in a linear manner as dry air is replaced by 100 per cent carbon dioxide.

Humidity has an additional effect which may be both serious and unsuspected. Films of moisture form on the surfaces of metals and other materials under such conditions that no true condensation is possible. Such films not only degrade the insulation resistance of apparatus but also affect the equivalent spacing of an air condenser. The variation is small, but can be significant in precise apparatus.

Cavity resonators are ordinarily filled with a dry gas, usually nitrogen, and completely sealed. They are then immune to the effects of humidity. They are also insensitive to pressure if the walls are sufficiently thick so as to avoid mechanical distortion. Coils and condensers may also be sealed to good advantage, but it is frequently sufficient to impregnate them under vacuum with a suitable highly-fluid wax or plastic.

Sealing, or impregnation, is desirable not only because it stabilizes the frequency but also because it increases and stabilizes the values of Q and of voltage breakdown. Special precautions must be taken if the apparatus is to operate under conditions of high humidity because damage due to mold and corrosion is greatly accelerated.[132, 246] Special precautions are also necessary to avoid arcing between terminals in components which must operate at low pressure due to high altitude.

6.5 Properties of condensers

In a majority of oscillators the resonator consists of a combination of coils and condensers. Because the reactive elements are very different in construction and properties it is appropriate to discuss them separately. Condensers are discussed first, because they are substantially free from losses and are somewhat simpler in behavior. Those who wish a general review of components are referred to Terman's *Handbook;*[307] and those who wish a more comprehensive treatment of condensers should read the books by Brotherton[39] or Coursey.[66] It is assumed that the reader has a fair knowledge of the properties and construction of typical components; and emphasis is placed upon the performance of components applicable to the present problem.

For fixed condensers the silvered-mica construction is very desirable because of its low temperature coefficient and good secular stability. Blocks of high-grade ruby mica, ordinarily imported from India, are first cut and split into thin sheets of suitable area and thickness. These are then coated on both sides with a thin layer of metal, usually silver, by vacuum evaporation or similar means. Several of these sheets are stacked to build up the desired capacitance, and leads are attached by soldering to the exposed area of the electrodes. Finally, the assembly is packaged as a unit, ordinarily by surrounding the actual condenser with a body of high-grade thermosetting plastic. This construction leads to a very low value of parasitic inductance.

Mica has high secular stability and an inherently low temperature coefficient of capacitance. These desirable properties are preserved in the present construction by applying the electrodes directly to the material. In typical specimens the temperature coefficient of capacitance[61] is substantially constant at a value $+20$ ppm per °C over the range -60 to $+80°$. The power factor is very low, of the order of 0.02 per cent. Silvered mica condensers are commercially available in capacitances ranging from about 5 to 5000 $\mu\mu$f. The effects of aging are so small as to be negligible in most applications.

Ordinary mica condensers are constructed of alternate layers of mica and metal foil. Their stability is inferior to that of silvered-mica units because the electrodes are not in such intimate contact with the surfaces of the mica. However, they are entirely satisfactory in many situations where the stability requirements are only moderate. Compact units having capacitances in the range of 5 to 10,000 $\mu\mu$f are generally available, and larger capacitances can be procured. Mica condensers of either construction have low losses and excellent d-c insulation. In typical units the power factor is substantially less than 0.1 per cent. Direct-current leakage is usually due principally to currents over the surface of the plastic jacket. It is therefore comparable to other leakage currents and is almost always negligible.

TABLE 6.2

ELECTRICAL PROPERTIES OF SOME SOLID DIELECTRICS AT 25°C

Material	Power factor at One Mc, %	ϵ_r	Temperature Coefficient, ppm/°C	Volume Conductivity, mhos/meter
Mica	0.015	6	$+20$	5×10^{-16}
Fused quartz	0.015	4.4	.....	2×10^{-17}
P100		12	$+100$	
P30		16	$+30$	
NP0		30	0	10^{-9}
Group A ceramics N30		31	-30	
based on N80	0.02	36	-80	to
titanium N150	to	41	-150	
dioxide N220	0.05	45	-220	10^{-14}
N330		50	-330	
N470		60	-470	
N750		85	-750	
Titanium dioxide	0.05	85	-750	

A variety of ceramic materials are now being used as dielectrics for condensers. In general, ceramic bodies have good secular stability and are not greatly affected by temperature, humidity, chemical attack, etc. However, the dielectric behavior of some of these materials, notably barium titanate, is very complicated, so that we must exercise some discrimination in choosing a ceramic capacitor.[205]

Ceramic materials which include compounds of titanium have two exceptional properties. The values of dielectric constant are far

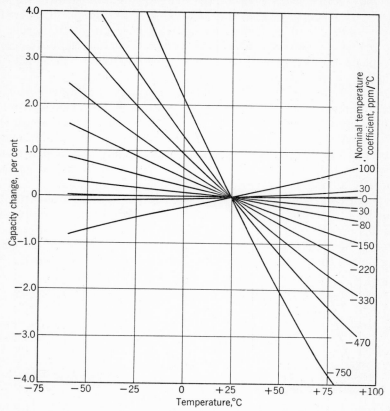

FIG. 6.5. Typical temperature coefficient curves for group A ceramic dielectrics at a frequency of 1 Mc.

higher than those of ordinary materials, and the temperature coefficient is negative. Large values of the dielectric constant are desirable because they lead to large capacitances in compact, light, noninductive structures. Negative temperature coefficients are desirable because they permit partial compensation of the positive coefficients, characteristic of most coils.

The ceramic materials which are most useful in the present application are prepared by mixing titanium dioxide with other more con-

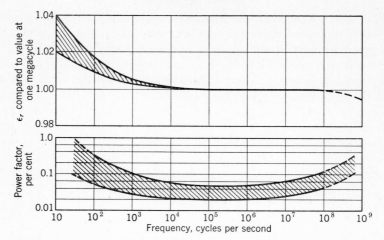

FIG. 6.6. Behavior of typical Group A ceramic dielectrics at 25°C.

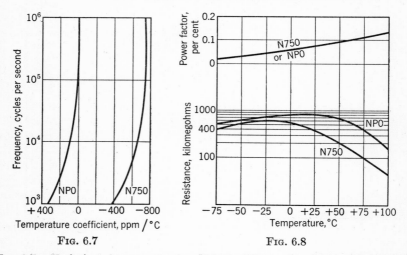

FIG. 6.7   FIG. 6.8

FIG. 6.7. Variation of temperature coefficient of Group A ceramic materials with frequency. Average coefficient over the range +25 to +85°C is shown for nominal 0 and −750 coefficient materials.

FIG. 6.8. Variation with temperature of power factor and insulation resistance of typical ceramic condenser units.

ventional compounds. The principal characteristics of a number of these ceramic materials, known to the trade as Group A, are presented in Table 6.2. Values for mica and for fused quartz are included for comparison. The principal characteristics of Group A ceramics, which are ordinarily designated in terms of the nominal temperature coefficients, are presented in Figs. 6.5 to 6.8. In Fig. 6.6 the range of variation indicated depends more upon process variations than upon the nominal temperature coefficient of the material.

Ceramic materials based on titanium dioxide but having still larger values of dielectric constant and negative temperature coefficients are available under the trade designation Group B. They may be used when a very large temperature compensating effect must be obtained in a small capacitance, but they have inferior values of power factor and of stability, and are generally undesirable for frequency control.

A number of ceramics known to the trade as Group C are based upon barium titanate. They have values of dielectric constant in excess of

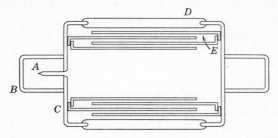

FIG. 6.9. Construction of a 50 $\mu\mu$f vacuum capacitor (simplified). Parts, which are assembled by welding, are: A, evacuation tube; B, end cap; C, fernico end cup; D, borosilicate glass body; and E, copper cylinders.

1000, but they are nonlinear and behave in a complicated manner with respect to temperature and frequency. They should therefore be avoided except for by-pass purposes.

Ceramic condensers are commonly manufactured in tubular or disk form. The electrodes are ordinarily produced by application of a metallic suspension which becomes integral with the dielectric when the unit is again fired to a temperature which fuses the metal. Leads are attached by soldering to the metallic electrodes, and the unit is finished by application of a waterproof wax or plastic coating. Condensers based on Group A dielectrics are generally available in the capacitance range of 1 to 1000 $\mu\mu$f. Capacitances up to about 0.03 μf are commonly available in Group B and Group C materials, but are subject to wide variations, as previously mentioned.

The techniques which permit the mass production of vacuum tubes are employed in the production of the vacuum capacitor. Because the dielectric is vacuum, these condensers are free from any inherent dielectric instability. Such capacitance changes as do occur result entirely from dimensional changes of the supporting structure. A temperature coefficient of $+30$ ppm per °C is typical of commercial units.[96] However, it appears that much smaller or even negative coefficients could be obtained by careful choice of materials and the use of differential expansion effects. The construction of a typical vacuum capacitor is shown in Fig. 6.9.

These capacitors have exceptionally low losses, typified by a power factor of 0.01 per cent at one megacycle, and show good secular stability. Atmospheric pressure and humidity affect only the exterior of the condenser and therefore have extremely little effect. The gravest faults of the construction shown are that the practical range of capacitance is rather small, perhaps 10 to 100 $\mu\mu$f, and the size is somewhat large.

Air dielectric condensers are also almost always variable, because suitable fixed condensers are more easily constructed in other ways. Variable air condensers have been the subject of extensive development and have been brought to a high stage of perfection. A wide variety of curves relating capacitance to rotor position may be obtained by shaping the rotor plates, and in large units the maximum capacitances may be as much as forty times the minimum. Maximum capacitances ordinarily lie in the range of 5 to 1000 $\mu\mu$f. The power factor may be made low, ordinarily less than 0.1 per cent, by the choice of suitable dielectric materials to support the stator. And, finally, proper design[119, 310] leads to a temperature coefficient which is small for all settings of the rotor. For these reasons adjustable frequency oscillators are almost always tuned by means of variable condensers.

The actual design of stable variable condensers is quite complicated, but the objective can be stated fairly simply. The shape and temperature coefficients of all the members used in the mechanical assembly should be such that there is no change of *shape* as a result of unavoidable changes of dimensions with temperature. If this objective is met, the behavior will be cyclic, and the temperature coefficient of capacitance will be equal to the coefficient of linear expansion, which is fairly small. If this objective is not met, the relative shape and spacing of the plates will change, and the capacitance variation with temperature will be complicated and ordinarily considerably increased. However, a very low or negative temperature coefficient may be secured in a condenser which has an aluminum frame and stator, and a rotor made partly from aluminum and partly from invar.[288]

The fact that a variable, or other, condenser is relatively stable with respect to slow temperature variations does not guarantee that it will be stable with respect to rapid temperature changes. The unequal temperature distributions which inevitably accompany rapid temperature changes are likely to produce differentials of expansion which warp the shape of the assembly and modify the capacitance. This difficulty is alleviated by constructing the condenser so as to have a good thermal conductivity and by insulating the entire assembly from ambient changes. Both these steps tend to reduce the temperature gradients which can exist.

Contact to the rotor is ordinarily made by means of a wiping or sliding spring. Unless the construction and the materials are carefully chosen, this contact will give trouble in the form of a high and variable resistance. This difficulty may be prevented by means of an elastic spring or pigtail, provided that the condenser is not capable of continuous rotation and that the appreciable and variable self-inductance of the pigtail is tolerable.

Soldered, brazed, or welded contacts throughout are greatly favored in the interest of long and reliable service. In addition, it is often necessary or desirable to electroplate all surfaces so as to prevent deterioration due to corrosion.

Paper condensers are not often used for frequency control. As ordinarily constructed, they have relatively poor secular stability and complicated and noncyclic behavior with respect to temperature. In addition, the power factor is poor and varies with respect to temperature and frequency. However, new materials and construction techniques offer promise of at least alleviating these limitations.[31] The performance of several types of paper condensers is shown in Fig. 6.10. The reason for avoiding these units, especially if low temperatures are encountered, is evident from these curves.

The technique of depositing metal directly upon dielectric paper for the construction of condensers has only recently been developed.* Condensers made with metalized paper are remarkably compact and light in terms of their capacitance and voltage rating; and they have the virtue of being self-healing if punctured by a voltage surge. However, both the equivalent series resistance and the shunt leakage conductance tend to be high; and it appears unlikely that these units will be significantly better than other paper capacitors for frequency control.

The remarkable advances in the field of plastics have led to the possibility of constructing condensers with a plastic film as the dielectric. The general construction is the same as that of paper condensers, but the performance with respect to frequency and temperature is markedly superior. Moreover, plastic materials are subject to excellent manufacturing control, so that desirable results, when once

* Information on the properties of such paper is available from Smith Paper, Inc., Lee, Mass.

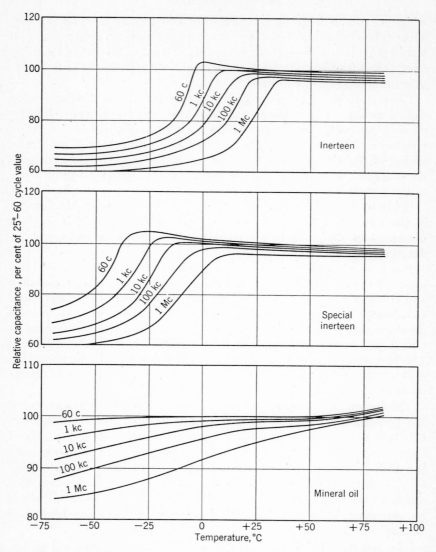

FIG. 6.10. Behavior of paper condensers impregnated with different fluids. Inerteen is a chlorinated biphenyl. Special Inerteen contains an addition of polychloroethyl benzene. (Redrawn by permission of authors and editor from L. J. Berberich, C. V. Fields, and R. E. Marbury, "Characteristics of Chlorinated Impregnants in Direct-Current Paper Capacitors," *Proc. I.R.E.*, **33**, 389–397 [1945].)

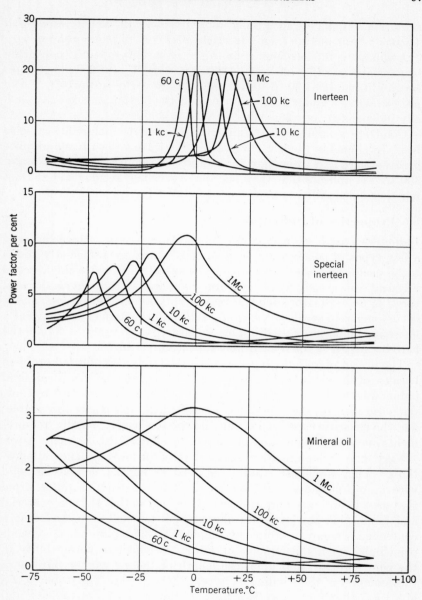

FIG. 6.10 (*Continued*)

achieved, should be accurately reproducible. In combination with silicone[23] impregnants these materials offer considerable promise.

Available compact commercial units have temperature coefficients of capacitance of $+700$ and -500 ppm per °C, capacitance values ranging from about 50 to 10,000 $\mu\mu$f, and are useful up to 75°C. The power factor is about 0.03 per cent, and the capacitance is substantially independent of frequency.

Condensers employing a thin film of glass for the dielectric have also been developed in the last few years. They are known to stand quite high voltages and to operate successfully at temperatures in excess of 300°C. It appears that they may have excellent secular and at least fair thermal stability.

6.6 Properties of inductors

Inductors exist in a great variety of forms and sizes. However, only a few types of construction lead to coils which are sufficiently stable to be useful for frequency-control purposes.[310] Because the losses in physical coils are nearly always large compared to those in condensers, the Q of LC resonators depends almost entirely on the coil loss, and it is customary to speak of the Q of a coil with the understanding that a loss-free condenser is used. This somewhat loose practice is followed here because it is convenient and almost universal.

The design of an inductance coil is a relatively complicated problem because of the many factors which must be considered.[275] The desired inductance must be obtained and must be stable with respect to time, temperature, etc; the effective Q must be high and reasonably stable; and the parasitic capacitance must not be too large. Finally, requirements on mutual inductance or coupling coefficient exist in many cases.

Very large inductances are required only for low-frequency applications. They are most readily obtained in multilayer coils of solid wire wound on laminated iron cores. The construction differs from that used in ordinary power transformers only in that the core material and lamination thickness are chosen with unusual care, and that a controlled air gap is ordinarily employed. The inductance depends principally upon the number of turns, the effective permeability of the core material, and upon the length of the air gap; variations of the geometry of the winding have very little effect. The stability of a given coil therefore depends mainly on the properties of the core and the manner in which the air gap varies. It is necessary to limit both direct and alternating currents through the coil; otherwise saturation may greatly change the effective inductance. Moderately good thermal and secular stability in inductance values ranging from 0.1

to 1000 henries may be obtained. The useful frequency range is about 20 to 20,000 cycles, and the Q value ranges from about 5 to 50.

At frequencies above a few kilocycles the eddy current losses in laminated iron cores are so large as to be prohibitive. However, cores made of finely divided iron powder or dust suspended in an insulating binder are useful to much higher frequencies of the order of 50 Mc. Ordinarily, the binder is some sort of plastic, and the mixture is molded under high pressure to an appropriate geometrical form. The magnetic properties of the final core depend upon the size and composition of the magnetic particles and the relative volume of iron and insulator. Effective permeabilities usually range from about 5 to 200.

Powdered-iron cores for use at frequencies upwards of one megacycle are ordinarily made in the form of a circular cylinder. Although the effective permeability is rarely in excess of ten, such cores are useful because they contribute to the values of Q and coupling coefficient which may be realized, and facilitate inductance adjustment. An excellent discussion of the properties and measurement of powdered-iron cores is given in papers by Foster and Newton,[99] and by Jaderholm.[155]

At frequencies of the order of 50 kc the core is commonly made toroidal, and the winding is uniformly distributed over its surface. The flux is almost entirely confined to the core so that the inductance is essentially independent of everything except the effective permeability. Moreover, a very high coupling coefficient between separate windings may be achieved; and undesired magnetic couplings to other circuits may be made negligibly small. The temperature coefficient may be made small and cyclic if the magnetic material is properly processed. Direct current should be avoided if possible; and other influences on the inductances are ordinarily negligible. Inductance values ranging from about one millihenry to one henry and Q values in the order of 150 are readily obtained in toroidal dust core coils.

Comparable results are achieved by interchanging the positions of the iron and copper. A multiple-layer coil, often of the universal form discussed in the following paragraph, is associated with a pair of molded cores which are shaped so as to produce a closed path to the magnetic flux. The principal advantage of this construction is the relative ease with which the windings may be made and adjusted.

In the frequency range of about 10 kc to one Mc and for inductances of about 100 μh to 100 mh the "universal" winding produces compact coils satisfactory for many purposes. Selectivity values as high as 250 are obtained, particularly when suitable powered-iron cores are associated with coils carefully wound of litz wire.

The construction is not particularly conducive to good thermal or secular stability because the winding is self-supporting, and any change in temperature or humidity is likely to change the size and relative location of the various turns. However, the stability of typical coils, particularly those which are impregnated with a good wax or plastic, is quite good.[118] A relatively simple but fairly precise machine is required for producing this sort of winding, and the setting of the various adjustments involves a considerable amount of mathematics.[162, 283]

The single-layer solenoid is the most flexible and generally useful form of coil in the frequency range of about 50 kc to 50 Mc. Powdered-iron cores are often used to improve the Q, especially in small coils, or to provide a convenient means for adjusting the self-inductance. Inductance adjustment may also be secured by means of conducting cores, such as copper, which act as short-circuited secondaries. However, it is best to avoid all such cores where good stability is required.

The inductance of an air core solenoid depends only upon the number of turns and the geometry, because the permeability of air differs from that of vacuum by only 25 parts in 10^9. However, the geometry of a physical coil is not readily subject to exact control. Moreover, the self-inductance of a given structure varies with the resistivity of the conductor and with frequency because of current redistribution due to skin and proximity effects. Since the resistivity of most materials changes rapidly with temperature, the inductance of a given coil may, at a given frequency, be sensitive to temperature even though no change of dimension occurs. The problem, therefore, is to design a coil in which the dimensions are independent of time, temperature, and atmospheric conditions and the current distribution is independent of temperature over the range of temperatures and frequencies in question.

Self-supported coils are sometimes made by winding a metal rod or tube in the form of a solenoid. One end is then rigidly supported, and the connection to the other end is made by means of a flexible lead such as copper braid. This construction results in reasonably stable coils having relatively low losses, but is unsuitable where severe vibration is encountered. The use of additional supports greatly reduces the difficulties due to vibration, but introduces new difficulties in controlling the temperature coefficients of the various members used. If a single support is used and if the metal is carefully annealed by repeated temperature cycles, the shape of the coil will not change with change of temperature, and all the dimensions will change according to the linear temperature coefficient of the metal. However, the temperature coefficient of inductance is still likely to be large. Such coils are necessarily of low inductance and therefore useful only at high frequencies, and at such frequencies the conductor thickness required for mechanical stability is many times the skin depth. Accordingly, the resistance change associated with a change of temperature will cause an appreciable change of current distribution and therefore of inductance.

That the self-inductance of a conductor is affected by skin effect, which is in turn a function of conductivity, is readily shown in terms of a coaxial structure. At very low frequencies the current flows uniformly throughout the cross section of the conductors, whereas at very high frequencies the current flow is confined to a shallow surface layer. Over some range of intermediate frequencies the current partially penetrates the conductors.[169] In this range the penetration, and hence the inductance, is sensitive to both frequency and resistivity. Because the resistivity of good conductors increases rapidly with increase of temperature, the inductance also increases with temperature. The temperature coefficient of resistivity of copper is about 4000 ppm per °C, and the temperature coefficient of inductance due to this cause alone may readily be as high as 100 ppm per °C.[123, 309]

A coil will possess cyclic behavior with respect to temperature only if there is no relative motion between the conductor and its support. The temperature coefficient will be low only if the dimensions are substantially constant and if the current distribution is independent of temperature. These several objectives are met in a coil made by depositing a thin helix of silver on the surface of a fused-quartz rod or tube. The thermal coefficient of linear expansion of fused quartz is exceptionally low, approximately $\frac{1}{2}$ ppm per °C. The quartz form will control the dimensions of the finished coil because of the good adherence which can be secured and because of the relatively large volume of the quartz with respect to the silver. The film should be very thin in comparison to the radius, but not appreciably thinner than the skin depth of silver at the operating frequency. If the metal has a thickness of 1.5 skin depths the current distribution will be virtually independent of temperature and the value of Q will be about 10 per cent higher than that obtained with a much thicker conductor.[339, 342]

Excellent coils may also be made by depositing silver or other metals on the surface of glass* or ceramic forms in cylindrical, toroidal, or other shapes. High conductivity and good adherence in the

* Coils made by depositing silver on the surface of a tube of pyrex glass are available on a commercial basis from the Corning Glass Works. See Bulletin ES-100, Electronic Sales Department, Corning Glass Works, Corning, New York.

metallic film, and good thermal and secular stability in the form are desirable, but ridges or grooves of any sort in the form are to be avoided because they promote nonuniform current distribution with consequent loss of Q and thermal stability. The conductor should occupy the largest practical fraction of the surface of the form in the interest of a high Q. One way of achieving this objective is to apply the metal uniformly over the entire surface and then grind a fine helical cut to produce the winding. However, the spacing between adjacent turns must not be too small or the distributed capacitance is excessive. The same general objectives are met in a coil produced by winding a very thin ribbon of copper or silver under tension on an unglazed ceramic form. With proper care this construction leads to a cyclic thermal behavior and good secular and thermal stability.

Variable inductances are rarely used in oscillators which must have good frequency stability, because it is difficult to achieve the necessary mechanical and electrical stability. They are occasionally useful where requirements are not severe or as an incremental adjustment.

An inductance ratio of about ten to one associated with a uniformly high Q may be obtained by inserting a suitable powdered-iron core into a long slender solenoid or "progressive universal wound" coil. When such a coil is associated with a fixed capacity, the frequency variation may be made almost linear with respect to the core position. This arrangement has been used in both commercial and military radio receivers and is capable of meeting fairly exacting requirements. It appears to be most suitable at frequencies of a few megacycles. The arrangement has the advantage that there are no moving contacts in the entire tuned circuit.

The variometer construction, widely used in early radios, is still occasionally used in variable-frequency oscillators. Relatively wide frequency ranges can be covered, but the construction is inherently expensive and presents serious problems of stability.

A useful continuously variable inductance may be obtained by sliding a contact along the conductor of a single-layer solenoid (helix) or a plane multiturn spiral. The entire coil is rotated about its axis, while an auxiliary mechanism guides the contactor longitudinally or radially so as to "track" the conductor as it slides by. Contact to one end of the coil is made by a suitable slip-ring or similar arrangement, and the unused portion is ordinarily short-circuited to avoid undesired coupled-circuit effects. This arrangement, which has received considerable commercial development, has the advantages of a long effective scale, typically more than ten complete rotations. The distributed capacitance of the coil is small, and the ratio of maximum to minimum inductance is readily made larger than ten to one, by the methods previously discussed. Moreover, in typical applications the impedance level is lower than that in a condenser-tuned oscillator, so that small capacitance changes inherent in vacuum tubes produce considerably less frequency shift. The principal drawback arises because the sliding contacts tend to give erratic performance, especially after the unit is exposed to dust and oxidation.

Because it is difficult and expensive to produce coils which have low or negative temperature coefficients of inductance, the use of negative-coefficient condensers for compensation has received considerable attention. Although simple in concept, the method presents serious problems in application. No significant compensation is possible unless the several elements are cyclic and have good secular stability. Moreover, from a production viewpoint, the method is worthless unless the characteristics of the several elements are reproducible within a range which is considerably narrower than the individual coefficients, and is less than the total performance tolerance. Finally, if the frequency must be adjustable by tuning, the temperature coefficient of the adjustable element must be independent of its setting. If, for example, a coil having a temperature coefficient of 10 ppm per °C is to be compensated and tuned by a variable condenser, the condenser including any padding must have a coefficient of -10 ppm per °C at all settings. This fact greatly restricts the usefulness of negative coefficient fixed condensers for temperature compensation.[50, 275, 292]

6.7 The butterfly circuit

Several tuned circuits, exceptionally useful for ultrahigh frequencies, have been devised by Karplus[163] and others of the General Radio Company. They are commonly referred to as butterfly circuits, because of the shape of the rotor, as shown in Fig. 6.11. An anti-resonant impedance is developed between points 1 and 2 of this figure. The structure may be thought of as two variable condensers in series shunted by two single-turn inductors in parallel. However, the equivalent inductance is not constant because the rotor serves as a short-circuited secondary which reduces the inductance as it is unmeshed to reduce the capacitance. The behavior of the unit of Fig. 6.11 is shown in Table 6.3 and in the curves of Fig. 6.12. The characteristic impedance is quite suitable for operation with typical vacuum tubes and is remarkably constant.

Because of the symmetry of the structure it is unnecessary to provide contact to the rotor, so that no sliding contact is present. It is therefore possible to drive the rotor continuously at very high speeds for special frequency-modulation applications. Moreover, the paths of current flow are such that no soldered, welded, or other contacts are involved. The secular stability of frequency and of Q and the uniformity between units are therefore very good. The temperature coefficient of frequency is comparable to the linear expansion of the

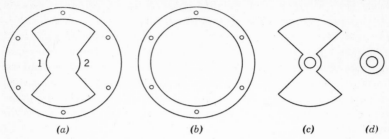

FIG. 6.11. Components of butterfly circuit for 220–1100 Mc. The parts are, respectively: (a) stator plate, (b) stator spacer, (c) rotor plate, (d) rotor spacer. Five rotor and six stator plates used. Drawn about half size.

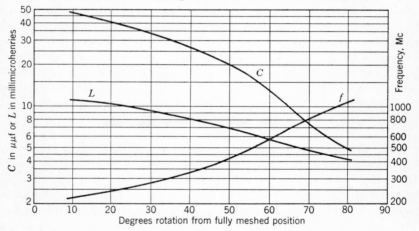

FIG. 6.12. Characteristics of butterfly circuit.

material, typically $+20$ ppm per °C for brass. By shaping the rotor plates it is possible to control the variation of frequency with respect to angle of rotation, much as in ordinary variable condensers.

A number of variations of the basic butterfly circuit have been devised for various applications. Karplus describes several, including coaxial structures well adapted to operate with disk-seal tubes of the "lighthouse" variety. A somewhat different structure having the same useful properties is due to Summerhayes.[302] Perhaps the most important limitation of butterfly structures is a tendency to resonate

TABLE 6.3
BEHAVIOR OF A BUTTERFLY CIRCUIT

Parameter	Symbol	Range	Nature of Variation
Frequency	f	200–1100 Mc	n^2
Inductance	L	0.011–0.0041 μh	n^{-1}
Capacitance	C	48–5 $\mu\mu$f	n^{-3}
Selectivity	Q	650–300	n^{-1}
Series resistance	$R = \omega L/Q$	0.023–0.095 ohm	n^2
Ratio	L/C	15.2–28.6 ohms	n
Impedance	$Z = QL/C$	9800–8600 ohms	Constant

at unwanted frequencies which are not simply related to the principal resonance. These undesired modes of resonance can ordinarily be suppressed or avoided, and in any event they are present in almost all forms of high-frequency resonators.

6.8 Transmission lines

Parallel-wire or coaxial transmission lines have been used as resonators for a long time, and information concerning their properties is commonly available.[306] This section will therefore be limited to a brief discussion of their application to oscillators and a compilation of formulas.

The parallel structure is inherently balanced, is convenient, and gives good performance, especially at moderate frequencies. The coaxial structure is inherently unbalanced and less convenient but has superior mechanical stability and is preferable at the highest frequencies because it is completely shielded. It therefore does not couple to adjoining apparatus or lose energy by radiation.

The arrangement most widely used is a line a quarter wavelength long at the frequency of interest, short-circuited at the far end. Near this frequency the line approximates a high-Q antiresonant circuit. However, a lumped antiresonant circuit has only one response, whereas the transmission line also gives a comparable response at 3, 5, 7, etc., times the frequency of the lowest antiresonance. Occasionally these higher order responses are used in oscillators; in which case special precautions are necessary to ensure that oscillation occurs at the desired rather than some other frequency.

Because circuits are commonly designed on the basis of lumped circuits, the equivalent circuit of Fig. 6.13 is convenient.[268] In this connection it may be noted that, *subject to a fixed inner radius of the outer conductor*, an air-filled coaxial line of a given conductivity has a maximum value of Q for a diameter ratio of 3.592, corresponding to a characteristic impedance of 76.64 ohms. However, with the same outer conductor a substantially higher antiresonant impedance is obtained with a smaller inner conductor corresponding to a diameter ratio of 9.185 and a characteristic impedance of 132.9 ohms. These and other useful relationships are very clearly presented by Smith.[289]

Subject to *fixed center to center spacing* D, parallel wire lines have a maximum value of Q when each conductor has a diameter d which is

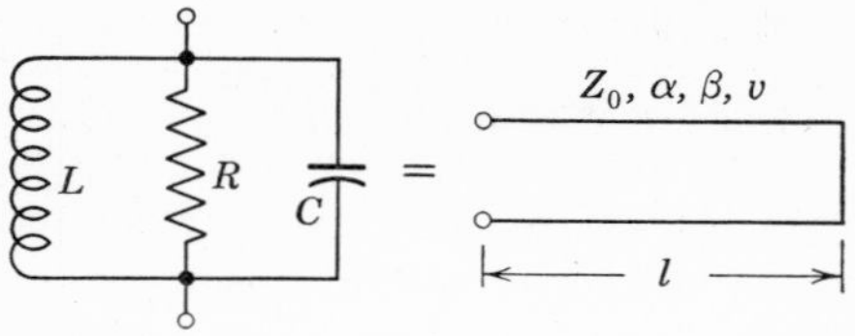

$$\text{if } \begin{cases} L = 8lZ_0/\pi^2 v \\ C = l/2Z_0 v \\ R = Z_0/\alpha l \\ \omega_0 = \beta v \\ Q = \beta/2\alpha \end{cases} \text{ or } \begin{cases} Z_0 = \pi\sqrt{L/2C} \\ l/v = \tfrac{1}{2}\pi\sqrt{LC} \\ \beta l = \pi/2 \\ \alpha = \beta/2Q \\ Q = R/\omega_0 L \end{cases}$$

Fig. 6.13.   Equivalence between line and lumped circuit.

$D/2$, corresponding to a characteristic impedance of 158 ohms.[306]   The maximum antiresonant impedance occurs for $d = D/4$, corresponding to a characteristic impedance of 347 ohms. In all the foregoing developments it was assumed that the short circuit at the end has negligible impedance. This is not true in all cases, and a suitable correction is necessary, as shown in the following section.

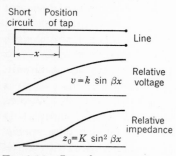

Fig. 6.14.   Impedance transformation obtained by means of a tap on a quarter-wave line.

If, as is often the case, the antiresonant impedance is larger than that desired, the appropriate impedance transformation is readily obtained by connecting to the resonator at some intermediate length. The situation is shown in Fig. 6.14 in terms of the free oscillation of a parallel wire line. If the Q is reasonably high, the voltage distribution is accurately sinusoidal, and the equivalent impedance transformation is therefore described by a factor of the form (sine^2). Impedance transformations in excess of ten to one are readily obtained in this way, usually with a marked improvement of frequency stability with respect to the driving system. The same effect is readily obtained in a coaxial structure by means of a hole or slot in the outer conductor.

Transmission lines may be made quite stable with respect to time and temperature. The thermal coefficient is equal to the linear coefficient of the material unless some distortion of shape occurs as a result of unequal expansion. With careful construction and choice of materials it is possible to reduce the temperature coefficient to a few parts per million per degree centigrade.

6.9 Cavity resonators

At frequencies in excess of about 100 Mc the unavoidable parasitic inductances and capacitances of leads and terminals become comparable with those of the desired elements. Poor frequency stability is ordinarily observed because the parasitic elements are not under control, and radiation losses are sufficient to be troublesome. It is clear that the radiation losses would vanish and that the other difficulties would be greatly reduced if the resonant circuits were made self-shielding. Cavity resonators which are inherently self-shielding and have very creditable values of Q are logical for this application. A particularly lucid account of the basic features of cavity resonators is given by Pierce and Shepherd on page 622 of their article.[241]

Cavity resonators may be thought of as the logical development from transmission lines. In fact, a half-wave coaxial line short-circuited at both ends is an important form of cavity resonator. The coaxial half-wave resonator is ordinarily long compared to its diameter and is employed in its *dominant* or lowest-frequency *mode* of resonance, which is the usual transverse electromagnetic mode in which the electric field is radial, and the magnetic field consists of circles concentric with the conductors. The magnetic field is most intense at the ends where the coaxial conductors are connected by disks, whereas the electric field is most intense halfway between. As in all resonators, the total energy is nearly constant; therefore, the electric and magnetic fields are in time quadrature.

The coaxial structure just described also resonates at three times the frequency previously described as a $\frac{3}{2}\lambda$ line. And in addition to this series of modes it is capable of resonating in many other modes, which are not in simple harmonic relation to the dominant frequency. A major problem of cavity design, therefore, is to obtain operation at the desired frequency or mode and to avoid the effects of other resonant modes. This subject already has an extensive literature and is far too complicated for treatment here.[346] It should, however, be noted that the problem of unwanted modes of oscillation arises in quartz crystal units as well as in cavity resonators; and that similar although less severe problems exist in connection with transmission lines, butterfly circuits, and even complicated LC circuits.

Where very large values of Q are required, particularly at frequencies upwards of 3000 Mc, the TE_{01} circular electric modes in hollow cylindrical cavities are useful. These modes have the desirable property that tuning may be achieved without the use of sliding contacts. Moreover Kinzer[172] has shown that, at a specified frequency, a prescribed high Q is obtained in the smallest possible volume by a TE_{01n} mode in a right circular cylinder. This is of importance because he has also shown that the total number of possible modes is approximately proportional to the volume; therefore, the problem of suppress-

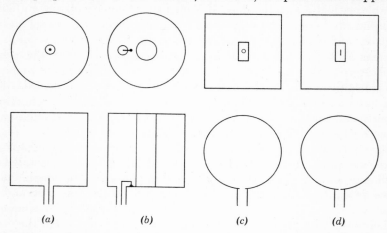

(a) (b) (c) (d)

FIG. 6.15.   Couplings to cavity resonators: (a) coaxial cable with probe coupled to TM_{010} mode in a hollow circular cavity; (b) coaxial cable with loop coupled to TEM mode in coaxial cavity; (c) rectangular wave guide coupled to TE_{011} mode in circular cavity by round iris; and (d) rectangular wave guide coupled to TE_{011} mode in circular cavity by slit iris.

ing or avoiding undesired modes of resonance is greatly simplified by a reduction of volume.

Because the walls of a cavity provide complete shielding, it is necessary to pierce the wall in one or more places to provide the necessary couplings.[127] As indicated in Fig. 6.15, there are three principal means for coupling to a cavity resonator. The probe may be thought of as coupling to the electric field within the cavity, and is therefore most suitable for use with modes which have a strong electric field perpendicular to the metal wall at some point. It is unsuited to TE_{01} modes in which the electric field is paralled to all boundaries. The loop may be thought of as coupling to the magnetic field and should therefore lie in a plane perpendicular to it. Loops are suitable for coupling to nearly all modes if properly located and oriented. The iris coupling also couples to the magnetic field at the wall of the cavity and is suitable for use with wave guides at the higher microwave frequencies. The slit iris is particularly desirable because it produces a minimum disturbance of the cavity boundary. The slit should be parallel to the magnetic field in both cavity and guide, and the coupling depends almost entirely on the length of the slit.

6.10 Resonator theorems

A number of general theorems apply to the behavior of resonators. Their presentation is logical at this point because they involve multiple responses and other ideas which have been developed in the previous sections. However, they apply to simple as well as complicated systems and give considerable insight into a variety of situations.

The principle of similitude is a special case of the Buckingham[76] pi theorem.[160] In the present context it states that all natural frequencies of a resonator system are increased by a factor N if all the dimensions are decreased by a factor N and vice versa. The application to quartz crystals and cavity resonators is obvious. It applies with equal validity to ordinary LC resonators, and since we can readily show that the capacitance of a parallel-plate condenser of a given shape is proportional to its linear dimensions we may conclude that the same statement applies to all condensers and all coils. The principle is very helpful in calculations of temperature coefficients and in modifying apparatus for operation at another frequency.

In the form given, the principle of similitude tells nothing about the change of selectivity with dimensions. However, in cavity resonators where the wall thickness is large compared to the skin depth, the selectivity, Q, of a given mode associated with a given metal varies inversely with the square root of the frequency or directly with the square root of the dimension. The same principle applies to single-layer solenoids associated with high Q condensers, provided all the coil loss is due to imperfect conductivity rather than dielectric losses.

Because the natural frequency of all types of resonators is dependent upon the dimensions, we are concerned with the coefficient of thermal expansion of various materials. Table 6.4 gives the expansion coefficients of a number of selected materials. It is seen that large temperature coefficients of frequency and noncyclic behavior will result unless materials and design are chosen with considerable care.

A second theorem, related to Foster's reactance theorem,[101] is that, if losses are neglected,[199, 200] the behavior of any resonator may be represented in terms of any one of the equivalent circuits of Fig. 6.16. In this connection it should be noted that an infinite number of elements are required for the complete representation of distributed systems such as cavity resonators.[270]

From a practical standpoint, the theorem just stated needs some amendment. Analysis indicates that in a specified cavity resonator each mode has a certain natural frequency and a certain value of Q.

TABLE 6.4

LINEAR EXPANSION OF MISCELLANEOUS MATERIALS

(Parts per million per °C at 20°C)

Aluminum	+23	Hard rubber	+50	Polystyrene	+70
Bakelite	+50	Invar	+0.9	Porcelain	+4
Brass	+19	Lucite	+80	Pyrex	+3
Catalin	+20	Magnesium	+25	Silver	+19
Celluloid	+110	Mica	+3	Solder	+25
Copper	+16	Monel	+14	Steatite	+8
Ebonite	+84	Nickel	+12	Steel	+11
Fused quartz	+0.5	Nylon	+100	Tantalum	+6.5
Glass	+8	Platinum	+9	Tungsten	+4
Graphite	+6	Polyethylene	+190	Vycor	+0.8

Moreover, in perfect rectangular, cylindrical, and spherical cavities the modes are orthogonal in the sense that any one can exist in the absence of the others. It is also known that the resonant frequencies change in an orderly way as the dimensions are modified and that the Q of each mode changes quite slowly with such tuning. We are there-

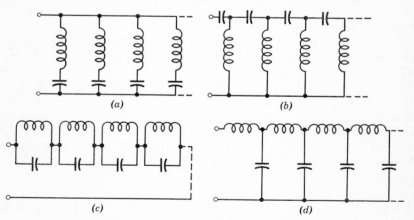

FIG. 6.16. Equivalent circuits for idealized resonators.

fore led to identify LC pairs of the equivalent network with particular modes within the cavity. This useful idea requires some qualification. In the first place, the relative impedance levels of the various circuit branches depends upon the extent to which the given input device is coupled to the mode in question. Even more important, any departure from the ideal geometrical shape introduces couplings between the elements of the equivalent circuit.

An equivalent circuit applicable to a physical loop-coupled cavity is shown in Fig. 6.17. The couplings are represented as magnetic fields within the cavity. They are ordinarily quite small and hence are negligible except where two modes have nearly identical frequencies. Then, complicated coupled-circuit effects are observed, and the effective Q of the system is likely to be seriously degraded. The control or avoidance of these couplings is one of the major problems in designing cavity and quartz-crystal resonators. If a given

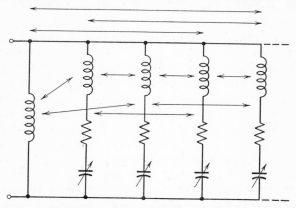

FIG. 6.17. Equivalent circuit of a practical resonator. The condensers are assumed to vary at different rates with respect to a common tuning control.

mode is not excited by the coupling device, it will be observed only by its influence on other modes which have external coupling, when the two are simultaneously resonant. This situation may be treated by allowing the impedance level in the appropriate arm of Fig. 6.17 to approach infinity or by representing the mode in question as an isolated resonant loop magnetically coupled to the rest of the systems.

6.11 Piezoelectricity

It is well known that certain crystalline substances are piezoelectric, that is, they change their dimensions when subjected to an electric field, and conversely generate an electric field when subjected to mechanical strain. The effect is distinct from electrostriction in that the deformation is proportional to the applied field and reverses with reversal of polarity. Piezoelectricity is of concern to us because it offers an excellent means of electromechanical coupling whereby the mechanical resonance of a solid body may control the frequency of an electrical oscillator.

Rochelle salt has a very large piezoelectric response and is widely used in electromechanical transducers such as phonograph pickups. However, crystalline quartz is the only piezoelectric material used to any considerable extent for oscillator applications. This material, which occurs rather commonly in nature, has a relatively large piezoelectric coefficient, is little affected by ordinary chemicals, and has excellent secular stability. The internal visocosity is very low, so that mechanical vibrations have a high inherent Q, and the crystalline structure is such that resonators having very low temperature coefficients may be produced. This combination of desirable properties is so exceptional that it appears quite unlikely that crystalline quartz will ever be replaced for the precise control of frequency. However, recent work[47] offers great promise that high-grade crystals may be produced synthetically from low-grade quartz in such quantity that importation from Brazil, the present principal source, may no longer be necessary. Dr. W. G. Cady[52] has contributed greatly to our understanding of the fundamental principles of piezoelectricity, and Dr. Heising[137] and others of the Bell Telephone Laboratories have done most of the work toward the practical application of crystal units for frequency control. The subject is so extensive and specialized that we can present only a few of the most important results. Papers by Van Dyke,[325, 326] Watanabe,[336] George,[110] and others serve to indicate the methods used and give typical numerical data.

6.12 General properties of crystal units

In the present connection, a crystal unit comprises a block of crystalline quartz supported between suitable electrodes so as to be usable in an oscillator. Ordinarily, the quartz has the form of a thin rectangular parallelopiped or circular disk, but long slender bars,[182] cylinders, and even toroidal shapes have been used. The electrodes are usually parallel metal plates close to or touching the faces of the quartz plate, but in many units the metal is actually deposited on the surface of the quartz by vacuum evaporation, cathode sputtering, or chemical reaction. The quartz plate and its electrodes are supported in some sort of holder which provides means for connection to the electrical circuit and protects the crystal from mechanical damage. The holder is usually hermetically sealed to exclude dust and moisture, and is often evacuated as well, to reduce damping by acoustic absorption. Several typical electrode arrangements for crystal units are shown in Fig. 6.18.

When an alternating electrical voltage is applied to the terminals of a crystal unit, an alternating electric field is created in the quartz between the electrodes, and a corresponding displacement current flows. Small alternating forces are set up in the volume of the quartz as the result of these displacement currents, but no considerable response occurs unless the electrical frequency corresponds very closely to a frequency of mechanical resonance of the quartz plate. In this event a considerable mechanical vibration occurs, and the current observed in the external circuit is greatly affected. As we might anticipate, the relative magnitude of this effect is greater if the

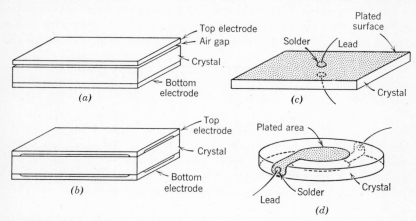

FIG. 6.18. Methods of mounting crystal plates: (a) with air gap, (b) pressure mounted; (c) plated and wire mounted, and (d) plated and mounted at the edges.

electrodes are close to the crystal, if the crystal has a large piezoelectric coupling factor, and if the mechanical vibration is not restrained. It is further observed that the piezoelectric coupling factor differs from material to material and depends upon the angles at which the plate is cut from the natural crystal. Imperfections in the crystal from which the plate was cut may affect either or both the mechanical vibration and the piezoelectric coupling.

From the discussion of Section 6.10 it is seen that the equivalent circuit of a quartz crystal unit has the form of Fig. 6.19, in which the heavy lines govern the behavior in the region of the desired response, and the remaining branches describe other responses. In this connection it should be noted that this equivalent circuit of the crystal resonator was independently identified by Van Dyke[324] before the general resonator theorems were derived. Ordinarily, the principal mesh is sufficient for analysis of the operation of a crystal unit over the range of interest, and the remaining branches of the network are ignored.   The extra responses *are* present, however, and often affect the measured response.

Natural quartz stones or crystals are rarely perfect throughout their volume.   It is therefore necessary to select the region of quartz as well as the angles of cut in order to secure a satisfactory resonator.   In addition to ordinary cracks, quartz crystals are subject to *inclusions* and *twinning*.   Inclusions usually are fine bubbles within the solid volume of the material, and may be filled with a gas, liquid, solid, or a mixture.   They are avoided as far as possible because they introduce mechanical damping, thereby degrading the Q of the finished resonator, and because they tend to reduce the amplitude of vibration which may be used without risk of fracture.   Twinning is a local reversal of the

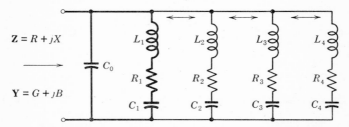

FIG. 6.19.   Equivalent circuit of a quartz crystal unit.

sign of the piezoelectric coupling and is due to a change of the inherent crystal structure into its mirror image or a reversal of the entire crystal orientation.   Twinned plates are to be avoided because the piezoelectric action of the separate regions tends to cancel, thus decreasing the overall coupling, and because the temperature coefficient of frequency is likely to be adversely affected.

The temperature coefficient of a quartz crystal unit depends upon the proportions and orientation of the block and upon the mechanical vibration employed.   A great deal of work has gone into the study of these factors and some remarkably stable units have resulted.   The secular stability of a quartz crystal depends greatly upon the methods used in its fabrication.   The usual grinding process leaves the surfaces covered with fine pits and scratches and in a state of stress similar to that which is employed in cutting ordinary window glass.   Unless this disoriented and partially dislodged surface material is removed with extreme care it will gradually loosen and separate from the finished unit, ordinarily raising the frequency.   Mechanical scrubbing, chemical etching, optical polishing, and baking[244] have been used to alleviate this effect, and it now constitutes a problem only in the most exacting applications.

In the region of its principal mechanical resonance the impedance of a quartz crystal varies in the manner shown roughly in Fig. 6.20. It is seen that there are two frequencies at which the reactance is zero, corresponding to unity power factor, and that the resistance is very low at one and very high at the other. In a general way, the lower frequency, at which the low impedance is observed, is referred to as the series resonant frequency, and the higher frequency corresponding to the high impedance is called the antiresonant frequency. In practical oscillators the crystal is sometimes operated at or near the series resonant frequency as in the Meacham oscillator. Ordinarily, however, the crystal is in parallel with an external capacitance, called

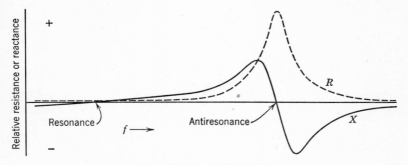

FIG. 6.20.   Impedance variation of a crystal unit.

the *load capacitance*, and the effective antiresonance of this combination is employed. The antiresonant resistance developed is referred to as the *performance index*, abbreviated *PI*. The equivalent circuit of Fig. 6.19 is important because, in this limited frequency region, it has a response which is closely equal to that of the actual crystal. Given the equivalent circuit, it is always possible to calculate the response, and vice versa.

6.13 Detailed properties of crystal units

From the application standpoint, a crystal unit is characterized by its frequency, selectivity, impedance level, capacitance ratio, and temperature coefficient. The following paragraphs discuss these parameters for the designs now in common use. The fundamental parameters are supplemented by auxiliary data, which are useful in selecting a crystal for a particular practical application. It is to be hoped that future developments will lead to still more desirable units.

Figure 6.21 shows the orientation* of the more widely used crystal resonator plates in terms of the natural axes of the parent crystal. It must be remembered that there are three distinct pairs of X and Y axes, so that a desired orientation may be obtained in three different ways from a given stone. It may be helpful to note that AT and CT cuts are nearly parallel to one of the three pyramidal caps of a perfect natural crystal. The precise angular measurements required to obtain desired orientations are made by means of x-rays and polarized light.

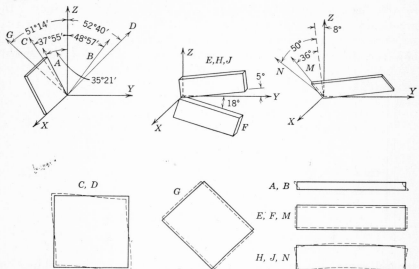

FIG. 6.21. Orientation and motion of the principal crystal elements.

Although every cut is capable of vibrating in many different ways, most of which have considerable piezoelectric coupling, desirable temperature characteristics are obtained only when the vibration and the cut are appropriately related. A crystal *element* consists of a plate or bar cut in a prescribed way from the natural stone and vibrating in a particular manner. Thus an A element consists of a plate having the AT orientation† or cut and vibrating in thickness shear. The dotted lines of Fig. 6.21 show the mechanical vibration used in the more important crystal elements. The only vibrations of any practical

* The notation of Fig. 6.21 follows that of "Standards on Piezoelectric Crystals," *Proc. I.R.E.*, **37,** 1378 (1949).

† Similarly, the B element corresponds to the BT cut, etc.; however, the E and F elements do not correspond to the little-used ET and FT cuts, which are approximately CT and DT plates operated on a mechanical overtone.

utility which are not shown are the mechanical overtones of the thickness shear mode, which are employed in some A and B type units. Both even and odd overtones may exist, but only odd overtones have appreciable piezoelectric coupling. These overtones bear nearly, but not exactly, integral ratios to the fundamental frequency.

Although quartz is not isotropic, the dielectric constant is substantially independent of direction and equal to 4.54. Therefore, if edge effects are neglected, the shunting capacitance of any fully plated crystal unit is given by the formula

$$C_0 = 4.54\epsilon_0 A/D \qquad \text{farads} \quad \text{or} \quad 0.402lw/t \qquad \mu\mu\text{f,} \qquad (6.3)$$

where A is in square meters and D is in meters, while l, w, and t are in centimeters. The equivalent series capacitance is smaller than the value above by the inherent capacitance ratio r_0 and is therefore given by the equation

$$C_1 = C_0/r_0 = 0.402lw/tr_0 \qquad \mu\mu\text{f.} \qquad (6.4)$$

The resistance depends very greatly upon the mounting used and other details of manufacture. Because Q values vary less with frequency area, etc., than resistance values it is convenient to obtain the resistance from the defining equation

$$R_1 = \omega L_1/Q = 1/\omega C_1 Q. \qquad (6.5)$$

Like other components, crystals may be damaged by excessively large values of current or voltage. In thickness-shear elements such as A or B, the limit is usually set by overheating. In typical units it is safe to dissipate continuously a power as great as 25 milliwatts, although an appreciable frequency change due to the resulting temperature rise may be observed. In other plates the limit is likely to be set by fracture or by excessive change of frequency, presumably due to nonlinearity in the mounting. For example, a typical 100-kc G type element shows a frequency change of 10 ppm when the current reaches a value of the order of one milliampere per centimeter of width. It appears that the current per unit width is a useful criterion in all extensional vibrations and may serve approximately for other modes; and that densities in excess of a few milliamperes per centimeter are to be avoided.

The effect of temperature upon the natural frequency of the various crystal elements is shown in Fig. 6.22. The curves are idealized in that they represent the response of a plate accurately cut from a substantially perfect block of quartz. Units achieved in quantity production vary somewhat from these curves.

In *B*, *C*, and *D* elements the temperature at which the temperature coefficient becomes zero, called the *turning point*, may be varied over a range of about 50°C by variation of the orientation angle.[213] That is, the curves may be shifted along the temperature scale without greatly changing their shapes. In *A* and *G* elements, on the contrary, the curve tends to rotate about the midpoint, without significant change of the temperature range covered. Other elements behave in a manner

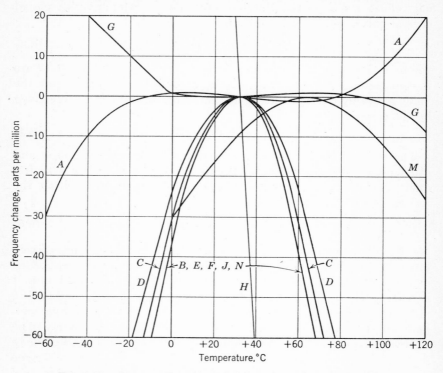

FIG. 6.22. Temperature characteristics of typical crystal units.

similar to the *B*, *C*, and *D*, but the temperature range over which the turning point may be adjusted is somewhat less. In elements of all kinds the cost is greatly increased if the temperature characteristic and nominal frequency must be controlled to very close limits.

The size of a practical crystal plate is limited by weight and availability on the upper side and by power dissipation, fragility, and techniques on the lower side. Operation over a wide frequency range is obtained by choosing the mode of vibration in addition to the dimensions of the plate. Approximate frequency ranges over which various

TABLE 6.5
PROPERTIES OF VARIOUS CRYSTAL CUTS

Cut	Mode*	Useful Range	Freq. Equation†	L_1, henries	C_1, μμf	Cap.‡ Ratio	R_1, ohms	PI§, ohms	Typical Q	Orientation	Typical Dimensions
A	ts	1–20 Mc	$166/t$	$\dfrac{2.62 \times 10^9}{lwf^3}$	$\dfrac{97lwf}{10^7}$	250	100	10^5	50,000	$(yxl)35°21'$ or $(yzw)35°21'$	$w = 0.95l = 29t$ $w = 1.05l = 32t$
B	ts	1.5–30 Mc	$256/t$	$\dfrac{10.5 \times 10^9}{lwf^3}$	$\dfrac{24.2lwf}{10^7}$	650	100	10^5	50,000	$(yxl) - 48°57'$ or $(yzw) - 48°57'$	$w = 1.02l = 24.4t$ $w = 0.98l = 24.8t$
C	fs	300–1000 kc	$307/l$	$233t$	$\dfrac{108}{tf^2}$	350	1,000	10^6	20,000	$(yxl)37°55'$ or $(yzw)37°55'$	$w = l = 20t$
D	fs	200–500 kc	$207/l$	$590t$	$\dfrac{43}{tf^2}$	400	1,000	10^5	20,000	$(yxl) - 52°40'$ or $(yzw) - 52°40'$	$w = l = 20t$
E	e	50–200 kc	$282/l$	$660t$	$\dfrac{38.3}{tf^2}$	125	1,000	10^5	20,000	$(xzl)5°$	$w = 0.15l = 10t$
F	e	50–200 kc	$256/l$	$840t$	$\dfrac{30.1}{tf^2}$	130	1,000	10^5	20,000	$(zyt) - 18°$	$w = 0.15l = 10t$
G	e	80–500 kc	$337/l$	$167t$	$\dfrac{152}{tf^2}$	350	100	10^6	200,000||	$(yxlt)51°14'/45°$	$w = 1.17l = 20t$
H	wf	4–50 kc	$500w/l^2$ or $75/l$	$14,200t$	$\dfrac{1.79}{tf^2}$	190	10,000	10^6	20,000	$(zyt)5°$	$w = 0.15l = 10t$
J¶	tf	1–10 kc	$560t/l^2$ or $11.2/l$	$10^4 t$	$\dfrac{0.0254}{tf^2}$	200	10,000	10^6	20,000	$(zyt)5°$ pair	$w = 0.1l = 5t$
M	e	50–500 kc	$280/l$	$382t$	$\dfrac{66.4}{tf^2}$	190	1,000	10^5	20,000	$(zytl)8°/36°$	$w = 0.4l = 5t$
N	wf	4–50 kc	$560w/l^2$ or $67.2/l$	$105,000t$	$\dfrac{0.242}{tf^2}$	900	10,000	10^6	20,000	$(zytl)8°/50°$	$w = 0.12l = 10t$
A	ots**	15–100 Mc	$166n/t$	$\dfrac{2.62n^3 \times 10^9}{lwf^3}$	$\dfrac{97lwf}{10^7 n^3}$	$250n^2$	100	10^4	75,000	$(yxl)35°21'$ or $(yzw)35°21'$	$w = l = 60t$

* ts = thickness shear, fs = face shear, e = extensional, wf = width flexure, tf = thickness flexure.
† Frequency in kilocycles corresponding to the governing dimension in centimeters.
‡ Capacitance ratio, $r_0 = C_0/C_1$.
§ Into a uniform load capacitance of 32 μμf, now commonly used.
|| Carefully mounted in vacuum.
¶ The J element is a cemented symmetrical pair of right and left-hand elements
** Using the mechanical overtone n of thickness shear.

elements are applicable, together with other properties, are given in Table 6.5.*

The symbols used in the orientation columns have a relatively simple interpretation. The resonator is a rectangular parallelopiped of thickness t, length l, and width w, respectively. The first two letters in parentheses represent, in order, the natural axes of the quartz crystal along which the thickness and length of the resonator lie before rotation. The third letter in the parentheses represents the dimension of the resonator which serves as axis for the first rotation. The fourth letter, when present, indicates the dimension which serves as axis for the second rotation. The angles which follow represent the magnitude and direction of the rotation angles. It is seen that these expressions are in agreement with Fig. 6.21.

The data of Table 6.5 are reasonably accurate except for the resistance and PI values, which are correct only in order of magnitude. Moreover, the temperature characteristics, capacitance ratios, and frequency constants are subject to considerable variation due to deliberate or accidental variations of orientation and relative dimensions. However, the compilation does show orders of magnitude, and contrasts the behavior of different units.

6.14 Magnetostriction resonators

The usefulness of quartz crystals as resonators stems from the fact that quartz is piezoelectric.† Another important class of resonators is based upon the property of magnetostriction.[344] This property is observed in a number of pure metals and alloys, notably those based on nickel, as a dependence of the mechanical dimension upon the magnetic condition. In a typical magnetostriction resonator,[239] application of a longitudinal magnetic field results in a shortening of a relatively long bar of the metal. However, the behavior depends greatly upon the material and the relative orientation of the field. Moreover, because the dimensional change is independent of the direction of the applied field, a simple proportionality cannot exist between cause and effect; and the dimensional change usually varies approximately as the square of the field. This difficulty is ordinarily avoided by biasing the material with a constant magnetic field which is substantially

---

* Substantially all the data for Table 6.5 and Figs. 6.21 and 6.22 was obtained by the Bell Telephone Laboratories and is taken from the section prepared by Dr. R. A. Sykes for the Prentice-Hall *Handbook on Electrical Communication*.

† Electrostriction has not found application in resonators because the electromechanical coupling is much inferior to that provided by piezoelectricity, and is inadequate for most purposes.

larger than the maximum value of the varying field. However, the basic length, the natural frequency, and the electromechanical coupling vary somewhat with variations of the biasing field.

Magnetostriction resonators have not been widely used, although they possess certain advantages over quartz or other alternates, especially at frequencies of a few kilocycles. This limited use is due in part to the difficulty of procuring and mounting suitable rods and in part to inherent difficulties associated with the smallness of the electromechanical coupling.

The equivalent circuit of a magnetostriction resonator is shown in Fig. 6.23. It differs from that of a quartz crystal in that the shunting capacitance is replaced by an inductance and resistance in parallel. These account for the reactance and losses of the winding in the absence of vibration of the rod, whereas the high-Q branch, L_1, R_1 and C_1, accounts

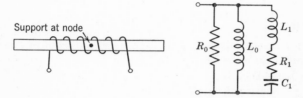

FIG. 6.23. Magnetostriction resonator and equivalent circuit.

for the desired response due to mechanical vibration. The inductance ratio L_1/L_0, together with the Q of the mechanical response, plays an important part in determining the characteristics which may be obtained. In available units this ratio is relatively high, in the order of 5000. The Q of the mechanical resonance is approximately 10,000; under these conditions we may show that the net reactance of the system is never capacitive. A corresponding situation exists in quartz crystals operated at a high mechanical overtone, and in both cases the driving system must be carefully designed if the output frequency is to be under adequate control of the mechanical vibration. In magnetostriction resonators this difficulty is sometimes evaded by using two coils so that the system acts as a highly selective four-terminal network.

The frequency of a simple bar vibrating in the extensional mode depends upon the length, density, and elastic constant of the material. In ordinary materials these quantities vary with temperature to an objectionable degree. However, Ide[153] has shown that an alloy of 8 per cent chromium, 37 per cent nickel, and 55 per cent iron has the relatively excellent response indicated in Fig. 6.24.

Recent work at the Armour Research Foundation has been directed toward producing magnetostriction resonators useful at frequencies in the order of a megacycle. Details of this work are not available, but it appears to have met with a reasonable degree of success.

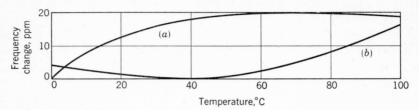

Fig. 6.24. Temperature characteristic of a magnetostriction resonator using extensional mode: (a) alloy annealed and operated in a field of 13,500 ampere turns per meter and (b) alloy quenched and operated in a field of 8100 ampere-turns per meter.

6.15 Tuning forks

The simple tuning fork has been used as a standard of frequency for acoustics and music for a long time and has received extensive development. It was, therefore, one of the first mechanical resonators to be used with electric circuits. In the earliest work the fork was driven magnetically by varying the current in an appropriate electromagnet and executed its control by opening and closing an electric contact in the driving circuit, as in an ordinary buzzer. This arrangement was never very satisfactory because of contact troubles and the mechanical loading due to the contact. Considerably better results were obtained when the contact was replaced by a pressure-sensitive resistance, similar to the ordinary carbon microphone. In fact, such units are still used to some extent because of their simplicity, compactness, and moderate power requirements.

Modern precise tuning fork resonators[222] are mounted in vacuum to avoid damping due to the air, are mechanically isolated from the support in such a way that very little energy is lost in the mounting, and are constructed of a material which leads to a very low temperature coefficient of frequency. A typical construction is shown in Fig. 6.25. One tine is driven by the varying pull of an electromagnet, while the other tine generates an alternating voltage in a second coil by its motion in conjunction with a permanent magnetic field.[184] Thus the unit acts as a four-terminal network in which the principal transmission takes place through the mechanical motion of the fork. The minimum loss is of the order of 40 db, but this presents no great difficulty because adequate gain may be secured by means of a single vacuum tube with suitable transformers.[223] However, there is some difficulty with undesired oscillation because of direct magnetic coupling through the fork and permanent magnet.

Tuning forks have been built for frequencies of about 100 to 10,000 cycles, and have a typical Q value of about 10,000. Temperature stabilities of the order of 0.1 ppm per °C have been achieved in some cases by careful choice of materials and construction, but a much larger

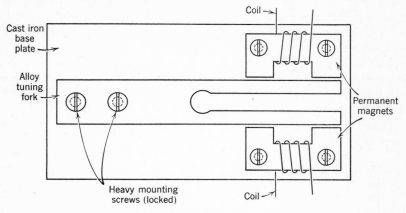

FIG. 6.25. Typical precision tuning fork.

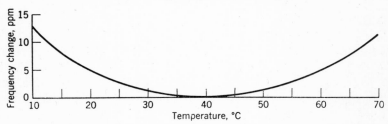

FIG. 6.26. Temperature characteristic of a tuning fork resonator.

coefficient is typical. The temperature characteristic of a good modern fork is shown in Fig. 6.26.

6.16 Molecular resonance

The resonators so far described are relative rather than absolute; that is, the natural frequency depends upon dimensions or other properties which are under control. An entirely different situation exists with respect to atomic and molecular resonances.

It has been known for a long time that the optical frequencies (or wavelengths) characteristic of various atoms are absolute, highly stable, and virtually independent of all known influences. However, this knowledge was of little use to the oscillator art because of the tremendous frequencies (order of 10^{15}) involved. Later it was discovered that ammonia and a number of other gases show selective absorption effects at frequencies of the order of 20,000 Mc. The ammonia response at 23,870.127 ± 0.003 Mc is particularly strong and has been extensively studied at the Bureau of Standards and elsewhere.[11, 139] The sharpness of response corresponds to a selectivity of about 100,000; and the central frequency appears to be absolutely independent of everything except static electric and magnetic fields, which are readily reduced to values producing negligible error.

The simplest device for making use of this effect is a section of rectangular wave guide with inside dimensions approximately one-half by one centimeter. The guide is fitted with air-tight mica windows and filled with dry ammonia gas at a pressure of about 10^{-5} atmosphere. Under these circumstances the unit acts as a band-rejection wave filter having; per meter length, a fixed loss of about one decibel and a variable loss increasing sharply by several additional decibels at the critical frequency. Alternative arrangements employ wave guides of enlarged cross section or cavity resonators in which the intrinsic Q is low compared to 100,000.

The sharpness of the response is degraded if the gas pressure or the electric field intensity becomes too high, presumably because of interaction between the molecules. Therefore, it is necessary to maintain a low and fairly uniform pressure and to limit the signal applied. Everything else being equal, it appears that the permissible power level is directly proportional to the number of molecules, hence the gas volume. Therefore, in cavity-type absorption resonators a large rather than a small ratio of volume to inherent selectivity is desirable.

At the present time circuits for use with this form of resonator are somewhat complicated and troublesome to maintain. However, the method shows promise of providing a standard of frequency, and time, which is superior to anything yet developed.

A still more exact standard of frequency exists in the molecular beam.[166] A beam of molecules of a suitable material is produced by evaporation and is projected through an evacuated region where it is subjected to alternating electric and magnetic fields. When the frequency of these fields has a particular value, characteristic of the molecule in question, the beam is strongly deflected. Exceptional features of this arrangement are the sharpness of discrimination, which corresponds to a Q of 10^7, and the fact that the critical frequency depends solely upon the kind of molecules used. The molecular beam, therefore, offers an absolute standard of frequency substantially superior even to the molecular resonance. However, from the practical standpoint it seems even farther from use as a working standard of frequency.

PROBLEMS

6.1. An antiresonant circuit has a capacitance of 1000 $\mu\mu f$, a Q of 200, and a natural frequency of one megacycle. What is its impedance level? What properties must an associated driving system have?

6.2. In a cavity resonator operating at 30°C and standard pressure the humidity changes from 20 to 70 per cent. What is the fractional change of natural frequency?

6.3. In Prob. 6.2, half of the air (at 20 per cent humidity) is replaced by carbon dioxide. What is the fractional change of natural frequency?

6.4. Prove that the temperature coefficient of capacitance of a condenser is equal to the linear coefficient of its material if the shape is the same at all temperatures.

6.5. Repeat Prob. 6.4 for an inductance.

6.6. A coaxial conductor is made of copper. The center conductor has a diameter of one centimeter and the outer tube has inner and outer diameters of 2 and 3 cm respectively. By suitable references determine the inductance per meter at very low and very high frequencies and the frequency region where the transition occurs (at 30°C).

6.7. A simple cavity resonator is made of brass. What is its temperature coefficient of frequency? Explain.

6.8. Design a coaxial quarter-wave resonator in which the temperature coefficient of frequency is canceled by differential expansion of aluminum and steel.

6.9. How might one distinguish between piezoelectricity and electrostriction: between piezomagnetism and magnetostriction?

6.10. A quartz crystal has parameters, $R_1 = 400$ ohms, $L_1 = 200$ henries, $C_1 = 0.02$ $\mu\mu f$, and $C_0 = 7\mu\mu f$. What is its performance index (PI) with a load capacitance of 30 $\mu\mu f$?

7

LINEAR OSCILLATORS

A great majority of the oscillators in practical use are nonlinear; that is, the vacuum tube simultaneously serves as amplifier and limiter. In such oscillators the current through the tube is far from sinusoidal, although the voltage wave forms are often almost pure because of the filtering action of tuned circuits. The use of the tube as limiter is effective and economical; and such oscillators adequately meet most application requirements. However, where the highest order of frequency and amplitude stability is required or where harmonics must be avoided and reliable operation over long intervals is needed, the linear oscillator is used.

Two principal classes of linear oscillators exist. In one, limiting is accomplished by means of a *thermistor*, that is, a thermally sensitive resistor. In a thermistor-controlled oscillator the amplitude of oscillation may be made almost independent of the condition of the vacuum tube and its bias voltages; however, it is necessarily dependent upon the ambient temperature. In the second class are electronically controlled oscillators in which the gain is varied as a function of amplitude by an auxiliary device in such a way that no appreciable non-linearity is produced. Certain multiple-grid tubes designed primarily for frequency conversion have characteristics suitable for accomplishing this end. In electronically controlled oscillators the amplitude depends mainly upon some reference voltage.

7.1 Thermistors for oscillator use

Thermistors are elements in which the resistance is a function of temperature but not of the instantaneous current. They are therefore well suited for use as limiters in oscillators because, for any but the lowest frequencies, *thermal inertia prevents the temperature, and hence the resistance, from changing appreciably during any one cycle of the oscillation.* The resistance is therefore a function of the oscillation amplitude but is linear from the standpoint of waveform distortion.

Two types of thermistors are commonly used in oscillator circuits.

Cheapest and most generally available is the tungsten filament lamp. The common feature of all tungsten lamps is that the resistance at incandescence is about ten times as great as that at room temperature. In oscillators it is undesirable to use this full range because of the relatively high power required to produce incandescence and because of the limited operating life which results. However, small filaments are raised to a temperature of about 900°K (corresponding to a dull red) by a power of only a few milliwatts. At this temperature the resistance is about four times that at room temperature, and the life is virtually unlimited.

7.2 Lamp characteristics

Tungsten filament lamps are manufactured in a great variety of physical forms for operation throughout a wide range of voltages and currents. For the present purposes, however, we need consider only lamps of small physical size designed for relatively low voltages and currents. The properties of interest are the resistance; its variation with respect to the current, voltage, or power; and the thermal time constant of the filament. The thermal time constant for a slender filament rated at about 30 ma is of the order of 0.02 second. For a somewhat heavier filament rated at 200 ma this increases to about 0.06 second.

Different points along the filament operate at quite different temperatures because of unequal radiation losses and the cooling effect of lead and support wires. For this reason the variation of overall resistance, which may conveniently be expressed with respect to the applied voltage, is relatively complicated. The variation of resistance with applied voltage for representative lamps is shown in Fig. 7.1. Voltage, rather than current or power, is chosen for the abscissa because the lamp voltage is closely proportional to the output voltage in a number of important thermistor-controlled oscillators. Logarithmic scales for both voltage and resistance are chosen to accommodate a wide range of variables and because *fractional* rather than absolute changes are of interest. The principal axes of voltage and resistance are supplemented by diagonals of power which are very helpful in actual design. It is seen that a great impedance range is available, and that a marked increase of resistance is obtainable with relatively small power dissipation. An example of the use of these curves follows in Section 7.5.

An important property of a thermistor is the sensitivity s defined*

* Our s is comparable to the parameter η_B used by Aigrain and Williams.[4] However, they refer the resistance to the current rather than the voltage.

by the ratio

$$s = \frac{dr/r}{dE/E} = \frac{d(\log r)}{d(\log E)},\qquad(7.1)$$

where E is the terminal voltage and r is the resistance. It is seen that s is simply the slope when the curve is plotted to logarithmic scales.

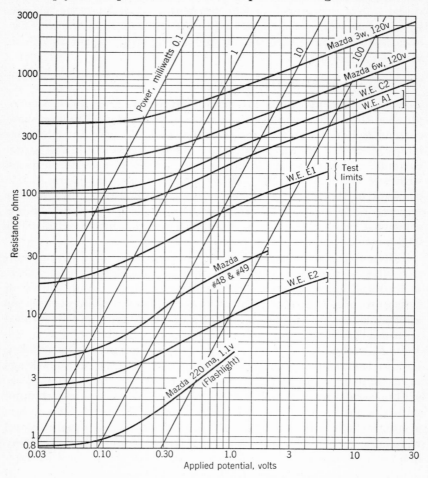

Fig. 7.1. Properties of tungsten lamps at 300°K.

Accordingly, attention is focused upon the steepest part of the curves of Fig. 7.1. Fortunately, the slope is near its maximum value over a wide region of low power input, so that long life is to be expected.

Two additional practical problems need to be considered, especially if quantity production is anticipated. Because lamps are manufactured in large numbers at small cost, there is a considerable variation between units; the circuit design must take account of this resistance variation, which is typically about ± 20 per cent for a given voltage. Unfortunately, because the sensitivity s is only about one-half for typical lamps the resistance variation may result in an output voltage variation as great as ± 40 per cent; a variation of more than two to one! When lamps are designed for illumination, there is no substantial contact problem, and the filament is often connected to the lead-in wire by a simple hook-clamp joint. Although this arrangement is satisfactory for lighting, it is likely to give trouble in an oscillator. In other lamps the filament is connected by spot welding or by pressing it into the softer lead-in wire. Neither of these constructions should give contact trouble. However, all lamps in which the filament has additional supporting hooks are subject to slight instabilities because the support wires short-circuit one or more of the tiny coils of the filament.

7.3 Semiconducting thermistors

Materials whose conductivity is much less than that of typical metals, but is much greater than that of good insulators, are called semiconductors. Carbon, silicon, and germanium are familiar examples of semiconductors. The behavior of semiconductors is very complicated and cannot be discussed here. It is sufficient to note that the number of mobile charges or current carriers, and hence the conductivity, is quite sensitive to the amount of impurity present, to the temperature, and to other influences such as radiation. Most semiconductors have high negative temperature coefficients of resistance. The thermal variation of resistivity of a typical semiconducting material is compared with that of tungsten in Fig. 7.2. This property is employed in semiconducting thermistors.

Thermistor units are manufactured for electrical application[24] in two distinct classes. Simplest are the *self-heated* thermistors which are simple two-terminal elements, comparable with lamps. More complicated and versatile are the *separately heated* thermistors in which the temperature may be controlled by heat generated in a coil of resistance wire associated with the semiconductor. The latter arrangement permits the control of very small signals by currents in an entirely separate network, and is desirable in a number of situations. Commercial units are quite small and resemble other circuit elements in general appearance. The characteristic of a sensitive self-heated thermistor designed for oscillator application is shown in Fig. 7.3.

Its resistance variation is opposite to and much greater than that of tungsten; however, this advantage is considerably offset by the marked effect of ambient temperature.

In a linear oscillator the gain is independent of the signal level, and is ordinarily quite insensitive to the ambient temperature. Therefore, equilibrium will demand a unique value of resistance and hence a unique temperature of the thermistor. Because the heat loss from the thermistor is a function of the ambient temperature, it is clear that the power, and hence the oscillation amplitude required to maintain the equilibrium, also depends upon the ambient temperature.

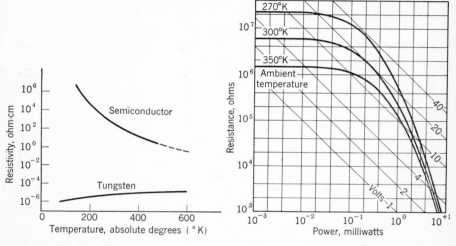

FIG. 7.2.   Resistivity of a semicon-   FIG. 7.3.   Characteristics of a semiconductor.   ducting thermistor.

In thermistors which operate near 1000°K, the principal heat loss is by radiation, which is little affected by the ambient. However, when the operation temperature is near 400°K the heat loss is largely by conduction, and is greatly affected by the ambient, as shown in Fig. 7.3. Unfortunately, semiconducting thermistors tend to drift in value if subjected to excessive temperatures, so that it is difficult to eliminate the temperature effect.

The undesirable effect of ambient temperature on the output of thermistor-controlled oscillators may, however, be greatly reduced by a balancing method. Ordinarily, the oscillator employs a bridge circuit in which the thermistor resistance substantially equals a fixed resistance. If the fixed resistance is replaced by a suitable second thermistor, then a first-order balance may be obtained over a considerable range of ambient temperature. The added thermistor must have a power rating or heat exchange rate which is large compared to that of the primary thermistor so that its resistance will be governed solely by the ambient temperature and not by the oscillation amplitude. If this added thermistor is to appear in an arm adjacent to the primary thermistor—the usual case—it should have a thermal coefficient of the same sign but smaller than that of the primary thermistor. Becker et al.[27] describe such arrangements in some detail.

The thermal time constant of semiconductive thermistors tends to be somewhat longer than that of lamps. The unit of Fig. 7.3 has a time constant of about 0.1 second, and is stated to be satisfactory for use in oscillators at frequencies above about 100 cycles.

7.4 A thermistor bridge oscillator

The oscillator shown in Fig. 7.4 is capable of excellent performance in that the output is nearly constant in amplitude and frequency and is virtually free from harmonics. The system is particularly convenient

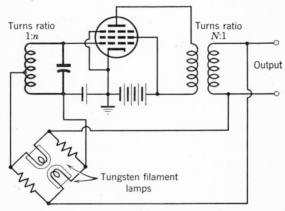

FIG. 7.4.   Lamp bridge oscillator.

for analytic purposes because the amplifier, limiter, and resonator functions are performed by separate portions of the circuit and because linear equations are adequate to describe the performance.

When the circuit is first energized, the lamp filaments are cold and have a relatively low resistance so that the bridge circuit is far from balance and has little loss. If the transformers are suitably wound and connected a considerable loop gain exists, and oscillations build up at the natural frequency of the resonator, that is, the tuned grid circuit. The oscillatory currents heat the filaments, thereby increasing their resistance and bringing the bridge nearer to balance. This action reduces the net loop gain, and decreases the rate at which the oscillations expand. Equilibrium is reached when the loss of the lamp bridge equals the gain of the rest of the system. It is practical to adjust the element values so that the equilibrium amplitude is considerably below the overload point of the tube, which then operates in a conservative class A condition.

The fact that limiting can be achieved without distortion is due to the thermal inertia of the lamp filaments. Although the temperature (and hence the resistance) changes rapidly enough to maintain equilibrium, the temperature does not change appreciably during any one cycle. Therefore, *with respect to the oscillatory current, the lamp acts like an adjustable linear resistor rather than a nonlinear resistor.*

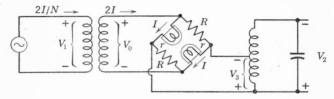

Fig. 7.5.   Equivalent circuit.

In the most exact sense the foregoing statements are only approximate. For, no matter how high the frequency of oscillation and how slow the thermal response of the lamp, there is necessarily *some* variation of resistance during the cycle, and therefore *some* distortion of the wave. If the frequency is in order of 100 kc, the variation is extremely small and the distortion is less than that inherent in the vacuum tube. At the lower audio frequencies, on the other hand, the resistance of ordinary lamp filaments *does* vary appreciably over the cycle, and significant distortion occurs.

To facilitate analysis of the lamp bridge oscillator, we assume that the plate resistance of the tube is infinite; that the output transformer is so tightly coupled as to be effectively ideal; that the input transformer has finite inductance but negligible loss and leakage; and that the loop gain is so large that the bridge is nearly balanced. These conditions are used to obtain Fig. 7.5 in which the transformer turns ratios correspond to Fig. 7.4. The governing equations are linear and relatively simple, in part because the tuned grid circuit is assumed to have no losses. Because of the symmetry of the bridge the driving current divides equally so that

$$V_3 = I(R - r). \tag{7.2}$$

Since the plate current is given by

$$2I/N = g_m n V_3, \tag{7.3}$$

the condition of sustained oscillation is obtained by eliminating I and V_3 to give

$$2 = g_m n N (R - r) = g_m n N R (1 - r/R). \tag{7.4}$$

7.5 Design parameters for bridge oscillator

The substitution of numerical values is frequently helpful in interpreting analytic results. Reasonable values for the present example are $g_m = 2000$ micromhos, $R = 200$ ohms, $N = 20$, and $n = 40$. Substitution in eq. 7.4 yields

$$2 = 40 \times 20 \times 0.002 \times 200(1 - r/R), \tag{7.5}$$

which requires

$$r = 198.667 \text{ ohms.} \tag{7.6}$$

The Western Electric type A1 Switchboard Lamp is suitable for this application.   As shown in Fig. 7.1, the resistance reaches 200 ohms at a voltage of about 1.3 volts.   In this region the curve is closely approximated by the empirical equation

$$r = 180E^{0.4}, \tag{7.7}$$

where E is the lamp voltage.   The sensitivity, s, which corresponds to the exponent is thus equal to 0.4.   Substitution of eq. 7.6 into eq. 7.7 requires that

$$E = 1.27 \text{ volts.} \tag{7.8}$$

The remaining circuit voltages are readily seen to be $V_1 = 51$, $V_0 = 2.55$, $V_3 = 0.008$, and $V_2 = 0.32$ volt, values which are consistent with highly linear class A amplification.   Under the assumptions made, the frequency is identical with the natural frequency of the grid circuit. In a practical circuit this condition is very closely approximated.

The operation of this circuit can be analyzed from another viewpoint which offers certain advantages.   The curve of Fig. 7.6 shows the variation of the output V_3 of the lamp bridge as a function of the applied voltage V_0.   The output first increases linearly with the input, but decreases from this relation as the temperature of the lamps increases.   The output reaches a maximum, then decreases rapidly toward zero as the input is further increased, passing through zero and reversing in phase as the input is increased through that value which balances the bridge.

Because the amplifier is linear, the voltages V_0 and V_3 are proportional to each other. This relationship is represented in Fig. 7.6 by the dot-dash line which has a slope equal to the reciprocal of the voltage amplification. The condition of sustained oscillation corresponds to the intersection of the dot-dash line with the characteristic curve of the lamp bridge. This construction shows clearly that a large change in the amplifier gain, corresponding to a large change in the

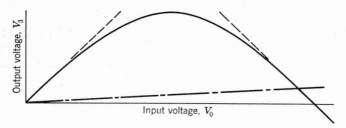

FIG. 7.6.   Loss characteristics of a lamp bridge.

slope of the dot-dash line, will produce only a small fractional change in the output voltage V_0. That is, the system has a large value of amplitude stability.

7.6 Amplitude stability of bridge oscillator

The preceding discussion of the bridge oscillator has shown, in a general way, that a large change in the tube transconductance produces only a small change in the output voltage, V_0. This general idea can be reduced to a quantitative relationship by the following mathematical process.   We begin by noting from Fig. 7.5 that the lamp voltage, E, is related to the amplifier output voltage V_0 by the simple expression

$$E = V_0 r/(R + r). \tag{7.9}$$

If we multiply eq. 7.9 by $(R + r)$ and take differentials, considering E, V_0, and r as variables, we obtain

$$(R + r)dE + E\, dr = V_0 dr + r\, dV_0. \tag{7.10}$$

Division by eq. 7.9 and use of the fact that the bridge is almost balanced so that r and R are nearly equal yield

$$dE/E - \tfrac{1}{2}\, dr/r = dV_0/V_0. \tag{7.11}$$

The loop gain eq. 7.4 is now differentiated with respect to g_m and r to obtain

$$g_m dr = (R - r)dg_m \quad \text{or} \quad dr/r = (R/r - 1)\, dg_m/g_m. \tag{7.12}$$

Combining eq. 7.1 with eq. 7.11 and 7.12 yields

$$(1/s - \tfrac{1}{2})\, (R/r - 1)\, dg_m/g_m = dV_0/V_0. \tag{7.13}$$

The amplitude stability with respect to transconductance is defined in Chapter 1 as

$$S_A = \frac{dg_m/g_m}{dV_0/V_0}. \tag{7.14}$$

Using eq. 7.4 to eliminate r from eq. 7.13 permits rewriting the amplitude stability as

$$S_A = \frac{2s}{2 - s} \cdot \frac{R - 2/nNg_m}{2/nNg_m} = \frac{s}{2 - s} \cdot (nNg_mR - 2). \tag{7.15}$$

It is clear that the amplitude stability approaches zero as the product $nNRg_m$ decreases toward two (the threshold of oscillation) and that it approaches infinity as s approaches two. We see by substituting numbers from the previous example, where the lamp sensitivity s was 0.4, that S_A may become quite high in practical cases,

$$S_A = \frac{0.4}{1.6}\, (40 \times 20 \times 0.002 \times 200 - 2) = 79.5. \tag{7.16}$$

That is, a 0.795-db change in transconductance would result in only 0.01-db change of output.

7.7 A linear tuned plate oscillator

A simple linear oscillator which has several interesting features is shown in Fig. 7.7. It differs from the conventional tuned plate triode oscillator in that the grid bias is produced in the cathode rather than the grid circuit, and by the addition of the lamp and inductance L_3.* The lamp serves to stabilize the amplitude by reducing the Q and impedance of the tuned circuit as the amplitude of oscillation increases. The compensating inductance L_3 serves to make the operating frequency independent of the lamp resistance, as shown in eq. 7.24 below. The cathode resistor, when adequately by-passed, provides a bias suitable for class A operation. Tests show that the amplitude and frequency stability are good and that the output is substantially free from harmonics.

* Except for the addition of the lamp, this circuit is identical with that of Mallett.[201] The operation, however, is quite different, because the addition of L_3 may actually degrade frequency stability when strong harmonics are present.

The conditions for oscillation are determined by reference to Fig. 7.8. Because there is no grid current, we may write.

$$\mathbf{V} = j\omega M \mathbf{I}_1, \tag{7.17}$$

$$\mathbf{V}_0 = \mathbf{I}_1(R_1 + j\omega L_1), \tag{7.18}$$

$$\mathbf{I}_2 = j\omega C_1 \mathbf{V}_0, \tag{7.19}$$

and

$$(r_p + j\omega L_3)(\mathbf{I}_1 + \mathbf{I}_2) = (\mu\mathbf{V} - \mathbf{V}_0). \tag{7.20}$$

Elimination of the current and voltage variables yields

$$r_p + j\omega L_3 + j\omega r_p C_1 R_1 - \omega^2 L_3 C_1 R_1 - \omega^2 L_1 C_1 r_p$$
$$- j\omega^3 L_1 L_3 C_1 = j\omega M \mu - R_1 - j\omega L_1. \tag{7.21}$$

The real terms must form a separate equation

$$R_1 + r_p = \omega^2(L_3 C_1 R_1 + L_1 C_1 r_p), \tag{7.22}$$

which becomes independent of R_1 and reduces to

$$1/\omega^2 = L_1 C_1 \tag{7.23}$$

provided

$$L_1 = L_3. \tag{7.24}$$

The equation based on the imaginary terms of eq. 7.21 becomes with eqs. 7.23 and 7.24

$$\mu = (L_1 + r_p C_1 R_1)/M. \tag{7.25}$$

It defines the gain and resistance conditions which must be met for oscillations to exist.

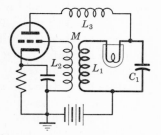

FIG. 7.7. Tuned plate oscillator.

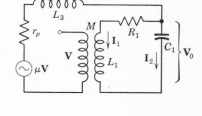

FIG. 7.8. Equivalent circuit.

Suppose that a frequency of one megacycle is to be produced, using the familiar 6J5 triode with $r_p = 7500$ and $\mu = 20$. A suitable lamp is the type 48 (or 49) switchboard lamp having characteristics shown in Fig. 7.1. As a reasonable compromise between sensitivity, freedom from ambient temperature effects, and the limited power available from a small tube let us operate the lamp at a resistance of 10 ohms, a voltage of 0.25 volt, and a current of 25 ma. It is appropriate to allow about 10 ohms additional resistance for the coil losses so that $R_1 = 20$ ohms. The reasonable assumption that the plate coil has an inherent Q of 100, together with a resistance of 10 ohms at a frequency of one megacycle, fixes the value of inductance by the relation

$$2\pi \times 10^6 L_1 = 10 \times 100 \text{ henries} \tag{7.26}$$

so

$$L_1 = L_3 = 159 \ \mu\text{h.} \tag{7.27}$$

Using eq. 7.23, we find

$$C_1 = 159 \ \mu\mu\text{f.} \tag{7.28}$$

Then, from eq. 7.25,

$$M = 9.15 \ \mu\text{h.} \tag{7.29}$$

Because the lamp resistance is 10 ohms only when the rms lamp current is 25 ma, the rms grid voltage is by eqs. 7.17 and 7.29,

$$V = 1.44 \text{ volts rms.} \tag{7.30}$$

The corresponding plate voltage is closely equal to the voltage across L_1, which by eq. 7.18 is

$$V_0 = 25 \text{ volts rms.} \tag{7.31}$$

A plate supply of 150 volts with a grid bias of 4 volts, which leads to an average current of 6 ma and calls for a self-bias resistor of 666 ohms, is appropriate. The direct current is small enough so that it does not contribute appreciably to heating the lamp. It is seen that all the element values are entirely reasonable in magnitude, and that the voltages are consistent with linear operating conditions.

In practice, there are a number of distributed capacitances which were not included in the analysis. Moreover, the dielectric losses of the coil are not effectively in series with the lamp. For these reasons it is usually necessary to adjust L_3 experimentally to a value somewhat smaller than L_1 for best frequency stability.

Although slightly more complicated, the oscillator of Fig. 7.4 is superior to that of Fig. 7.7 in several respects. First, it is much less critical with respect to the values of the elements, because the relatively large loss normally designed into the bridge will accommodate considerable variations of transconductance and transformer performance. For the same reason, the amplitude of the output is more nearly constant. Finally, the frequency of the bridge oscillator is inherently independent of the lamp resistance, so that no frequency stabilizing reactor is necessary.

7.8 Amplitude stability of tuned plate oscillator

The amplitude stability of the linear tuned plate oscillator is readily determined by methods already established. Since in practice the amplification factor of a triode is much more constant than the plate resistance, it is appropriate to differentiate eq. 7.25, regarding only r_p and R_1 as variables. If the notation of Fig. 7.8 is used, the resulting equation is

$$dr_p/r_p + dR_1/R_1 = 0. \tag{7.32}$$

The resistance R_1 represents the sum of the lamp resistance, which may be designated r, and the coil resistance, which may be represented by the constant k. With this substitution and use of eq. 7.1 we obtain

$$dr_p/r_p = -dr/R_1 = -(sr/R_1)(dv/v), \tag{7.33}$$

where v represents the lamp voltage itself, and is given by

$$v = I_1 r. \tag{7.34}$$

Differentiation of this expression leads to

$$dv/v = dI_1/I_1 + dr/r. \tag{7.35}$$

Because large values of Q are commonly used, the output voltage, V_0 is almost proportional to I_1, so differentiation of eq. 7.18 leads (with only a very small error) to

$$dV_0/V_0 = dI_1/I_1. \tag{7.36}$$

The overall amplitude stability now becomes

$$S_A = \frac{dr_p/r_p}{dV_0/V_0} = \frac{-sr\, dv/v}{R_1(dv/v - dr/r)} = \frac{-sr}{(1 - s)(r + k)}. \tag{7.37}$$

Substituting in this equation the values $r = k = 10$ used in the example in the preceding section and the sensitivity $s = 0.7$ corresponding to the selected operating point in Fig. 7.1, we have for the amplitude stability the relatively low value of 1.15. The negative sign arises from the fact that an increase in output is associated with a decrease of the plate resistance.

7.9 The Wien bridge oscillator

A circuit which has proved exceptionally convenient for variable frequency oscillators in the audio range[25] is shown in Fig. 7.9. It is a linear, thermistor-controlled oscillator, which has excellent amplitude control. Although many variations are practical and are sometimes used,[164] the arrangement shown is ordinarily regarded as most advantageous.

The key feature of this oscillator is the slightly modified Wien bridge which serves as both limiter and equivalent resonator. It is well known that such a bridge is balanced, provided

$$R_1 = 1/\omega C_1, \tag{7.38}$$

and

$$R_2 = 2r. \tag{7.39}$$

Oscillation occurs at a frequency such that eq. 7.38 is satisfied to an accuracy limited only by the presence of unavoidable phase shifts in

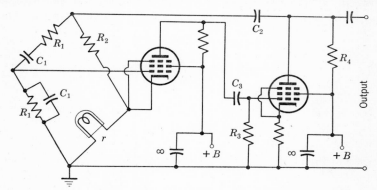

FIG. 7.9. Wien bridge oscillator.

other parts of the circuit. The equilibrium amplitude is such as to heat the lamp nearly, but not quite, to a resistance consistent with eq. 7.39. In practice, R_1 is usually large compared to R_2, so as to obtain audio frequencies with practical values of capacitance.

The Wien bridge may be connected in several ways, of which only one yields suitable oscillations under any particular set of conditions. It is therefore necessary to examine the system behavior with some care.[338] The essential facts are presented in a Nyquist diagram determined from the following equations, based on the equivalent circuit of Fig. 7.10:

$$V_3 = V_2 - V_1, \tag{7.40}$$

$$V_1(r + R_2) = V_0 r, \tag{7.41}$$

and

$$V_2 = V_0 \frac{R_1/(1 + j\omega C_1 R_1)}{R_1/(1 + j\omega C_1 R_1) + mR_1 + 1/j\omega n C_1} \tag{7.42}$$

or

$$\mathbf{V}_0/\mathbf{V}_2 = 1 + m + j\omega m C_1 R_1 + 1/n + 1/j\omega n C_1 R_1. \quad (7.43)$$

Elimination of $\mathbf{V}_1$ and $\mathbf{V}_2$ yields

$$\mathbf{V}_3/\mathbf{V}_0 = \frac{1}{1 + m + 1/n + j\omega m C_1 R_1 + 1/j\omega n C_1 R_1} - \frac{1}{1 + R_2/r}, \quad (7.44)$$

which may be put in the symbolic form

$$\mathbf{V}_3/\mathbf{V}_0 = \frac{1}{a + jb\omega + 1/jc\omega} - d. \quad (7.45)$$

This equation is in the form of a ratio of phasor voltages and therefore determines a Nyquist diagram. The denominator of the first term corresponds to a straight vertical line in the complex plane. There-

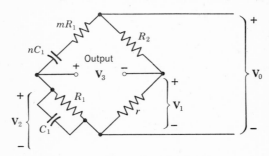

Fig. 7.10. Generalized Wien bridge.

fore, the complete expression 7.45 represents a circle of diameter $1/a$ displaced from the origin by the distance d. Two cases, one for d small, the other for d large, are shown in Fig. 7.11. In both cases, increasing frequency corresponds to clockwise rotation. Because m and n are inherently positive, the constant a always exceeds one, and the circle diameter is less than one. Therefore, from eq. 7.45 the circle will cross the axis to the right of the origin only if the ratio R_2/r is of the order of one. In particular, an increase in r also increases d and shifts the entire diagram to the left. Since a shift to the left corresponds to a reduction of loop gain, *a thermistor having a positive temperature coefficient of resistance must be used as r, to secure proper limiting action* (that is, reduction of loop gain with increase of amplitude). Alternatively, a negative coefficient thermistor may be used in the R_2 position if r is replaced by a fixed resistor.

The two vacuum tubes produce no net phase reversal and thus serve only to magnify Fig. 7.11 without changing its shape or frequency scale.

Accordingly, with appropriate scale change, this constitutes a universal Nyquist plot for the system. Stable oscillations are anticipated if r is a positive-coefficient thermistor. The diagram readily encircles the point $(1, 0)$ for small amplitudes, but with increase of amplitude the diagram is displaced to the left so as to pass through the point $(1, 0)$. This behavior is in interesting contrast to that of the oscillator of Fig. 7.4, whose Nyquist diagram shrinks radially as the limiter takes effect.

Inspection of eq. 7.45 shows that each point on the circle of Fig. 7.11 corresponds to a specific frequency and vice versa. When d is nearly equal to $1/a$, therefore, a relatively small change in frequency results in a large loop phase shift. This property is common to all bridge circuits which are nearly balanced and are sensitive to frequency. It

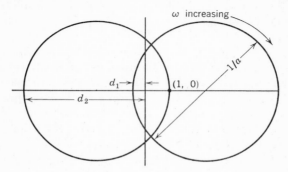

FIG. 7.11. Nyquist diagrams.

is desirable in oscillators because unavoidable phase shifts in the amplifier (driver) unit are automatically corrected by a slight change of frequency.

A bridge composed of fixed linear elements also has this desirable property of phase magnification. However, it is impractical to achieve the desired accuracy of balance because of changes of element values with respect to age, temperature, etc. Moreover, a separate limiter would be required in any event. Therefore, the use of a thermistor as one arm of the frequency-controlling bridge must be regarded as a necessity in any practical bridge oscillator.

Ordinarily, the tube adjacent to the bridge in Fig. 7.9 is adjusted for large linear voltage amplification of a small signal. Care must be taken to see that the total direct cathode current does not contribute too much heat to the thermistor, which is commonly a 3-watt, 120-volt tungsten-filament lamp. The other tube is designed as a linear power amplifier. However, it must operate into a relatively low impedance and must produce a sufficiently large alternating current to heat the thermistor. The cathode by-pass condenser *must* be omitted from the voltage amplifier in order to preserve the desired bridge operation; and it is commonly omitted from the power amplifier to avoid difficulty with phase shifts at the lower frequencies. The time constant of the coupling circuit C_3R_3 (of Fig. 7.9) can be made sufficient to avoid low-frequency phase shift without serious difficulty. However, because r and R_2 have a resistance of only a few thousand ohms, it is necessary to use for C_2 a relatively large capacitance (such as 40 μf) to avoid excessive phase shift at low frequencies. An additional problem is to secure suitable operating conditions in the power amplifier without reducing R_4 so far that it produces a serious effective shunt across the bridge. This problem is alleviated, at the expense of the coupling problem, by lowering the bridge impedance. A considerable advantage is secured by setting $n = 2$ and $m = \frac{1}{2}$ in Fig. 7.10, in which case balance occurs for $R_2 = r$.

Finally, it is possible to interchange the reactive arms of the Wien bridge. This arrangement can be used in the oscillator of Fig. 7.9, provided the cathode and grid leads are reversed to account for the reversal of phase and if r is a negative-coefficient thermistor. In practice, the connection of the cathode into the reactive arm of the bridge leads to intolerable difficulties with d-c conditions in the first tube, and is never used.

A number of other linear resistance capacitance oscillators exist.[282] However, they possess few features not already discussed, and are omitted here.

7.10 The Meacham bridge oscillator

The circuit which produces oscillations of the greatest frequency stability yet recorded is due to L. A. Meacham;[209] it is used in the frequency standards of the Bell System, the National Bureau of Standards, and the British Post Office. The essential features of the circuit are shown in Fig. 7.12. A tuned amplifier provides a relatively high gain at zero phase shift. The bridge, which is the heart of the circuit, provides the combined functions of limiter and resonator. As will presently be shown, the balancing action of the bridge tends to increase the effective Q of the series resonant circuit by magnifying the phase shift produced as a result of any frequency deviation. Consequently, a considerable phase shift in the driving system produces only a very small shift in the operating frequency. This action is also present in the Wien bridge oscillator just described, but the stability of available RC elements is so poor that it offers little advantage in the Wien circuit. The operation of the Meacham circuit is conveniently explained in terms of the series resonant circuit shown, although, in practice, the latter is usually replaced by a quartz crystal.

The inherently low harmonic output produced by the tube is further reduced by the action of the tuned input and output transformers. The thermistor produces limiting with negligible harmonic distortion because the circuit is ordinarily used only at frequencies above the audible, where the resistance is unable to vary appreciably during any one cycle. In the circuit described in Meacham's original paper the second and third harmonics were respectively 67 and 80 db below the fundamental. Because three of its arms are pure resistors, the bridge can approach balance only at the series-resonant frequency,

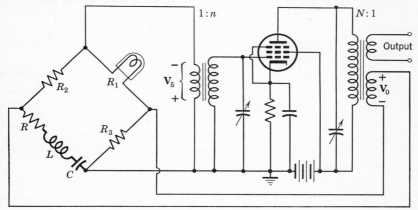

Fig. 7.12.   The Meacham bridge–stabilized oscillator.

where the reactance of the fourth arm vanishes. Under balanced conditions the bridge is purely resistive.

During oscillation, the amplitude must adjust itself so that the loss of the bridge is equal to the gain of the amplifier. Also, the frequency of oscillation must adjust itself so that the phase shift of the bridge is equal and opposite to that of the amplifier, which is adjusted by means of input, output, and interstage networks to have as small a phase shift as possible. With the simplifying assumptions that the amplifier input impedance is large compared to the bridge resistances and that no phase shifts exist, it is possible to describe the system by means of relatively simple equations:

$$\mathbf{V}_0 = \mu \mathbf{V}_5 \tag{7.46}$$

and

$$\mathbf{V}_5 = \mathbf{V}_0 \left[\frac{R_2}{(R_1 + R_2)} - \frac{R}{(R_3 + R)} \right], \tag{7.47}$$

where μ is the effective voltage gain of the amplifier.

Because the bridge is operated at a condition very near balance, it is convenient to express the situation in terms of δ, the degree of unbalance, defined by

$$R_1 = (1 - \delta) \frac{R_2 R_3}{R}. \tag{7.48}$$

Introducing δ (which equals zero when the bridge is balanced) into eq. 7.47 and then using eq. 7.46, we obtain

$$1 = \mu \left[\frac{R}{(1 - \delta)R_3 + R} - \frac{R}{R_3 + R} \right]$$

$$= \mu R \left[\frac{1}{R + R_3 - \delta R_3} - \frac{1}{R + R_3} \right]. \tag{7.49}$$

Because δ is very small we may write to an adequate approximation

$$\frac{1}{1 - \delta} \doteq 1 + \delta. \tag{7.50}$$

Use of this approximation in a slightly modified form converts eq. 7.49 to

$$1 = \mu R \left[\frac{R + R_3 + \delta R_3}{(R + R_3)^2} - \frac{R + R_3}{(R + R_3)^2} \right] = \mu \delta \cdot \frac{R R_3}{(R + R_3)^2} \tag{7.51}$$

If an equal-arm bridge is used,

$$R_3 = R. \tag{7.52}$$

For this relationship eq. 7.51 requires that

$$\mu \delta = 4. \tag{7.53}$$

The equal-arm condition is desirable because, consistent with a prescribed value of μ, it leads to maximum amplitude and frequency stability. If the equality of eq. 7.52 is not achieved, an increase of the product $\mu \delta$ is required for oscillation. Thus, when

$$R_3 = 4R \text{ or } R/4, \tag{7.54}$$

the required unbalance is increased to

$$\mu \delta = 6.25. \tag{7.55}$$

In a typical example $\mu = 400$ and $R_3 = R$; then $\delta = 0.01$, and oscillation occurs when R_1 is only one per cent below the value which produces exact balance. Where the absolute maximum in performance must be achieved, the amplifier unit may consist of two or even three tubes in conjunction with transformers and interstage elements, carefully adjusted with respect to the overall gain and phase-shift characteristics. Ordinarily, however, a single tube in conjunction with tightly coupled, high impedance input and output transformers is sufficient. Suitable transformers for frequencies in the region of 100 kc usually employ toroidal cores of powdered iron. Accordingly, the design of the bridge represents the chief problem. Several questions as to the proportioning of the bridge are discussed in the following section.

7.11 Design of the Meacham bridge

The principal requirements which govern the design of the bridge circuit are these.   (1) A maximum possible rate of change of phase

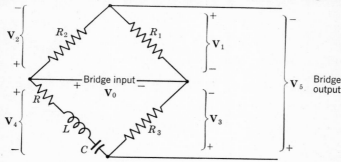

FIG. 7.13.   Bridge circuit.

shift with respect to frequency is desired to minimize the change of frequency which results from a change of amplifier phase.   (2) In terms of ratios, a maximum change of bridge loss for a small specified change of thermistor resistance is desired to minimize the change of output which results from a change of amplifier gain.   (3) A certain maximum amount of current or power is safely allowable in the resonator, especially when a quartz crystal is used.   (4) A certain minimum amount of power or current is required to operate the lamp thermistor.

The phase magnification will be calculated first in terms of the bridge circuit of Fig. 7.13 and the associated phasor diagram of Fig. 7.14, in which the magnitude of the unbalance has been exaggerated for the sake of clarity.   The governing equations are

$$V_5 = V_3 - V_1, \tag{7.56}$$

$$V_1(R_1 + R_2) = V_0 R_1, \tag{7.57}$$

and

$$V_3(R_3 + R + j\omega L + 1/j\omega C) = V_0 R_3. \tag{7.58}$$

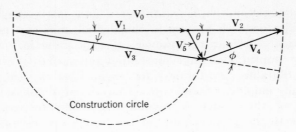

FIG. 7.14. Phasor diagram of Meacham bridge.

A complete solution, although practical, is unnecessary, because interest is confined to conditions near the balance point, which is reached when

$$\psi = \theta = \phi = 0 \tag{7.59}$$

and

$$R_1 R = R_2 R_3. \tag{7.60}$$

For conditions of small phase shift we may write

$$\tan \psi = \psi, \tan \theta = \theta, \text{ and } \tan \phi = \phi. \tag{7.61}$$

The use of similar triangles then yields

$$\phi/\psi = V_0/V_4 \quad \text{and} \quad \theta/\psi = V_3/V_5. \tag{7.62}$$

Division yields

$$\theta/\phi = V_3 V_4/V_0 V_5 = (V_3/V_0)(V_4/V_0)(V_0/V_5)$$
$$= (V_3/V_0)(V_4/V_0)\mu. \tag{7.63}$$

But

$$V_3/V_0 = R_3/(R + R_3) \quad \text{and} \quad V_4/V_0 = R/(R + R_3). \tag{7.64}$$

Therefore, we may use eq. 7.51 to obtain the relationship

$$\theta/\phi = 1/\delta, \tag{7.65}$$

which is important because it proves that *a bridge which yields optimum frequency stability also yields optimum amplitude stability and vice versa.*

7.12 Parameters for optimum stability

The proportioning of the bridge is affected by the power rating of the resonator and the power required by the thermistor. In systems designed for the greatest frequency stability, the resonator is a *GT* cut quartz crystal, and must be operated at a power level substantially lower than that required by the lamp. Therefore, it is often necessary to use a bridge composed of unequal arms.

It is assumed that the power rating P_4 and elements of the resonator are fixed, and that the thermistor requires a specific power P_1 for its operation but that its resistance may be chosen at will. Consistent with usual conditions, it is also assumed that the grid and plate resistances of the tube are effectively infinite, and that the associated transformers have negligible loss. However, the impedance levels (number of turns) of the high impedance windings of the transformers are limited by parasitic capacitance and other considerations, and this fact must be considered in the analysis.

The design problem now reduces to choosing R_1, R_2, and R_3 so as to obtain the smallest fractional unbalance δ and hence the greatest possible amplitude stability consistent with a given transconductance g_m, prescribed plate and grid circuit impedances, and power levels consistent with resonator and lamp limitations.

Near the balance point we may write

$$P_1 = V_1{}^2/R_1 \quad \text{and} \quad P_4 = V_4{}^2/R. \tag{7.66}$$

Introducing the dimensionless parameter k, and taking advantage of the fact that $V_1 \doteq V_3$, we may obtain the relationship

$$k^2 = P_1/P_4 = R_3/R_2. \tag{7.67}$$

Near balance the grid and plate impedances are, respectively,

$$Z_g = n^2(R_1 + R_3)(R_2 + R)/(R + R_1 + R_2 + R_3) \tag{7.68}$$

and

$$Z_p = N^2(R_1 + R_2)(R_3 + R)/(R + R_1 + R_2 + R_3). \tag{7.69}$$

Consistent with the assumed conditions, we may calculate μ as defined in eq. 7.46 in terms of g_m, Z_g, Z_p, and the bridge resistances. Substitution of the resulting expression in eq. 7.51 yields the useful relationship

$$\frac{1}{\delta} = g_m\sqrt{Z_g}\,\sqrt{Z_p} \cdot \frac{RR_3}{(R + R_3)^2} \cdot \frac{\sqrt{R_1 + R_2}}{\sqrt{R_1 + R_3}}\,\frac{\sqrt{R + R_3}}{\sqrt{R + R_2}}. \tag{7.70}$$

Introduction of the parameter

$$m = R_3/R, \tag{7.71}$$

and use of eqs. 7.60 and 7.67 reduces this expression to

$$1/\delta = g_m\sqrt{Z_g}\,\sqrt{Z_p}\,(km)/(m + 1)(m + k^2). \tag{7.72}$$

Differentiating to minimize δ shows that the conditions for greatest stability are

$$R_1 = R, R_2 = R/k, \text{ and } R_3 = kR. \tag{7.73}$$

Like other typical conditions for minima, eq. 7.73 is relatively broad.

It sometimes happens that current rather than power is the important parameter in limiting the performance of the bridge thermistor. This condition is represented by the equation

$$V_1/R_1 = KV_4/R. \tag{7.74}$$

Under these conditions differentiation for a minimum value of δ leads to the relationships

$$R_3 = R \text{ and } R_1 = R_2 = R/K. \tag{7.75}$$

At the present time it is possible to produce 100-kc crystals which have resistances of about 10 ohms and Q values in excess of 10^6, but, unfortunately, such crystals are adversely affected by currents in excess of a hundred microamperes. On the other hand, the power and current required to actuate a tungsten filament thermistor do not continue to decrease as the diameter and length of the filament are reduced. The E1 lamp operating at a resistance of 30 ohms appears to approximate the limit which can be reached in this way. Therefore, it is not always possible to employ the optimum relationships. The relationships developed in the following section indicate the extent to which performance is sacrificed by such a compromise.

7.13 Amplitude and frequency stability

Conditions for optimum stability were established in the preceding sections; it remains to show what actual stability factors result when these conditions are met. Because the frequency stability is of principal concern it will be treated first.

In terms of the simple tuned circuit of Fig. 7.13 the phase shift $d\phi$ is related to the selectivity of the resonator at frequencies near resonance by the equation

$$d\phi = 2Q \, d\omega/\omega. \tag{7.76}$$

Moreover, from eq. 7.65, we have

$$d\phi = \delta \, d\theta. \tag{7.77}$$

Therefore, consistent with Chapter 1, we have as the frequency stability with respect to amplifier phase shift the relationship

$$S_F = \frac{d\theta}{d\omega/\omega} = \frac{2Q}{\delta}. \tag{7.78}$$

In terms of Fig. 7.12, with eq. 7.72, this reduces to

$$S_F = 2Q g_m \sqrt{Z_g} \sqrt{Z_p} \frac{km}{(m + 1)(m + k^2)}. \tag{7.79}$$

In practice, increments in the amplifier phase shift θ usually result from variation of the plate-to-ground and grid-to-ground capacitances of the vacuum tube. It is therefore appropriate to investigate this relationship. In the normal operating condition the grid faces a pure resistance equal to Z_g. The phase angle $d\theta$ which results from a capacitance increment dC is, therefore,

$$d\theta = Z_g \omega \, dC, \tag{7.80}$$

where the angle and its tangent are taken as equal. The frequency stability with respect to the grid capacitance therefore is

$$\frac{dC}{d\omega/\omega} = \frac{2Q}{\omega Z_g \delta} = \frac{2Q g_m}{\omega} \sqrt{Z_p/Z_g} \frac{km}{(m + 1)(m + k^2)}. \tag{7.81}$$

This equation shows that, with respect to grid capacitance variations, the frequency stability is increased by increasing the plate impedance and decreasing the grid impedance. However, it is clear that eq. 7.81 (with Z_p and Z_g inverted) also represents stability with respect to C_p; therefore, a compromise is necessary.

In typical pentodes the grid capacitance is about ten times less stable than the plate capacitance. *Therefore, typical random deviations in these capacitances will produce the smallest total frequency deviations if the contributions are made equal by letting* $Z_p \doteq 10 Z_g$.

The amplitude stability is obtained by differentiating eq. 7.57 to obtain

$$R_1 \, dV_1 + V_1 \, dR_1 + R_2 \, dV_1 = R_1 \, dV_0 + V_0 \, dR_1. \tag{7.82}$$

Division by eq. 7.57 yields

$$\frac{dV_1}{V_1} + \frac{V_1}{V_0} \frac{dR_1}{R_1} = \frac{dR_1}{R_1} + \frac{dV_0}{V_0}. \tag{7.83}$$

Substitution of eq. 7.1 and the parameter m yields

$$\frac{dV_0}{V_0} = \frac{1 + m - s}{1 + m} \cdot \frac{dV_1}{V_1}. \tag{7.84}$$

Differentiation of eq. 7.51 and its reuse leads to

$$\frac{d\mu}{\mu} = -\frac{d\delta}{\delta},$$ (7.85)

in which g_m may be substituted for μ because only the fractional variation is of interest. Making this substitution and introducing the derivative of eq. 7.48 gives

$$R\,dR_1 = -d\delta\,R_2R_3.$$ (7.86)

Finally, introducing the value of δ from eq. 7.70 gives

$$S_A = \frac{dg_m/g_m}{dV_0/V_0} = g_m\sqrt{Z_g}\sqrt{Z_p}\frac{skm}{(1+m-s)(m+k^2)}.$$ (7.87)

7.14 Numerical example

Let us design a single-tube Meacham oscillator using the type 6AC7 pentode at a frequency of 100 kc. Reasonable numerical values are:

$R = 100$ ohms　　　　　　　$I_4 = 2$ ma max. in crystal
$Q = 10^5$ (quartz crystal)　　$I_1 = 8$ ma min. in lamp
$Z_g = 10^4$ ohms　　　　　　$g_m = 0.01$ mho
$Z_p = 10^5$ ohms

If eq. 7.75 were followed, we would have $R_3 = 100$ ohms and $R_1 = R_2 = 25$ ohms. However, no available lamp has this resistance and from Fig. 7.1 we choose as most suitable the E1 lamp with a resistance of 50 ohms and a current of 8 ma at 0.4 volt. As a compromise between eq. 7.73 and 7.75 we choose $R_3 = 200$ ohms and $R_2 = 25$ ohms.

From eqs. 7.68 and 7.69 we have $n = 10.9$ and $N = 34.6$. Consistent with the bridge currents and resistances we have $V_0 = 0.6$ volt corresponding to the conservative rms plate voltage of 24.5. Because the tube has a voltage gain of 1000, the grid voltage is only 24.5 mv.

From eq. 7.70 we have $\delta = 0.0168$, corresponding by eq. 7.65 to a phase or Q magnification of 59.8. Thus by eq. 7.78 the frequency stability against phase shift is 1.2×10^7. That is, the frequency will change only one part in 10^8 if the amplifier introduces a phase shift of 0.12 radian (about 7°). By eq. 7.80, a capacitance increment of about 6 $\mu\mu$f in the grid circuit (or 0.6 $\mu\mu$f in the plate) would produce this phase shift.

The amplitude stability is obtained from eq. 7.87. The value $s = 0.5$ obtained from Fig. 7.1 yields $S_A = 35.8$. That is, a transconductance change of 3.58 db would result in a change of only 0.1 db in the output.

7.15 Automatic output control

At approximately the same time Arguimbau[14] in America and Groszkowski[122] in Poland announced independently the invention of a linear oscillator in which the gain of the vacuum tube is controlled to produce amplitude limiting by means of a bias derived from the output signal. A similar principle had already been used to stabilize the output of an amplifier subjected to a variable input signal. The terms automatic volume control (avc) or, preferably, automatic output control (aoc) are used to identify both amplifiers and oscillators of this kind. Oscillators of this sort compare favorably with the Meacham in regard to amplitude stability and purity of wave form. They are inferior to the Meacham in frequency stability because they lack the phase-magnifying property of the bridge circuit.

The electronic problem common to all automatic output devices is to provide a tube in which the transconductance may be varied through a considerable range by means of a bias voltage, without at the same time introducing intolerable nonlinearity and signal distortion. In amplifiers for radio receivers the problem is not difficult because the linearity requirements are moderate and because the control may be exercised in early stages where the signal amplitude is very small. A conventional remote cutoff (variable transconductance) pentode with both signal and control bias applied to the first grid meets this need very nicely.

In an oscillator, we ordinarily wish to produce signals approaching the power rating of the tube. Moreover, the problem of providing a suitable control bias is complicated if the amplitude of oscillation must be small. Because the remote cutoff pentode is ill fitted to the present application we are led to investigate the properties of other types of tubes. The closest parallel to the present problem in the existing art appears to be the volume expander,[252] sometimes used to increase the dynamic range of recorded speech of music. Volume expanders sometimes employ thermistors in circuits similar to those already described in this chapter. Of greater present interest, however, are the electronic expanders which employ pentagrid tubes, such as the 6L7, 6SA7, 6SB7-Y and FM-1000. All these tubes have the common feature that the plate current is a function of the potential of the first and third grids, whereas the second and fourth grids are internally connected to serve as a positive screen, and the fifth grid serves as a simple suppressor. The essential fact, which is ably presented by Wing,[347] is that, for a fixed screen voltage, the plate current may be represented by a simple product, $i_p = F(e_1) \cdot F(e_3)$, where $F(e_1)$ depends only upon the voltage of the first grid, and $F(e_3)$ depends only upon the voltage of the third grid.

The 6L7 is a double-ended tube in which the first grid (cap connection) has a remote cutoff characteristic whereas the third grid is designed for sharp cutoff. The 6SA7 and 6SB7-Y are single-ended

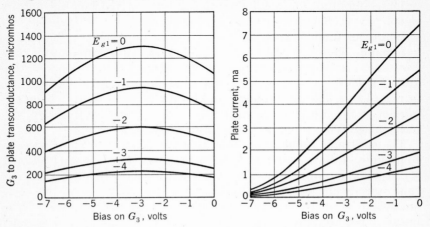

FIG. 7.15. Characteristics of a typical FM–1000. Conditions $E_{g5} = 0$, $E_{g2} = E_{g4} = +100$, $E_p > +40$ volts. (Courtesy Philco Corporation.)

tubes in which the cutoff characteristics of the first and third grids are reversed from the 6L7. The FM-1000 is a single-ended tube of the lock-in type. The characteristics of both the first and the third grids are essentially linear; and the fifth (suppressor) grid may also be used as a control electrode, though its effective transconductance is quite low. In all these tubes the cathode current depends principally upon the potentials of the first and second grids. Although the plate current is substantially independent of the plate voltage, as in other multiple-grid tubes, it is affected by the potential of the third grid, which controls the fraction of the cathode current which escapes the screens and reaches the plate. Characteristics of the FM-1000 are shown in Fig. 7.15. It is seen that signals having a peak amplitude of several volts may be applied to the third (or first) grid, and that by means of a reasonable bias on the first (or third) grid the transconductance to the plate may be reduced from about 1300 micromhos to zero without producing serious nonlinearity. Moreover, both grids are negatively biased so that they require negligible current and power for operation.

7.16 An automatic output control oscillator

A great variety of oscillators employing automatic control have been constructed. All the essential principles are, however, illustrated by the circuit of Fig. 7.16, which differs from a conventional tuned plate oscillator only by the choice of the tube and the manner in which bias is applied to the first and third grids. For small oscillations the peak voltage induced in the auxiliary coil L_3 is less than that of the bias battery V_B, and no current flows through the rectifier. The first

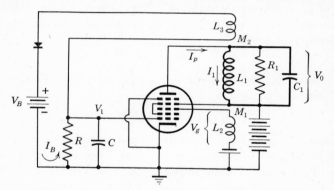

FIG. 7.16.   Automatic output control oscillator.

grid, therefore, is at cathode potential, and the plate current and transconductance are normal. The tube operates as a linear amplifier, and the oscillations are sinusoids which expand with time.

As the amplitude of oscillation increases, the voltage induced in L_3 increases proportionally and presently reaches a value in excess of V_B. Rectification then occurs, and the resulting current through the high resistance R biases the first grid negative with respect to the cathode. This bias voltage reduces the cathode current, with the result that the effective transconductance drops to such a value that the loop transmission is (1,0). The equilibrium is stable because a reduction in amplitude results in an increase of transconductance, and vice versa. It is readily shown that the condition for sustained oscillation is

$$g_m R_1 M_1 = L_1. \qquad (7.88)$$

The wave forms of both voltage and current are nearly sinusoidal if the circuit constants are properly chosen. Fortunately, the calculation of the parameters is greatly facilitated by the fact that the tube operates in a linear fashion in such a manner that its properties may be calculated from the curves of Fig. 7.15.

The design of the bias system involves several factors which are not capable of exact specification. However, the FM-1000 will operate well if the following conditions are realized: $V_0 = 10$ volts rms, $V_g = 1$ volt rms, $V_1 = -2$ volts, and $V_B = +10$ volts. Moreover, these conditions are readily obtained with circuit elements of convenient size.

7.17 Amplitude stability of controlled oscillator

Like other linear oscillators, the automatic output control system is capable of good amplitude stability. The extent of this stabilization may be evaluated by using the equations already developed. From Fig. 7.16 we may write

$$M_2 V_0 = L_1(V_B - V_1). \tag{7.89}$$

Since a change in the tube parameters will affect only V_0 and V_1, we may differentiate to obtain

$$M_2 \, dV_0 = -L_1 \, dV_1. \tag{7.90}$$

In the desired operating region the transconductance, g_m (between third grid and plate), may be expected to vary in a linear manner with the bias voltage, V_1, according to the simple relation

$$g_m = g_0 + kV_1, \tag{7.91}$$

which when differentiated yields

$$dg_m = k \, dV_1. \tag{7.92}$$

If the circuit parameters do not vary, a change in output can occur only if a change in the inherent properties of the tube tends to modify g_m, thus necessitating a modification of V_1 to restore g_m to the value required by eq. 7.88. The fractional change of the inherent tube transconductance may thus be written

$$\frac{dg_m}{g_m} = \frac{kR_1 M_1 \, dV_1}{L_1}. \tag{7.93}$$

The amplitude stability, S_A, is then by definition

$$S_A = \frac{dg_m/g_m}{dV_0/V_0} = \frac{kV_0 M_2}{g_m L_1} = -\frac{kV_0 R_1 M_1 M_2}{L_1{}^2}, \tag{7.94}$$

which shows the desirability of large values of k, R_1, and M_2, and of the ratio $M_1:L_1$.

7.18 Illustrative design

Suppose that a frequency of one megacycle is to be generated, that coils having a Q of 100 are available, and that the plate swing is to be 40 peak volts. The FM-1000 is chosen for the reasons already given, although comparable results may be obtained with other pentagrid types. The nominal transconductance is about 1300 micromhos, but allowance for variation of circuit parameters and the gain-reducing action of the third grid requires that this be approximately halved to 500, for a margin of safety. The static characteristics of Fig. 7.15 indicate that a high degree of linearity will be achieved by use of a plate load resistance of 50,000 ohms with a screen bias of $+100$ volts and a bias of -3 volts on the third grid.

If no useful power is to be drawn, the load resistance will consist solely of the coil losses which, on the basis of $Q = 100$, fixes the reactance of L_1 and C_1 at 500 ohms, corresponding to an inductance of approximately 80 μh and a capacitance of approximately 320 $\mu\mu$f. The mutual inductance is then found by eq. 7.88 to be 3.2 μh. Consistent with this value, a peak alternating plate voltage of 40 volts leads to a control grid voltage of $V_g = 1.6$ volts.

Inspection of Fig. 7.15 shows that the required transconductance will be obtained provided $V_1 = -2.2$ volts. In the interest of amplitude stability let us choose $V_B = +20$ volts, which with eq. 7.89 calls for $M_2 = 44.4$ μh. The curves of Fig. 7.15 show that k has the value 0.0003 in the region of interest. Use of this value in eq. 7.94 gives as the amplitude stability the value $S_A = 13.5$.

An important feature of all automatic output control oscillators is that the amplitude is substantially independent of the tube parameters and plate voltage but varies in a nearly linear fashion with the control voltage V_B. When an accurately constant output is required it is therefore necessary to stabilize this voltage in an adequate manner. Alternatively, it is possible to modulate the amplitude of oscillation by deliberate variation of V_B. More is said of this matter in Chapter 16.

7.19 Design considerations

The automatic output control oscillator just discussed involves several questions which have not been answered. Perhaps first among these is the nature and magnitude of nonlinearities present. This question may, for the system of Fig. 7.16, be divided into three questions, concerning the vacuum tube, the rectifier, and the RC bias holding system. The vacuum tube may, in principle, be made linear to any prescribed degree by suitable construction, choice of operating voltages, and

restriction of amplitude. In practice, the degree of linearity may be
made quite good, so that with the aid of the tuned circuit it is reasonable to expect all harmonic voltages to be at least 50 db down from
the fundamental.

The simple rectifier shown loads the resonator with a current which
flows through L_3 in short pulses. It therefore tends to introduce
harmonics in the output, and to degrade the frequency stability as
shown in Chapters 3 and 4. In principle, this effect can be made
negligibly small by increasing the bias resistor to a value sufficiently
large in comparison with the tank resistance R_1. This increase is not
always practical, but there are other means for obtaining the bias
voltage which do not reflect nonlinearity into the tuned circuit. Two
such means which immediately suggest themselves are the use of a
buffer amplifier in conjunction with a diode or the so-called infinite
impedance (cathode-follower) detector.

The bias-holding system is readily controlled to meet its principal
requirement, that the bias shall not change enough during the period
of any one cycle to affect appreciably the tube transconductance. The
effect is readily calculable in terms of the transfer characteristics of
the tube and may be made adequately small in practice.

A second basic problem is the separation of signal paths. The
previous discussion assumes that the first grid introduces only a
control bias, completely free from voltage at the oscillation frequency.
In practice, it is not only impossible to achieve such a perfect separation but even difficult to secure an adequate one. Because the signal
which leaks through the bias system is likely to be substantially out of
phase with that deliberately returned to the third grid, the operating
frequency is likely to differ from the resonator frequency by an amount
which varies with the degree of control being exercised. This difficulty
may be alleviated by the use of a symmetrical (push-pull) rectifier
which tends to balance out the oscillation frequency and by use of
additional filtering elements which attenuate this frequency without
unduly affecting the time constant and low-frequency behavior of the
system.

A third problem is inherent stability, discussed at much greater
length in Chapter 10. For the present it is sufficient to say that
intermittent oscillation, which often occurs in bias-controlled oscillators, will be avoided if the RC time constant is very long and if the
operating conditions are such that the loop gain at the operating frequency steadily decreases with increase of oscillation amplitude for a
fixed control bias. The latter criterion is readily tested by manually
adjusting the bias and observing the amplitude of oscillation, which

should be a continuous single-valued function of the bias.   Chapter 10 shows that the criterion just described is sufficient but not necessary, and is indeed rather severe.   However, it is met in the circuit of Fig. 7.16, provided the bias on the third grid is such that operation occurs at the inflection point of the transfer characteristic (maximum transconductance).

PROBLEMS

7.1. Calculate the curve corresponding to Fig. 7.6 for a bridge of E1 lamps and 50-ohm resistors.

7.2. Using the above bridge, design an oscillator to operate at 300 kc, using $N = n = 30$ and $g_m = 5000$ micromhos.

7.3. Calculate the amplitude stability and operating voltages of the above oscillator.

7.4. Calculate for your design the frequency deviation which will result if the grid capacitance is increased by one micromicrofard.

7.5. Verify the correctness of eq. 7.73 and defend the associated assumptions.

7.6. Verify the correctness of eq. 7.75.

7.7. It would appear that the frequency stability of the Meacham oscillator with respect to changes of tube capacitance could be reduced by addition of a stable padding capacitance.   Prove that this is not true.

7.8. Discuss the use of unequal impedance levels in grid and plate circuits in the interest of frequency stability.

8

CONVENTIONAL HARMONIC OSCILLATORS

Chapter 7 has described in some detail a number of linear oscillator circuits, which generate waves of great purity having good amplitude and frequency stability. However, the circuits most widely used in practical apparatus operate in a markedly nonlinear manner. The present discussion is devoted to a presentation of these widely used circuits and their properties; it has been deferred to this point in order to present the extensive background which is necessary to the understanding of a number of important features of such circuits.

This chapter is concerned principally with low-power oscillators which operate at ordinary frequencies, have moderate values of amplitude and frequency stability, and are characterized by simplicity and economy. However, most of the results are independent of frequency. The problems which are peculiar to high-power levels are discussed separately in a later chapter.

The exact analysis of nonlinear systems is so difficult and cumbersome that some alternative must be found if useful engineering results are to be obtained. On the other hand, some form of analysis is necessary if the performance of existing oscillators is to be understood and if new circuits are to be designed intelligently. The following analysis is based on idealized class C operation; it is a form of the method of equivalent linearization discussed in Chapter 4. No effort is made to obtain a frequency correction term.

8.1 The tuned plate oscillator

The circuit of the conventional tuned plate oscillator is shown in Fig. 8.1. The schematic diagram is a very close approximation to the actual physical system, the principal idealization being the representation of the load as a pure shunt resistor R. In actual operation some grid current always flows, but if R_c is relatively high the effects of grid current are negligible. The tube is assumed to have an idealized cutoff characteristic. That is, the curves of plate voltage versus grid voltage, with plate current as parameter, are assumed to be uniformly spaced parallel straight lines with slope equal to $-\mu$ as shown in Fig. 8.2.

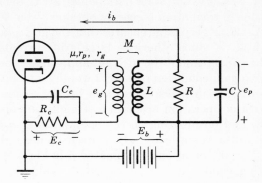

FIG. 8.1. Tuned plate oscillator.

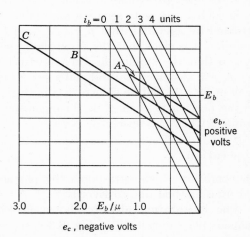

FIG. 8.2. Idealized triode characteristics and paths of operation.

The analysis is begun by assuming that the tube has a small negative bias, consistent with class A operation, and that the circuit parameters are adjusted so that oscillations just begin. With this idealization it is possible to employ linear equations, which at the natural frequency of L and C take the form

$$e_p/e_g = L/M \quad \text{and} \quad e_p = \mu e_g R/(R + r_p). \tag{8.1}$$

Eliminating the amplitudes to obtain the conditions for sustained oscillation, we have

$$\mu = (R + r_p)L/RM \quad \text{or} \quad r_p/R = \mu M/L - 1, \tag{8.2}$$

where μ and M, as well as the other parameters, are taken as positive.

The amplitude of oscillation is readily obtained from Fig. 8.2. The assumption that R_c is very large ensures that the grid cannot be driven appreciably positive, since otherwise large grid currents would flow. Moreover, the tube cannot be driven appreciably beyond cutoff, because the loop gain condition of eq. 8.2 would be violated. Finally, e_g and e_p are exactly in phase opposition by the assumptions made, so that the path of operation becomes a straight line of slope $-L/M$ centered on E_b and terminating on the boundaries $i_b = 0$ and $e_c = 0$. The grid bias will automatically adjust itself to meet this condition. The resulting path of operation is designated A in Fig. 8.2.

The operating condition just described is evidently unstable and undesirable, because any decrease in R or μ will cause the oscillations to stop. We therefore need to explore the consequences of modifying the parameters in such a way as to secure a margin of safety. This is conveniently treated by assuming that μ, r_p, M, and L are fixed and that R is increased. It is clear that the small-signal loop gain is now larger than one, so that the amplitude will tend to increase. When this occurs the bias will also increase, and plate current will flow during only part of each cycle. It will be shown that both the amplitude of oscillation and the portion of each cycle during which plate current flows are determined when R is specified.

8.2 Class C operation

The equilibrium condition which corresponds to a particular value of R is best obtained by a method due to Everitt.[88, 89] The calculation is based on the tube idealization already shown in Fig. 8.2. That is, the instantaneous plate current i_b of Fig. 8.3 is represented by the expression

$$i_b = (e_b + \mu e_c)/r_p = g_m(e_c + e_b/\mu) \tag{8.3}$$

subject to the physical restriction that i_b cannot be negative. *The principal assumption of this method is that the alternating grid and plate voltages are sinusoidal and 180° out of phase.* Introducing the excitation ratio h which is characteristic of the circuit and defined by

$$h = E_{pm}/E_{gm}, \tag{8.4}$$

we may establish an artificial driving voltage

$$E' = (E_{gm} - E_{pm}/\mu) = E_{gm}(1 - h/\mu). \tag{8.5}$$

Using the variable $\theta = \omega t$, we may express the current as

$$i_b = g_m(E' \cos \theta + E_0), \tag{8.6}$$

where

$$E_0 = (E_b/\mu - E_c) \tag{8.7}$$

is the amount by which the bias differs from the cutoff value.

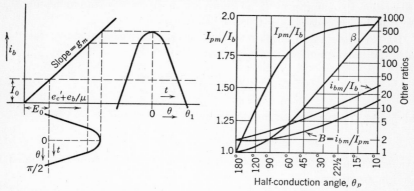

FIG. 8.3.   Calculation of plate current.   FIG. 8.4.   Parameters for idealized class C operation.

The fundamental component of the plate current is evaluated by use of the Fourier series expression

$$I_{pm} = \frac{1}{\pi} \int_0^{2\pi} i_b \cos \theta \, d\theta = \frac{2}{\pi} \int_0^{\pi} i_b \cos \theta \, d\theta. \tag{8.8}$$

Because the current is zero and eq. 8.4 does not apply over part of the cycle, it is desirable to modify the limits by use of the new variable

$$\theta_p = \cos^{-1} (E_0/E'), \tag{8.9}$$

which represents *half* the angle over which plate current is conducted. The maximum value of the fundamental component of plate current is now

$$I_{pm} = \frac{2g_m}{\pi} \int_0^{\theta_p} (E' \cos \theta + E_0) \cos \theta \, d\theta \tag{8.10}$$

Integration and substitution of limits yields, after simplification,

$$I_{pm} = g_m E' \frac{2\theta_p - \sin 2\theta_p}{2\pi} = \frac{g_m E'}{\beta_p}, \tag{8.11}$$

where

$$\beta_p = \frac{2\pi}{2\theta_p - \sin 2\theta_p}. \tag{8.12}$$

The parameter β_p is useful in all kinds of class C calculations; its variation with θ_p and some related parameters are given in Fig. 8.4. The principal result of the foregoing analysis is that *in class C operation the effective transconductance is decreased and the effective plate resistance is increased by the factor* β_p. The transconductance reduction is immediately apparent. The increase in plate resistance is demonstrated by setting $E_{gm} = 0$ ($h = \infty$) in eq. 8.5.

By an integration similar to that of eq. 8.8 we may show that the average component of plate current is given by

$$I_b = g_m E' \frac{\sin \theta_p - \theta_p \cos \theta_p}{\pi} \tag{8.13}$$

and that the maximum instantaneous plate current is

$$i_{bm} = g_m E'(1 - \cos \theta_p). \tag{8.14}$$

An additional relationship which is often useful is shown in Fig. 8.4 and is given by

$$B = \frac{i_{bm}}{I_{pm}} = \beta_p(1 - \cos \theta_p). \tag{8.15}$$

8.3 Effect of grid current

The current which is rectified in the grid circuit flows through the grid leak to produce the bias. If the resistance of the grid leak is high compared to other circuit impedances, the grid is never driven appreciably positive and the associated power loss is small. The equilibrium amplitude of oscillation is readily calculated, and the associated operation is conducive to good frequency stability but small power output.

A substantially greater power output is obtained by lowering the grid leak resistance to a value comparable to the plate load impedance. The losses in the grid circuit are somewhat increased by this change, but the power output is increased by a much larger amount. The losses in the grid circuit and the corresponding effective grid circuit impedance, R_g, may be calculated by a process similar to that employed in the previous section.

Experimental results show that, in typical triodes and pentodes, the current drawn by the control grid when positive is approximately proportional to the grid voltage and not greatly affected by the plate voltage. The corresponding grid resistance r_g is usually about one thousand ohms. Evidently, the ratio of this resistance to that of the grid leak will determine the bias developed and the extent to which the grid is driven positive.

Following the indicated analysis, we find that the *equivalent a-c grid resistance* R_g is equal to $\beta_g r_g$, where β_g is defined by eq. 8.12 in terms of θ_g, the angle of *grid current conduction*. Unfortunately, this form for the expression is inconvenient and may lead to serious error in numerical work. Therefore, the results presented in the curves of Fig. 8.5 are recommended for ordinary use.

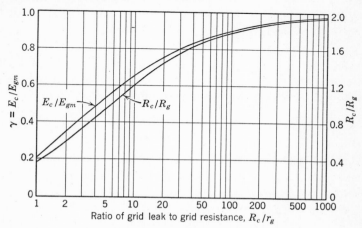

FIG. 8.5. Effect of grid rectification.

When the grid leak is subjected to an alternating as well as a direct voltage, as in the circuit of Fig. 8.6, an additional power loss is incurred. This has no effect upon the rectified bias, but increases by one the value of the ratio R_c/R_g. If, for example, we have $R_c/r_g = 100$, the ratio R_c/R_g is equal to 2.8.

Returning to the circuit of Fig. 8.1, we find that grid rectification has two principal effects. First, there is an additional loading which may be accounted for by substituting for R, in eq. 8.2, the quantity

$$R' = \frac{L^2 R R_g}{M^2 R + L^2 R_g} = \frac{h^2 R R_g}{R + h^2 R_g}. \tag{8.16}$$

Second, the extent to which the grid is driven positive must be taken into account by writing

$$E_c = \gamma E_{gm}, \tag{8.17}$$

where γ is given by Fig. 8.5.

8.4 Prediction of the amplitude of oscillation

The amplitude of oscillation in the tuned plate circuit may be predicted by appropriately combining the information now available. From eq. 8.2, modified to account for R_g, by means of Fig. 8.5, we may determine the parameter β_p and hence the conduction angle θ_p. Then from eq. 8.15 or Fig. 8.4, we may obtain the additional parameter B. These are sufficient to determine the amplitude as shown in the following paragraph.

Using eqs. 8.4, 8.7, 8.9, 8.15, and 8.17 we may eliminate E_0, E_c, E_{gm} and θ_p to obtain the maximum alternating plate voltage

$$E_{pm} = \frac{h\beta_p E_b}{(\mu - h)(B - \beta_p) + \mu\gamma\beta_p}. \tag{8.18}$$

It is seen that the amplitude is proportional to E_b, increases with increase of h, and is affected by β_p, B, μ, and γ. In class B operation, where $B = \beta_p = 2$, the expression simplifies to

$$E_{pm} = \frac{hE_b}{\mu\gamma}, \tag{8.19}$$

which is readily checked by direct calculation.

Because eqs. 8.18 and 8.19 do not depend upon the circuit configuration, and because the development involves only the assumption that grid and plate voltages are sinusoidal and 180° out of phase, they may be applied to any circuit which meets this condition; that is, they are applicable to nearly all practical oscillators.

The amplitude of oscillation just calculated represents a stable equilibrium in most practical cases. That this is true may be shown by assuming that the amplitude is momentarily increased (or decreased) by some external influence. A consideration of the class C process shows that there is a strong tendency for the amplitude to return to its original value.

There are, however, two situations in which stability may be lacking. In high-power oscillators where maximum efficiency and power output are desired the grid is driven considerably positive with respect to the cathode, and may even become positive with respect to the plate. Under these conditions secondary emission of electrons may occur, the grid current is greatly increased, and the plate current is reduced. Because the situation differs widely from that assumed in the foregoing analysis the results may be in great error. More is said of this in Chapter 11. Under other conditions the time constant of the grid circuit is excessive compared to the envelope time constant of the tuned circuit. We may then observe intermittent oscillations, discussed in detail in Chapter 10.

8.5 Illustrative design of tuned plate oscillator

To illustrate the application of the equations developed above, let us design an oscillator to operate at a frequency of one megacycle and yield a relatively large output from a 6J5 triode. The approximate parameters of this particular tube are $\mu = 20$, $r_p = 8000$ ohms, $g_m = 2500$ micromhos, and $r_g = 1000$ ohms. We may choose as reasonable values the additional parameters $E_b = 300$ volts, $h = 6.0$, $\theta_p = 60°$, and $\gamma = 0.70$. With these values we have, from Fig. 8.4, $\beta = 5.0$ and $B = 2.5$. Therefore, from eq. 8.17, we have

$$E_{pm} = 256 \text{ peak volts}, \tag{8.20}$$

from which we obtain $E_{gm} = 42.66$ and $E_c = 29.9$ volts. The curves of Fig. 8.5, together with $r_g = 1000$, yield the grid leak resistance $R_c = 15r_g = 15{,}000$ ohms and $R_g = R_c/1.3 = 11{,}500$ ohms.

Introducing β_p and R' into eq. 8.2, we have

$$R' = 17{,}170 \text{ ohms.} \tag{8.21}$$

Now using h and eq. 8.16, we have as the actual plate load $R = 17{,}900$ ohms.

If we select as a reasonable value of capacitance $C = 120$ $\mu\mu$f, we find for resonance at one megacycle $L = 210$ μh and $M = 35$ μh. Assuming a selectivity of $Q = 100$, we find that the equivalent shunt resistance of the coil is $R_L = Q\omega L = 132{,}000$ ohms. Evidently, the power delivered to the useful load is reduced by that lost in the coil. Correcting for this effect, we have an equivalent load resistance of 20,800 ohms. The maximum alternating plate current is $256/17{,}100$ or 15.0 ma. The average plate current is, from Fig. 8.4, $15.0/1.80 = 8.33$ ma. The useful power output is $256^2/(2 \times 20{,}800)$ or 1.57 watts. The efficiency, which is relatively high, is $(1.57 \times 10^3)/(300 \times 8.33) = 62.5$ per cent. The design is completed by selection of a grid condenser, which should be large compared to the internal capacitance of the tube; $C_c = 200$ $\mu\mu$f is a suitable value.

8.6 The Colpitts oscillator

The circuit diagram of a practical form of the Colpitts oscillator is shown in Fig. 8.6. In fundamental principles, this circuit differs very little from the tuned plate oscillator just described, but a number of practical differences exist. The grid leak is connected directly from grid to cathode so that an a-c as well as a d-c loss will occur unless a suitable choke is used in series with it. Both the plate and grid are returned directly to ground through the condensers C_p and C_g of the resonator or tank. This is an advantage, because the highly distorted grid and plate currents, characteristic of high-efficiency operation, can return to the cathode without impedance from coil resistance or leakage reactance. However, if the frequency is to be adjustable, the two condensers should be varied in such a way as to preserve their ratio; otherwise the excitation ratio and performance are modified with tuning.

The conditions for oscillation are conveniently determined with reference to the generalized circuit of Fig. 8.7. Using the principle of

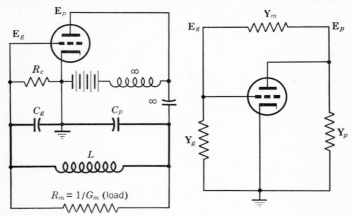

FIG. 8.6. Shunt-fed Colpitts circuit. FIG. 8.7. General oscillator circuit.

equivalent linearization in the form of the preceding sections, we may write the phasor nodal equations

$$\mathbf{E}_g(\mathbf{Y}_g + \mathbf{Y}_m) - \mathbf{E}_p\mathbf{Y}_m = 0, \qquad (8.22)$$

$$-\mathbf{E}_g\mathbf{Y}_m + \mathbf{E}_p(\mathbf{Y}_p + \mathbf{Y}_m) = -\mathbf{E}_g g_m', \qquad (8.23)$$

in which $\mathbf{Y}_m$, $\mathbf{Y}_p$, and $\mathbf{Y}_g$ are taken to include the internal admittances of the vacuum tube, and g_m' represents the *effective transconductance*, defined by

$$g_m' = g_m/\beta_p. \qquad (8.24)$$

Elimination of the voltage variables yields the generally useful equation

$$-g_m' = \mathbf{Y}_p + \mathbf{Y}_g + (\mathbf{Y}_p\mathbf{Y}_g/\mathbf{Y}_m). \qquad (8.25)$$

Neglecting the grid-plate capacitance in the Colpitts oscillator of

Fig. 8.6, and representing the total conductances of grid and plate circuits by G_g and G_p, respectively, we may write

$$\mathbf{Y}_g = G_g + j\omega C_g; \ \mathbf{Y}_p = G_p + j\omega C_p; \text{ and } \mathbf{Y}_m = G_m + (1/j\omega L). \quad (8.26)$$

Substitution of these values in eq. 8.24 yields

$$-g_m' = G_g + j\omega C_g + G_p + j\omega C_p$$
$$+ \frac{j\omega L(G_g G_p - \omega^2 C_g C_p + j\omega G_p C_g + j\omega G_g C_p)}{1 + j\omega L G_m}. \quad (8.27)$$

In each of the admittances, the real part is small compared to the imaginary part. Therefore, negligible error is produced when several squared terms are neglected in rationalizing the last term of eq. 8.27 to obtain by separation of real and imaginary parts

$$C_g + C_p = \omega^2 L C_g C_p - \omega^2 L^2 G_m (G_g C_p + G_p C_g) \quad (8.28)$$

and

$$g_m' = -G_p - G_g + \omega^2 L(G_g C_p + G_p C_g) + \omega^4 L^2 G_m C_p C_g. \quad (8.29)$$

In typical situations the last term of eq. 8.28 is very small compared to the others, and the operating frequency represents series resonance of L with C_g and C_p. Using this value of ω, together with the excitation ratio

$$h = E_{pm}/E_{gm} = C_g/C_p, \quad (8.30)$$

we obtain from eq. 8.29 the gain equation

$$g_m' = hG_p + G_g/h + G_m(h + 1)^2/h. \quad (8.31)$$

If a pentode is used, G_p is effectively zero; moreover, the term G_g/h may often be made negligible. Under these circumstances the effective transconductance required for oscillation with a fixed value of G_m reduces to a minimum value of $4G_m$ for an excitation ratio of unity. Equation 8.31 is useful in adjusting the impedance level of the circuit because the last two terms represent the total admittance presented as load to the plate of the vacuum tube. With this modification, the amplitude of oscillation may be predicted by use of eq. 8.18. As previously noted, the two condensers should be varied in the same ratio if the excitation ratio is to remain constant as the frequency is varied.

8.7 The Hartley oscillator

The circuit diagram of the series-fed Hartley oscillator is shown in Fig. 8.8. It is seen to bear considerable resemblance to both the tuned plate and the Colpitts circuits. It differs from the tuned plate oscillator principally in that the grid leak is in shunt and that the tank condenser and load resistance are connected across the entire coil rather than the plate section only.   The circuit will operate if there is no mutual inductance between the two sections of inductance. However, it is much simpler to construct the coil as a single continuous tapped winding, and this is almost always done because the overall efficiency and performance are considerably improved thereby.   The coupling coefficient between the two portions of the coil should be made as large as possible, because the leakage may be represented as an inductance in series with the cathode lead.   Such an inductance inter-

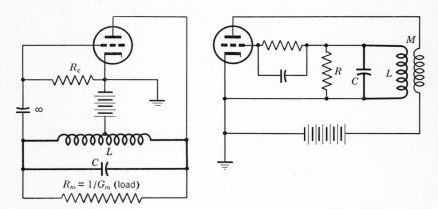

FIG. 8.8.   Series-fed Hartley cir-   FIG. 8.9.   Tuned grid oscillator
          cuit.

feres with efficient class C operation.   This circuit has the practical advantages that it is readily tuned by means of a single variable condenser, and that the total number of components is small.

The operating frequency is very nearly that of resonance between C and the total inductance, and the excitation ratio h is the effective turns ratio of the coil.   The general eq. 8.25 or the specific eq. 8.31 developed in the preceding section may be used to calculate the conditions for oscillation; eq. 8.18 may again be used to predict the amplitude.

When the Hartley circuit is used to generate large amounts of power it is customary to modify the circuit to employ *shunt feed* such as that shown in Fig. 8.6.   An additional choke and blocking condenser are required, but the tank now has no direct potential to ground, and therefore constitutes much less of a hazard to operating personnel. The same objective is achieved in various ways in almost all high-power oscillator applications.   Additional discussion of the Hartley oscillator is given by Heising[135] and Record and Stiles.[253]

8.8 The tuned grid oscillator

An oscillator circuit which is occasionally useful is shown in Fig. 8.9. It is seen to differ from the tuned plate oscillator only in that the load and tuning condenser are transferred from the plate to the grid coils. It is, therefore, also closely related to the Hartley circuit.   All three of these circuits become identical, except for impedance levels, as the coupling coefficient of the coils becomes unity.   Of the three, however, this circuit suffers the most from imperfect coupling.   Its principal advantage is that one end of the tank may be grounded.

The operating frequency is very close to the natural frequency of L and C, provided proper account is taken of the effects of parasitic grid and plate capacitances.   The effective plate load impedance R' is

$$R' = Rh^2, \qquad (8.32)$$

where the excitation ratio h is the turns ratio of the plate to the grid coil.   Using this relation and eq. 8.31, we may calculate the amplitude and frequency of oscillation by the method developed for the tuned plate oscillator.

8.9 The Clapp oscillator

An oscillator circuit having exceptional practical advantages has been described by Clapp.[63]   The circuit diagram, shown in Fig. 8.10, differs from the Colpitts oscillator of Fig. 8.6 in three respects.   A pentode is used instead of a triode, the plate rather than the cathode is at a-c ground potential, and the tank coil, L, is replaced by the series combination of L_e and C_3.   The tank change is the important one, although the others are necessary to obtain the frequency stability which thereby arises.   An incidental advantage of the system is that it is readily tunable over considerable frequency ranges by means of the single condenser C_3.

The best frequency stability obtainable with this arrangement is theoretically equal to that of an ordinary Colpitts oscillator employing the same tube and a coil of equal Q.   The difference lies in the fact that the Clapp arrangement lends itself to a much closer realization of the theoretical limit.

The analysis of the Clapp oscillator is facilitated by assuming that the effective plate resistance of the tube is infinite, that grid circuit losses are negligible, and that the effective transconductance is represented by g_m'.   In typical oscillators operating in class C the effective transconductance is only about one fifth of the nominal value. However our purpose is to determine the effect upon frequency stability of the added capacitor C_3; and it is therefore appropriate to assume that g_m' is a prescribed constant. The relatively long analysis* which follows is included because it gives considerable insight into the behavior of all kinds of oscillators, and because it is directly applicable to the important Pierce crystal oscillator.

The problem to be solved is this. Assuming that the Clapp circuit is to oscillate with a given transconductance g_m', and that the coil has a specified value of Q, how shall C_g, C_p, and C_3 be adjusted so that an

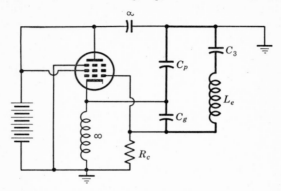

FIG. 8.10.   Clapp's oscillator.

arbitrary increment in C_g or C_p produces the smallest frequency deviation?

The analysis starts by making the substitutions

$$C_g = hC_p = kC_3. \tag{8.33}$$

At the normal operating frequency we see that

$$\omega^2 L_e = 1/C_3 + 1/C_p + 1/C_g = (k + h + 1)/C_g. \tag{8.34}$$

Now if the grid capacitance increases by an amount δC_g the frequency changes to a value represented by

$$(\omega + \delta\omega)^2 L_e = 1/C_p + 1/C_3 + 1/(C_g + \delta C_g). \tag{8.35}$$

Neglecting second-order terms and using the approximation valid for small values of x,

$$1/(1 + x) \doteq 1 - x, \tag{8.36}$$

---

* The following analysis is almost identical with that of Gouriet,[117] which, however, did not come to the author's attention until the present section was completed.

we obtain

$$\omega^2 L_e(1 + 2\delta\omega/\omega) = (1 - \delta C_g/C_g + h + k)/C_g. \tag{8.37}$$

The value of L_e is eliminated by means of eq. 8.34 to obtain

$$\frac{\delta\omega}{\omega} = -\frac{\delta C_g}{C_g}\frac{1}{\lfloor 2 + 2h + 2k\rfloor}. \tag{8.38}$$

It is clear at this point that large values of h, k, and C_g are desirable in order to reduce the frequency deviation; however, these values are limited by the fact that only a given transconductance is available to produce oscillation. To determine the extent to which C_g may be

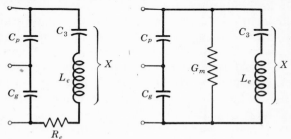

FIG. 8.11. Clapp's resonator.

increased we must obtain an expression for the conductance of the resonator. Referring to Fig. 8.11, we may write

$$R_e/X = XG_m \tag{8.39}$$

and

$$X = 1/\omega C_g + 1/\omega C_p = (1 + h)/\omega C_g. \tag{8.40}$$

Neglecting grid and plate circuit losses in eq. 8.31, we have

$$g_m' = G_m(h + 1)^2/h = R_e(h + 1)^2/X^2 h. \tag{8.41}$$

Introducing the selectivity

$$Q = \omega L_e/R_e, \tag{8.42}$$

we obtain

$$g_m' = \omega C_g(1 + h + k)/Qh. \tag{8.43}$$

Combination of eqs. 8.38 and 8.43 to eliminate C_g yields the important result

$$\delta\omega/\omega = -\omega\delta C_g/2Qhg_m'. \tag{8.44}$$

Because the parameter k, which fixes the value of C_3, disappears in the final substitution, we conclude that in itself the added capacitor C_3 contributes nothing to frequency stability. That is, subject to a fixed *value of Q, a properly proportioned Colpitts oscillator is just as stable as a properly proportioned Clapp oscillator.* However, the Clapp arrangement is much the more flexible, because the inductance value may be chosen on the basis of convenience, selectivity, stability, compatibility with available tuning condensers, etc. The impedance level presented to the tube may then be adjusted for best operation by means of C_g and C_p. In this way all the important parameters are under good engineering control. In the Colpitts oscillator, on the other hand, the reactances required for optimum stability are often impracticably small; and an attempt to realize the calculated values is frustrated by poor values of Q, impracticably large variable condensers, and other similar limitations.

The development of eq. 8.44 is such that by substituting δC_p for δC_g the same expression may be used to determine frequency changes due to increments of plate capacitance. Assuming that C_p and C_g are subject to equal random deviations, we obtain best results by setting $h = 1$. In many cases, however, C_p is about ten times more stable than C_g. When this is true the smallest total frequency deviation results when $h = \sqrt{10} \doteq 3$.

A numerical example may be helpful. Suppose then a frequency of 159 kc ($\omega = 10^6$) is to be generated by a 6SJ7. It is assumed that the nominal transconductance of 1600 micromhos is reduced to an effective value of 200 by class C operation, and that coils having a selectivity $Q = 200$ are available. From eq. 8.43 we have the values $C_g = 5000$ $\mu\mu$f, $C_p = 1667$ $\mu\mu$f, $C_3 = 250$ $\mu\mu$f, and $L_e = 4.8$ mh, corresponding to the choice $k = 20$ and $h = 3$. These values are quite appropriate at the given frequency and are consistent with the assumed value of Q.

In the ordinary Colpitts circuit we have $k = 1$; therefore, consistent with $h = 3$, $C_g = 30,000$ $\mu\mu$f, $C_p = 10,000$ $\mu\mu$f, and $L_1 = 133.3$ μh. This value of inductance is too low to be convenient at the given frequency, and in any event the large values of capacitance preclude tuning over any appreciable frequency range.

8.10 The Meissner circuit

A circuit which is principally of historical interest is the Meissner, shown in Fig. 8.12. It reduces to the Hartley oscillator if the coupling coefficients are unity and if the number of turns in L is equal to the total number of turns in the grid and plate coils. It provides d-c isolation of the tank and flexibility in the choice of impedance level at the price of additional complexity and a serious tendency to oscillate at undesired frequencies which depend upon parasitic inductances and capacitances. This tendency toward spurious oscillation results from the several leakage inductances inherent in the arrangement and is not readily controlled.

Closely related to the circuits of Meissner and Clapp is that due to Lampkin[181] and illustrated in Fig. 8.13. As in the Clapp circuit, the size of the coil and condenser is chosen on the basis of Q, tuning range, and convenience; the tube is then attached in such a way as to produce oscillation with a minimum of disturbance of the natural frequency. The present arrangement is most desirable at low and moderate frequencies, where relatively tight coupling may be produced. If

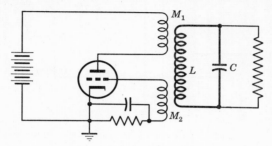

FIG. 8.12. Meissner oscillator.

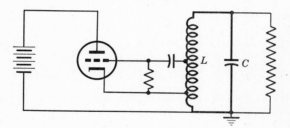

FIG. 8.13. Lampkin's oscillator.

tight coupling is not achieved the circuit is likely to generate spurious oscillations at some relatively high frequency which depends upon the leakage inductance.

8.11 The tuned grid–tuned plate circuit

A circuit which is the basis of the familiar Miller crystal oscillator is shown in Fig. 8.14. Its analysis is of further interest because triode amplifiers and frequency multipliers often generate undesired oscillations in accordance with the design principles of this circuit. Such oscillations do not have good frequency stability because the grid-plate capacitance of the tube is an important element in the frequency-determining circuit; however, relatively good stability may be obtained by adding a stable capacitance to C_3 and reproportioning the other elements. The circuit may be interpreted as a Hartley oscillator in which the mutual inductance has become zero and the effective inductance of each coil has been increased by partial tuning.

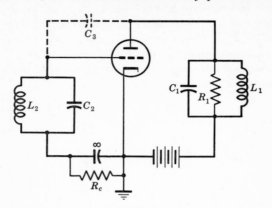

FIG. 8.14. Tuned grid–tuned plate circuit.

Referring to Fig. 8.7, we may substitute

$$\mathbf{Y}_m = jB_m = j\omega C_3,$$

$$\mathbf{Y}_g = jB_g = j\omega C_2 + 1/j\omega L_2, \tag{8.45}$$

and

$$\mathbf{Y}_p = G_p + jB_p = G_1 + j\omega C_1 + 1/j\omega L_1.$$

Substituting in eq. 8.25 and taking advantage of the fact that $\mathbf{Y}_m$ and $\mathbf{Y}_g$ are pure imaginary, we have

$$B_m g_m{}' + G_1(B_g + B_m) = 0, \tag{8.46}$$

and

$$1/B_m + 1/B_g + 1/B_p = 0. \tag{8.47}$$

The first of these equations represents the transconductance required for oscillation, and shows that B_g and B_m must be of opposite sign; that is, the grid circuit must be inductive. The second equation shows that oscillations are sustained at the frequency at which the reactive elements alone produce a resonant loop.

Introducing the excitation ratio, which is

$$h = -(B_g + B_m)/B_m, \tag{8.48}$$

we may reduce the loop gain equation to the form

$$g_m{}' = hG_1. \tag{8.49}$$

In practical oscillator circuits the losses in the grid circuit are usually small but not always negligible. The analysis is considerably complicated by including these losses, which have as their principal consequences an increase in the required transconductance and a slight modification of the operating frequency.

8.12 The Gunn circuit

An interesting circuit which secures phase reversal by the use of two tubes was described by Gunn.[126] The arrangement, as shown in Fig. 8.15, is symmetrical, and requires well-shielded tetrodes or pentodes for best results. Because the power output is not large, and two con-

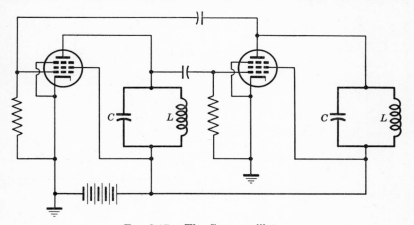

FIG. 8.15. The Gunn oscillator.

densers must be varied in tuning, its use is limited to applications where frequency stability is the primary concern. Gunn explained its operation in terms of an infinite series process considering successive transmissions around the loop, but it appears that the more conventional analyses also apply here, and that his analysis could be applied to any oscillator. Whether the frequency stability is actually superior to that of a properly adjusted one-tube oscillator remains dubious.

Since the two stages are identical, the small-signal voltage gain of each need be only slightly in excess of unity. Even with low transconductance tubes, this permits the use of quite low impedance tank circuits with correspondingly large values of the C/L ratio. The frequency shift which will result from a given change in tube capacitance or harmonic content may thus be made very small. The output, which is not large, may be taken at any convenient point in the circuit,

provided the usual precautions to avoid frequency change due to the
load are observed.

8.13 The Franklin oscillator

A circuit due to Franklin[102] which has excellent frequency stability
is shown in Fig. 8.16.   Although developed independently, it differs
from the Gunn circuit mainly in that the two tuned circuits are
replaced by load resistors, and that the resonator is very loosely
coupled to the resulting driving system because C_1 and C_2 have
capacitances of only about 1 $\mu\mu f$ each.[180]   Limiting occurs principally

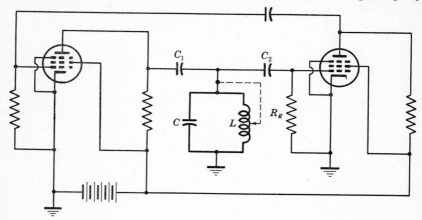

FIG. 8.16.   The Franklin oscillator.

in the tube at the left, and the other tube may well be provided with a
cathode biasing resistor to increase the impedance which the grid
presents to C_2.   This is desirable because the grid conductance in
conjunction with the input capacitance affects the phase angle of the
equivalent voltage divider, thereby affecting the frequency.

At frequencies near 500 kc, where the circuit is usually operated, the
load resistances may be made so small with respect to the associated
capacitances that the phase shift in each stage is substantially 180°.
The operating frequency is then very nearly the natural frequency of
the resonant circuit.   The arrangement has the advantages that tuning may be accomplished by means of a single variable inductor or
capacitor, and that one side of the tuned circuit is directly grounded.
In the original models the tuned circuit was a relatively massive unit
constructed with great care so as to minimize drift due to aging and
temperature change.[185]   However, the same construction could be
used profitably with other circuits, so that the merits of the circuit

and of the resonator should be considered separately.   In both this and the Gunn circuit it may prove desirable to use a tapped coil as indicated by the dotted line.   This preserves the advantages of a low impedance level without requiring an inordinately large tuning condenser, as discussed in Sections 8.9 and 8.10.

8.14 Electron coupling

In simple triode oscillators the operating frequency varies appreciably with load impedance.   The effect is always present, and takes on troublesome magnitudes when the frequency must be accurately controlled or the tube must be operated for maximum output.   This

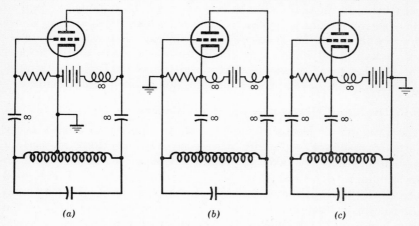

(a)   (b)   (c)

Fig. 8.17.   Choice of ground point.

difficulty is greatly reduced by the use of multiple-grid tubes such as tetrodes, beam tetrodes, or pentodes.   A basic property of these tubes, is that all the electrode currents are independent of the plate voltage, *provided the plate is sufficiently positive with respect to the cathode*.   To see how this property may be exploited let us examine the effect of grounding different points in an oscillator.

Figure 8.17 shows a shunt-fed Hartley oscillator grounded respectively at the cathode, grid, and plate.   For clarity, an actual physical ground is shown in each case, although the direct potential of the cathode ordinarily is small or zero for practical reasons.   Here, as in a preceding section, the operation of the oscillator is not affected by the choice of the grounding point, since the energy transfer depends only upon the relative voltages of the various tube electrodes.   Practical oscillators employ all three arrangements; however, the grounded plate arrangement is of the greatest present interest.

The next step in the development is to replace the triode by a corresponding ideal tetrode in which the screen and plate are connected together. It is seen that no change in operation is involved. *The crucial step is that there will be no change in operation if the screen and plate voltages differ in any manner whatever, so long as the plate voltage never becomes too small.* Therefore a load having any phase angle whatever, or tuned to an entirely different frequency, may be connected in the plate lead without affecting the frequency or amplitude of oscillation. Oscillator circuits using this idea were introduced by Dow[78] and are called *electron coupled.*

To obtain perfect decoupling it is necessary that perfect screening exist between the plate and the control grid. If coupling external to the electron stream is present it allows the load impedance to affect directly the operating frequency. If coupling exists within the electron stream the dynamic plate conductance is not zero, and additional coupling between load and resonator is introduced. Practical tetrodes and pentodes achieve a close approximation to such ideal shielding.

8.15 Design of electron-coupled oscillators

The principle of electron coupling can be applied to almost every form of oscillator, ordinarily with good results. However, certain precautions must be taken if the full advantage of the method is to be obtained. The electron-coupled Hartley oscillator of Fig. 8.18 serves to illustrate the discussion. In the first place, the maximum alternating voltage in the output circuit must not exceed E_{b2} or the plate voltage will fall below the screen voltage during part of the cycle. Such a situation is objectionable because the plate current is affected by the plate voltage in this region. Therefore, the impedance of the plate circuit must be chosen with suitable regard for the applied voltages and the actual amplitude of oscillation.

Because the cathode current is not affected by the plate voltage, the oscillator portion of the circuit may be designed from a knowledge of the tube as an equivalent triode, without regard to the division of the current between screen and plate electrodes. *Specifically, the full transconductance of the tube is available for feedback, in contrast with other arrangements to be described later.* Although practical designs are ordinarily achieved by cut and try, it is clear that a method differing only in detail from that used in connection with the tuned plate oscillator may be used to obtain adequate engineering results.

Finally, pentodes with the suppressor internally connected to the cathode are not desirable in this circuit because the direct capacitance introduced between plate and cathode at least partially defeats the purpose.   Beam tubes, which almost always have internal connections, are objectionable on the same basis, although the direct capacitance is frequently small enough to be tolerable.   Pentodes with available suppressor leads operate well in this circuit if the suppressor is connected to a fixed (by-passed) potential equal to the maximum alternating voltage of the cathode.   Shielding is preserved, and conduction occurs at times when the cathode and suppressor are at practically the same potential.

In summary, the optimum tube for Fig. 8.18 is a tetrode with excellent shielding, a large ratio of plate to screen current, high transconductance, and a high ratio between the safe plate voltage and the required screen voltage.   Available tubes such as the 24A and 36

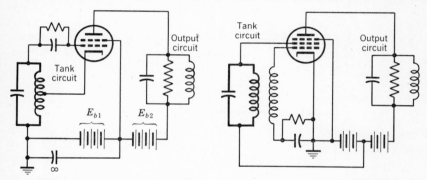

FIG. 8.18.   Electron-coupled Hartley oscillator.

FIG. 8.19.   Electron-coupled pentode oscillator.

approximate these objectives reasonably well.   Pentodes with separate suppressor leads are equally desirable and more commonly available. When a pentode with internal suppressor connection must be used a neutralization scheme similar to one described in a following paragraph may be employed.

An essentially different form of electron coupling is shown in Fig. 8.19.   The cathode is grounded and the second or screen grid is used as an equivalent plate in a tuned plate oscillator.   In this circuit the current which flows through the tank circuit to produce oscillations is not the entire cathode current but is only the fraction thereof captured by the screen.   The effective transconductance to be used in calculating the performance is given by the approximate relation

$$g_m' = (g_m/\beta_p) \cdot (I_{c2}/I_b), \tag{8.50}$$

where g_m is the normal control-grid-to plate transconductance, β_p is the class C parameter given in Fig. 8.4, and the average screen and plate currents are evaluated at some representative point on the characteristic.

In designing this circuit it is desirable to use an abnormally low value of the excitation ratio, in the order of $h = \frac{1}{2}$, so as to obtain adequate voltages in the control grid circuit without producing large voltages in the screen circuit. Otherwise, adequate values of plate current are not produced because the instantaneous screen voltage is reduced too greatly from its average value. The power output of this circuit is good, because the alternating plate voltage may be allowed to approach the total B voltage. As in the circuit of Fig.

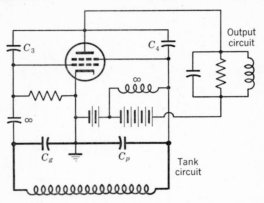

Fig. 8.20.   Capacitance compensated electron-coupled tetrode oscillator,

$$(C_3/C_4 = h = C_g/C_p).$$

8.18, however, the load impedance must be suitably controlled or the proper operating range will be exceeded.

Finally, a good shield between screen and plate is required. Otherwise, the alternating voltage in the plate circuit would react upon the frequency of oscillation through the direct screen to plate capacitance. Pentodes having a relatively fine suppressor mesh are preferred for this circuit because of their superior shielding. Internal connection is acceptable because both cathode and suppressor are to be grounded.

If a suitable pentode is unavailable, the desired result may be obtained by means of a bridge balance. The method is applicable to any of the conventional configurations but is most readily explained in terms of the Colpitts circuit of Fig. 8.20. Under the specified conditions, the oscillations present in the control and screen grid circuit would deliver no current to the plate circuit except through the actual electron stream because the contributions through C_4 and C_3 cancel. By reciprocity, therefore, reactances which may exist in the plate circuit are unable to affect the frequency or amplitude of the oscillations in the controlling circuit. Ordinarily, C_4 represents only the unavoidable internal capacitance of the tube and C_3 is a small neutralizing condenser adjusted for the desired balance. The pentode arrangement of Fig. 8.19 is preferable to the balanced arrangement of Fig. 8.20 because of the larger plate voltages which may be employed and because of the difficulty of achieving and preserving a suitable balance.

The basic principles of Figs. 8.18, 8.19, and 8.20 may be applied with minor changes to a great variety of oscillators. In all cases, the output circuit may be tuned to a harmonic of the frequency being generated. If the tube is operating well into class C, as is usually the case, the output is a substantial fraction of that which would have been obtained at the fundamental. The design of the load circuit requires a knowledge of the desired component of plate current, which may be obtained by applying Fourier analysis to the actual plate current wave.

8.16 Reactance stabilization of frequency

Both theory and experiment show that the frequency stability of practical oscillators is improved by the use of small L/C ratios in the tank circuits. However, where tuning by means of a variable condenser is necessary, or for various other reasons, it may not be possible to achieve the required stability in this way. In such cases the reactance stabilization of Llewellyn[192] is useful.

Llewellyn's analysis is based upon the principle of equivalent linearization, although the term was not in general use at that time. He assumed that the tank circuit is entirely free from loss, so that the power produced in the plate circuit equals the power lost in the grid circuit, principally in the grid leak. As shown in Section 8.4, the amplitude of oscillation will automatically adjust itself to such a value that the loop gain and phase requirements are satisfied. The idealizations of that section lead to values of plate and grid resistance which are independent of the applied voltage, but in actual oscillators these resistances change somewhat with the amplitude of oscillation. In general, the frequency of oscillation depends somewhat upon the resistances as well as the reactances present in the circuit. Therefore, changes in the applied voltages will lead to a change in frequency by changing the values of the tube resistances.

If, however, the grid and plate voltages are exactly 180° out of phase, the frequency is independent of the equivalent tube resistances and hence of the applied voltage. Llewellyn's paper shows a variety of arrangements for accomplishing this objective.   Unity coupling between the coils of the Hartley or tuned plate oscillator would clearly meet this requirement, and Llewellyn also shows how to obtain the desired effect without actually obtaining perfect magnetic coupling.   In the standard Colpitts oscillator, for example, the desired phase relationship is obtained by the addition of a small inductance in series with the plate or grid leads.

The analysis leads to the following logical procedure: (1) Use the lowest ratio of L/C consistent with the situation.   (2) Use the largest practical grid leak in order to obtain a large value of effective grid resistance.*   (3) Obtain the highest practical coefficient of coupling between the coils if magnetic coupling is used.   (4) Use a compensating reactor to correct the remaining departure from 180° phase. Llewellyn and others have obtained very stable oscillators following this procedure.

The foregoing discussion does not include the effects of intermodulation, as discussed in Chapter 4.   In most class C oscillators the equivalent reactance due to intermodulation is quite small.   Since the harmonic content is nearly independent of the applied voltage, the frequency variation with respect to applied voltage due to this cause is relatively unimportant, in marked contrast to the dynatron and related oscillators.   Additional information on this subject is presented by Jefferson.[156]

8.17 Resistance stabilization of frequency

Oscillators employing resistance stabilization can be made to produce remarkably constant frequency, especially in or somewhat above the audio range.   A Hartley oscillator employing resistance stabilization is shown in Fig. 8.21.   The coil is tightly coupled and has a large value of Q, and the L/C ratio is low.   The grid bias is fixed at a value slightly below the optimum value for class A operation.   The feedback resistor R_1, which is high compared to the plate resistance of the tube, is adjusted to a value only slightly smaller than that corresponding to the threshold of oscillation.   Under these conditions the tube operates with low distortion, the voltage across the tuned circuit is very nearly free from harmonics, and the frequency is quite insensitive to the conditions of the tube and to variations of the applied voltage.

Although the superior performance of such oscillators is in large part due to the care with which they are ordinarily built and operated,

---

*Intermittent behavior, which may occur if the grid leak is too large, is discussed in Chapter 10.

the feedback resistor contributes to this performance in two ways.   It provides a very practical and reproducible means for controlling the feedback to a value near the threshold of regeneration, and it isolates the tuned circuit from the plate of the tube, thereby improving the wave form and minimizing the reaction of varying plate resistance upon the output frequency.   Because of the fixed bias and the absence of a grid leak the amplitude of oscillation is limited in a way which is quite different from that in other oscillators.   During oscillation build-up the operation is almost linear, and the ordinary exponential expansion occurs; the grid draws no current, and the plate current increases very slightly because of unavoidable curvature in the tube characteristics.   The amplitude stabilizes at such a value that the grid is driven positive at the peak of each cycle, at which point the

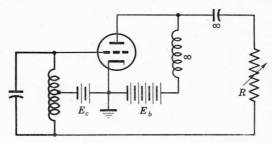

Fig. 8.21.   Resistance-stabilized Hartley oscillator.

marked loading in the grid circuit rapidly decreases the loop gain. The average bias is fixed by the battery so that a small change in amplitude produces a relatively great change in grid circuit loss. Accordingly the amplitude stability is quite good.

Terman[305] recommends the use of a triode having low plate resistance and an amplification factor between 6 and 10 in conjunction with a center-tapped, tightly coupled, high Q coil.   The recommended feedback resistor has a value between two and five times the plate resistance.   Finally, the plate choke and the blocking condenser should have reactances respectively very high and very low compared to the plate resistance.   It appears probable that desirable results could also be obtained with a pentode if the plate choke were replaced by a suitable load resistor.

8.18 Phase shift oscillators

Inconveniently large coils and condensers are required to generate the lower audio frequencies in ordinary LC oscillators.   The use of resistance and capacitance permits the generation of these frequencies much more conveniently. A very simple circuit for obtaining oscillations in a resistance-capacitance circuit was described by Ginzton and Hollingsworth,[111] and is shown in Fig. 8.22.

At first glance it may seem surprising that such a circuit can generate harmonic oscillations. It is well known that a passive circuit of resistance and capacitance is completely incapable of oscillation, and is characterized by roots which are real and negative. As shown in Chapter 5, however, the addition of gain or negative resistance in the form of a vacuum tube greatly modifies this situation. For appropriate values of the parameters the roots become pure imaginary, and the Nyquist plot passes through the point $(1, 0)$ corresponding to sustained oscillation.

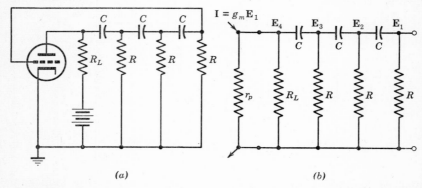

FIG. 8.22. Phase shift oscillator: (a) circuit arrangement, and (b) equivalent circuit.

The conditions for sustained oscillation may be determined by means of linear equations in connection with the equivalent circuit of Fig. 8.22b. As in other oscillators, the actual gain provided is in excess of that calculated, and nonlinear operation results. However, the operating frequency corresponds very closely to the calculated value, and the gain equation serves as a basis for the design of practical circuits.

The algebra presented by Ginzton and Hollingsworth is relatively complicated, and is omitted here in the interest of space. However, the results of their calculations for a variety of circuit arrangements are presented in Fig. 8.23. Throughout this figure the symbol A represents the amplification which would be observed for the given tube operating with the load resistor R_L. That is,

$$A = \mu R_L/(R_L + r_p). \tag{8.51}$$

The arrangements which employ condensers in shunt are particularly attractive for variable-frequency oscillators because variable condensers usually have a grounded common rotor connection. And variable condensers are preferred to variable resistors because they are much more stable and reproducible. Moreover, the gain equation is unaffected if all condensers are varied alike because the frequency readjusts itself so that the susceptances are not varied. *It is important to note that in this, as in other RC oscillators, the frequency varies inversely with the RC product so that relatively wide frequency ratios are easily covered.*

Phase Shifting Network	Frequency of Oscillation	Required Amplification
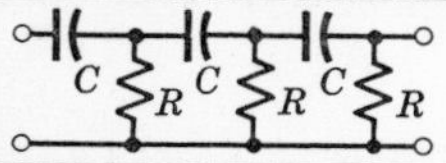	$\dfrac{1}{2\pi\sqrt{6}\,RC}$	29
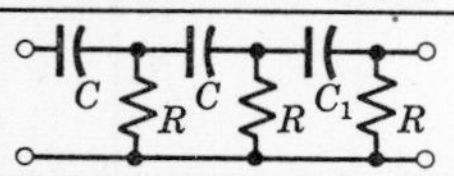	$\dfrac{1}{2\pi RC_1\sqrt{\dfrac{C}{C_1}\left(5+\dfrac{C}{C_1}\right)}}$	$16+10\dfrac{C_1}{C}+3\dfrac{C}{C_1}$
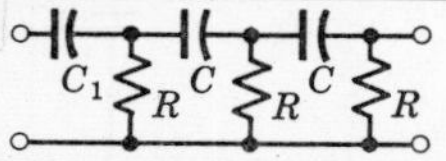	$\dfrac{1}{2\pi RC_1\sqrt{3\dfrac{C}{C_1}\left(1+\dfrac{C}{C_1}\right)}}$	$14+3\left(\dfrac{C_1}{C}+4\dfrac{C}{C_1}\right)$
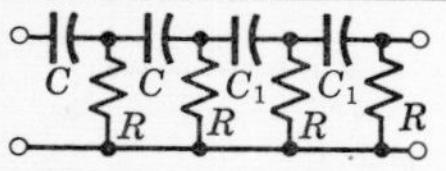	$\dfrac{1}{2\pi RC_1\sqrt{\dfrac{3\left(\dfrac{C}{C_1}\right)^2+7\dfrac{C}{C_1}}{4+3\dfrac{C}{C_1}}}}$	$\dfrac{9\left(\dfrac{C}{C_1}\right)^3+114\left(\dfrac{C}{C_1}\right)^2+352\left(\dfrac{C}{C_1}\right)+342+84\left(\dfrac{C_1}{C}\right)}{\left(4+3\dfrac{C}{C_1}\right)^2}$
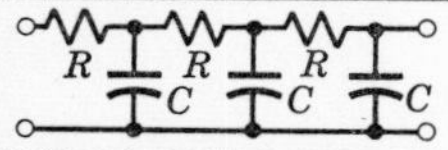	$\dfrac{\sqrt{6}}{2\pi RC}$	29
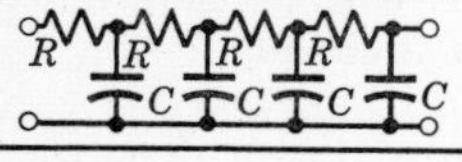	$\dfrac{\sqrt{10/7}}{2\pi\,RC}$	18.4

FIG. 8.23. Equations for design of phase shift oscillators.

It is easy to show that the amplification A required for oscillation is decreased by the use of more RC networks in tandem and by progressively increasing the impedance level of the networks. The results which may be secured in this way are discussed by Johnson.[159] Additional design information is given in papers by Hinton,[140] Sulzer,[301] Vaughan,[329] and Artz.[17]

The results of Fig. 8.23 do not include the effects of grid-to-plate or other capacitances in the tube. These are sure to become important at high frequencies, and may be significant at the upper audio frequencies if very high impedances are used to obtain such frequencies with variable air condensers of moderate capacitance.

The frequency stability of phase shift oscillators is adequate for nearly all audio frequency applications. The frequency is quite insensitive to the applied voltage if the tube is operated with only moderate gain margin. And the use of good components renders the frequency reasonably stable with respect to temperature and aging.

Related to the phase shift oscillators are the polyphase resistance-capacitance oscillators of Bartlett.[22]	These are useful in a few special applications where polyphase sinusoidal currents of variable frequency are required. A great variety of such arrangements are possible.

8.19 The DeLaup oscillator

A resistance-capacitance oscillator of exceptional simplicity has been devised by DeLaup.[75]	The circuit arrangement, shown in Fig. 8.24,

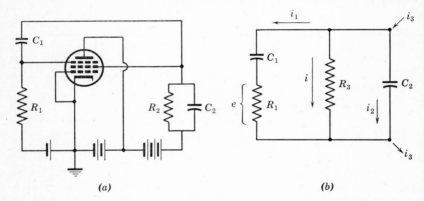

(a)	(b)

FIG. 8.24. Resistance-capacitance oscillator using negative transconductance: (a) circuit diagram and (b) simplified equivalent circuit.

is identical with that of the van der Pol relaxation oscillator described in Chapter 12. It is of little practical importance because the frequency stability and wave form are very poor unless the parameters are controlled within narrow limits. It is discussed because analysis of this critical behavior serves to explain the behavior of other oscillators.

The simplified equivalent circuit is shown in Fig. 8.24b, where R_3 represents the parallel combination of R_2 with the dynamic screen grid resistance of the tube. The use of g_m for the transconductance from suppressor to screen grid leads to the group of equations:

$$iR_3 = \int_0^t \frac{i_2}{C_2}\, dt, \tag{8.52}$$

$$iR_3 = i_1 R_1 + \int_0^t \frac{i_1}{C_1}\, dt, \tag{8.53}$$

and

$$g_m e = i_3 = i_1 + i_2 + i. \tag{8.54}$$

Differentiating eq. 8.53 and substituting to eliminate the current and voltage variables, we obtain as the differential equation of the system

$$\frac{d^2 i}{dt^2} + \left(\frac{1}{C_2 R_3} + \frac{1}{C_1 R_1} + \frac{1}{C_2 R_1} - \frac{g_m}{C_2} \right) \frac{di}{dt} + \frac{i}{C_1 C_2 R_1 R_3} = 0. \tag{8.55}$$

The substitutions

$$C_2 = n C_1, \tag{8.56}$$

$$\omega_0{}^2 = \frac{1}{C_1 C_2 R_1 R_3}, \tag{8.57}$$

and

$$m = \omega_0 R_1 C_1 = \frac{1}{\omega_0 R_3 C_2} \tag{8.58}$$

reduce the differential equation to the form

$$\frac{d^2 i}{dt^2} + \left(m\omega_0 + \frac{\omega_0}{m} + \frac{\omega_0}{mn} - \frac{g_m}{C_2} \right) \frac{di}{dt} + \omega_0{}^2 i = 0. \tag{8.59}$$

It is readily shown that sustained oscillations occur if the coefficient of the first derivative is zero and that their frequency is given by eq. 8.57.

For other values of the transconductance the oscillations expand or contract exponentially and the period is increased. Consistent with Chapter 2, we find that the roots of the auxiliary equation traverse a circle in the complex plane and are displaced from the horizontal axis by an angle ϕ given by

$$\phi = \tan^{-1} \sqrt{ \frac{4 m^2 n^2}{(m^2 n + m + n)^2 (1 - k)^2} - 1 } \tag{8.60}$$

where

$$k = \frac{m^2 n R_3 g_m}{1 + n + m^2 n}, \tag{8.61}$$

represents the ratio of the actual transconductance to that required for sustained oscillation.

The angle ϕ can be real, corresponding to sinusoidal oscillations, only if the fraction in eq. 8.60 is greater than one. This will be true over the widest range of the gain variable k if

$$m = 1 \quad \text{and} \quad n \gg 1. \tag{8.62}$$

These relationships justify the usual procedure of making

$$R_1 \gg R_3 \quad \text{and} \quad R_1C_1 = R_2C_2 = 1/\omega_0. \tag{8.63}$$

Subject to these conditions ϕ is real, provided

$$0 < k < 2. \tag{8.64}$$

Decaying sinusoidal waves are produced if $0 < k < 1$, expanding sinusoidal waves are produced if $1 < \overset{*}{k} < 2$, and relaxation oscillations are produced if $k > 2$.

Figure 8.25 shows Nyquist plots and the system roots for the circuit of Fig. 8.24 having parameters consistent with eq. 8.62. Condition A

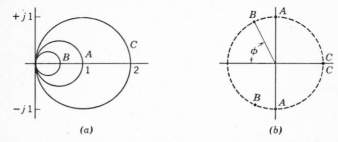

(a)   (b)

FIG. 8.25.   Properties of the circuit of Fig. 8.24: (a) Nyquist plot and (b) position of roots in complex plane.

represents sustained oscillation ($k = 1$) whereas B and C represent $k = \frac{1}{2}$ and $k = 2$, respectively.

8.20 Nyquist diagrams and system roots

The analysis of the preceding section has used the roots of the auxiliary equation to explain the otherwise puzzling fact that the DeLaup oscillator is very critical as to the transconductance of the tube. The same general analysis is now applied to other oscillators. The tuned plate oscillator, which has already been extensively studied, is treated first.

If the grid leak-condenser combination of Fig. 8.1 is replaced by a fixed bias battery, we may obtain the Nyquist diagram by inspection. The plot is a circle with diameter proportional to the amplification factor of the tube and a frequency scale uniquely fixed by the effective Q of the tank circuit. It therefore differs from that of the DeLaup oscillator only in that the rate of change of phase with respect to frequency is much greater. As shown in Chapter 5, this behavior is associated with roots much nearer the real frequency axis and correspondingly improved frequency stability.

The extent to which μ may be increased above the value correspond-ing to the threshold of oscillation before relaxation oscillations occur is of importance. That it is a large ratio is inferred from the Nyquist plot. The exact ratio is obtained by finding the roots of the auxiliary equations.

Referring to eq. 5.25, we see that the roots are pure real provided

$$4\omega_0{}^2 = (Mg_m\omega_0{}^2 - G/C)^2, \tag{8.65}$$

where $G = 1/r_p + 1/R$, and $\omega_0{}^2 = 1/LC$. Similarly the roots are pure imaginary corresponding to the threshold of oscillation, provided

$$Mg_m\omega_0{}^2 = G/C. \tag{8.66}$$

Taking the ratio of these two transconductances, we have

$$k = 1 + 2\omega_0 C/G. \tag{8.67}$$

The last factor is recognized as twice the selectivity of the tuned circuit as loaded by the dynamic plate resistance. Therefore, we conclude that relaxation oscillation can occur in a tuned plate oscillator only if the transconductance exceeds the threshold value by the factor $(1 + 2Q)$, which is readily made large in practical systems, so that a generous margin exists.

Occasionally we wish to damp the oscillation of a tuned circuit by means of a vacuum tube. This can be accomplished by reversing the sign of M or g_m in eq. 8.65; critical damping results when this reversed equation is satisfied.

Actual oscillators are almost never so simple as the system used to develop these results. Consideration of the grid leak and condenser combination always leads to an additional negative real root. More-over, additional meshes in the system and roots in the corresponding equation are contributed by the effects of parasitic inductance or capacitance and imperfect coupling in realizable transformers. How-ever, the results obtained give a correct general idea of the situation in the more usual forms of oscillators.

The phase shift oscillator presents an intermediate situation. Treatment of the general case will not be attempted because algebraic difficulties cloud the results unduly. If, however, we premise that each section of the phase shift network of Fig. 8.22 has an impedance large compared to that of the preceding one, we can obtain the Nyquist plot and the roots reasonably simply.

The differential equations for the several meshes of the system, using $p = d/dt$, have the common form

$$e_4/e_3 = e_3/e_2 = e_2/e_1 = 1 + 1/pCR. \tag{8.68}$$

Assuming that $r_p \gg R_L$ or that R_L represents the parallel value of the two resistors, we have

$$e_4 = -g_m e_1 R_L. \tag{8.69}$$

Elimination of the voltage variable leads to the system equation

$$(1 + 1/pCR)^3 + g_m R_L = 0. \tag{8.70}$$

As is well known, this equation may also be interpreted as the auxiliary equation which yields the desired roots. Let us examine it in this

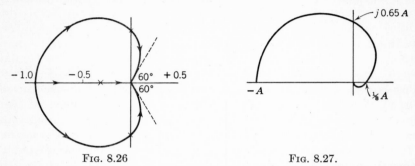

FIG. 8.26.   FIG. 8.27.

FIG. 8.26.   Variation of roots of phase shift oscillator (plot of p relative to $1/CR$).
FIG. 8.27.   Nyquist diagram for a three-section phase shift oscillator.

light.   First, with the tube off, corresponding to $g_m = 0$, the root is triple and has the anticipated value

$$p = -1/CR. \tag{8.71}$$

For the value of transconductance which corresponds to the threshold of oscillation, p must be a pure imaginary, whereas the other coefficients of eq. 8.70 are pure real. This is possible provided the cubed quantity represents a complex number having an angle of 60°. That is, if

$$p = \frac{\pm j}{\sqrt{3}\,CR}. \tag{8.72}$$

Substitution shows that eq. 8.72 satisfies eq. 8.70, provided $g_m R_L = 8$.

As g_m is varied from zero to infinity, the three roots at $-1/CR$ separate, tracing the paths shown in Fig. 8.26, and reconverge at the origin. *The exceptional feature of this circuit, which behaves differently from any previously studied, is that it cannot generate relaxation oscillations because p cannot become real and positive.*

The Nyquist diagram for the phase shift oscillator is readily plotted because it represents three times the phase and attenuation character-istic of a single RC section, modified by a negative factor A, which is the inherent amplification of the tube, as shown in Fig. 8.27. It is an interesting fact, which may or may not have significance, that for the systems here studied there is a considerable resemblance between the Nyquist plot and the path traced by the roots as the transconductance is varied.

8.21 Beat-frequency oscillators

A beat-frequency or heterodyne oscillator consists of two separate oscillators and a modulator or mixer for producing an output at the difference (or occasionally the sum) of these frequencies. The arrange-ment is widely used for generating audio frequencies, but is also applicable to a variety of other applications for measurement and signaling. Arbitrarily low frequencies can be produced in this way provided that adequate measures are taken to avoid synchronization between the two oscillators; however, the resulting frequency stability is relatively poor. To obtain reasonable stability it is customary to make the two oscillators as stable and as nearly identical as possible. Thus the two drift in a similar manner, and the difference is relatively constant. Ordinarily, the frequency of the oscillators is about ten times the maximum output frequency.

A major problem in the design of heterodyne oscillators is the elimination of spurious frequencies in the output. Unless suitable precautions are taken, the output of each oscillator contains the com-plete series of harmonics, and the modulator produces all possible sum and difference frequencies. If we represent the oscillator funda-mental frequencies as a and b, respectively, and assume $a > b$, we find in addition to the desired difference frequency $a - b$, components at $2a - 2b$, $3a - 3b$, $3b - 2a$, etc. A great many other frequencies are also produced, but are so remote that they are readily removed by means of filters. The terms such as $2a - 2b$ are most readily sup-pressed by designing the oscillators so that they produce practically pure sinusoids, and by designing the modulator so that it produces only sum and difference frequencies. Linear oscillators are suitable from the standpoint of frequency stability and low harmonic constant. A multiple-grid tube, such as the FM-1000, in which the input is applied to separate electrodes each of which exerts a *linear* control over the electron stream is suitable for the modulator. The detailed design of heterodyne oscillators is beyond the purpose of this work. The interested reader is referred to papers by Slonziewski,[288] Moore,[215] and Kirby.[173]

8.22 Decade oscillators

An oscillator which is convenient for many purposes is arranged so that the operating frequency may be set by means of additive decade dials similar to those used in ordinary resistance boxes.[85]   A very high accuracy of setting is achieved in this way without recourse to elaborate dial mechanisms; though the actual frequency stability is evidently no better than that inherent in the circuit.   The method depends upon the fact that the frequency of resistance-capacitance oscillators varies *inversely* with some RC product or *directly* with the reciprocal product of conductance and stiffness GD.   A decade oscillator results if an appropriate decade of conductance or stiffness is used.   Such decades may be made by connecting resistors in parallel or capacitors in series by switching arrangements appropriate respectively to capacitance and resistance decades.

If, for example, the phase shift circuit of the fifth line of Fig. 8.23 is to be used, it is appropriate to use three-gang switches to vary the three stiffness decades required.   Because only four separate capacitors are required for each decade, the number of elements required is not prohibitive.   The same objective is reached in the Wien bridge oscillator of Chapter 7 by means of only two stiffness decades.   An oscillator employing this arrangement has been described by Young.[351]

8.23 Low-frequency oscillators

Oscillators of the phase shift variety are readily adjusted to operate at frequencies as low as about 10 cycles; and substantially lower frequencies may be generated in this way if suitable precautions are taken.   The most important single factor is leakage, which may occur in the condensers or in the associated elements and leads.   The series capacitor arrangement indicated in Fig. 8.22 is preferred at low frequencies because it is little affected by parasitic capacitances and leakage conductances.   Using this arrangement and a thermistor amplitude control, Fleming[94] has produced a calibrated oscillator having low harmonic output and good stability in the frequency range of 0.9 to 10,000 cycles.

At still lower frequencies it is possible to employ the thermal time constant of a thermistor as the frequency-controlling parameter. Using a 400-μf condenser and a Western Electric 1-B thermistor, Stone[298] has produced oscillations variable over the frequency band of 0.02 to 0.1 cycle.   A relatively pure wave form at an adjustable-frequency is obtained by varying the feedback provided through a d-c amplifier.

Oscillations lower in frequency by another order of magnitude may be obtained by means of capacitances and mechanical relays. Because the system is inherently nonlinear, a pure wave form is obtained only if adequate filtering is provided. Means for producing such oscillations are described by Ives.[154]

8.24 Wide-range oscillators

Although it is possible to obtain a frequency which varies over a wide ratio by means of the heterodyne method, it is sometimes desirable to achieve the same result in a different way. Methods for directly producing oscillations over wide-frequency ratios have been devised by Anderson[7] and by Willoner and Tihelka.[345]

The oscillator due to Willoner and Tihelka is of the phase shift type, as shown in Fig. 8.28, but it uses an artificial line of inductance and capacitance rather than of resistance and capacitance. The transformer produces a stepdown so that the line may operate at a convenient impedance level; it does not produce a phase reversal. Limiting is produced in the tungsten lamp, which is heated by the alternating current fed to the phase-shifting line. Oscillation occurs at a frequency such that 180° phase shift is produced in the portion of line included in the oscillating loop in accordance with the setting of the potentiometer P. It appears that an even wider range of adjustment could be secured by means of a sliding contact on a continuously distributed line.

The "seven league" oscillator of F. B. Anderson[7] achieves a comparable result in a somewhat different manner. The basic element of this system is a bridge in which the transmission through a complicated RC network is partially balanced by a simple voltage divider. The general configuration and response of the bridge is shown in Fig. 8.29. By properly proportioning the six RC combination it is possible to secure the characteristic indicated, in which V_0, *the component of V_3 in quadrature with V_1, is almost constant over a very wide band of frequencies.* Therefore, for each setting of the potentiometer and associated voltage V_2, the frequency adjusts itself so that the desired quadrature relationship exists. Oscillation is obtained by using two of these bridges in tandem to secure the 180° phase reversal required in ordinary vacuum tubes. The frequency of oscillation varies approximately logarithmically with the setting of a linear potentiometer.

The actual circuit configuration, shown in Fig. 8.30, is somewhat complicated by the fact that vacuum tubes are used to obtain high impedances to prevent interaction between bridge arms. Tubes T_1 and T_2 serve as a two-input amplifier to take the required difference $V_3 - V_2 = V_0$. The output of T_1 represents the amplified quadrature

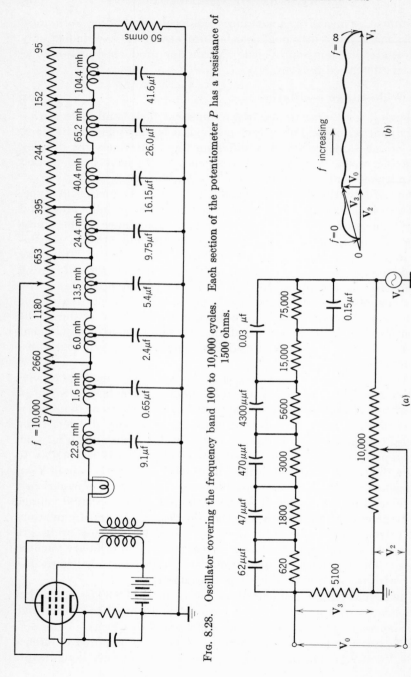

FIG. 8.28. Oscillator covering the frequency band 100 to 10,000 cycles. Each section of the potentiometer P has a resistance of 1500 ohms.

FIG. 8.29. Quadrature bridge: (a) circuit and (b) response.

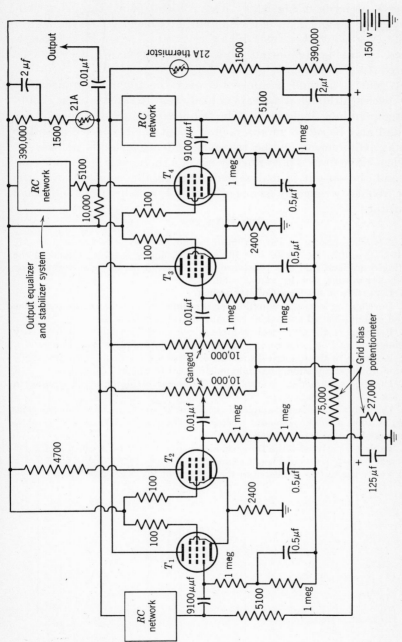

Fig. 8.30. Seven-league oscillator using 6AK5 tubes and covering the frequency range 20 cycles to 3 Mc. (Reproduced with permission of author and editor from F. B. Anderson, "Seven League Oscillator," *Proc. I.R.E.*, **39**, 881–890 [1951]).

voltage V_0 in terms of Fig. 8.29.   This voltage applied through a similar bridge to T_3 and T_4 produces an output which may be thought of as V_1.   A single rather than double reversal of phase in the loop is secured by taking the output from T_3 rather than T_4, as would be required for symmetry.

The general method is applicable over the frequency range 0.01 to 10^7 cycles, although it appears unlikely that the entire range should be attempted in a single unit.   The frequency is stable to about 2 per cent and may be set to an accuracy of about one-half per cent.   The tracking requirement on the two-gang potentiometer is not severe. Excellent wave form is preserved by use of a thermistor amplitude control, and the output is maintained substantially constant over the entire frequency range by means of a suitable equalizer and additional thermistor.

PROBLEMS

8.1. A triode oscillator similar to that of Section 8.5 has the parameters $\mu = 70$, $r_p = 10^5$, $r_g = 10^3$, $E_b = 250$, $h = 10$, $\theta_p = 50°$, and $\gamma = 0.75$.   Calculate the operating conditions, grid leak resistance, and resonator parameters, assuming no useful power output, $\omega = 10^7$ and $Q = 50$.

8.2. Repeat Prob. 8.1 for a Colpitts oscillator.

8.3. Develop the loop-gain equation for the tuned-grid oscillator, assuming the grid coil is shunt-loaded and taking account of grid rectification.

8.4. Referring to the numerical example of Section 8.5, calculate the frequency deviation produced by adding one micromicrofarad to the plate capacitance.

8.5. Referring to the numerical example of Section 8.9, calculate the frequency deviation produced by adding one micromicrofarad to the grid capacitance.

8.6. Develop a numerical example of a Meissner oscillator corresponding to Prob. 8.1.

8.7. Develop a numerical example of the Franklin oscillator based on pentodes with $g_m = 2000$, a 500-kc resonator with $Q = 150$ and $C = 1000\mu\mu f$, and coupling condensers of one micromicrofarad each.

8.8. Explain clearly why the transconductance available to produce oscillation is different in the circuits of Figs. 8.18 and 8.19.

8.9. Verify the results presented in the last line of Fig. 8.23.

9

CRYSTAL-CONTROLLED
OSCILLATORS

Crystal-controlled oscillators are characterized by the use of a piezoelectric crystal rather than a tuned circuit as the frequency-determining element. Logically, therefore, they are merely harmonic oscillators, and might well be classified with the other oscillators of that group. They are treated separately here because their properties are significantly different from those of other oscillators and because separate treatment is customary. The outstanding property of crystal-controlled oscillators is an exceptional degree of frequency stability. This is a direct result of the high Q and low temperature coefficient of the crystal unit employed. The difference, although of degree rather than of kind, is so great as to justify separate consideration.

Because the frequency is principally determined by the crystal, it is possible to obtain relatively simple expressions for frequency stability by combining appropriate partial derivatives. This procedure is illustrated in the following sections.

The subject matter of the chapter was arranged with a view to presenting a number of useful ideas in a logical order. It is perhaps unfortunate that the most widely used circuits operate in a relatively complicated manner and are therefore described near the end. The reader who wishes an independent and fairly elementary discussion of crystal oscillators is referred to the paper by Anderson.[8]

9.1 The transformer-coupled oscillator

The circuit of Fig. 9.1 is chosen to introduce the subject of crystal oscillators because it illustrates several basic and important ideas. Although applicable over a wide range of frequencies, it is most useful at frequencies between about 20 and 150 Mc in conjunction with crystals operating at series resonance on an overtone of the thickness-shear vibration.[206] To obtain these frequencies the capacitances of the grid and plate circuits are reduced to the minimum possible value, and the transformers consist of small single-layer air-core solenoids. The autotransformer arrangement is favored because it leads to a desirable high coupling coefficient between low- and high-impedance windings. The tube operates in class C with grid-circuit limiting, and the useful load is represented by the resistor R in shunt with the plate

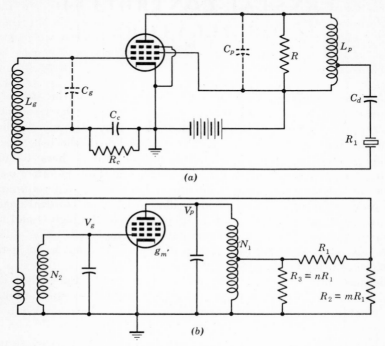

(a)

(b)

Fig. 9.1.   Transformer-coupled oscillator: (a) schematic and (b) idealization for analysis.

transformer. The operation differs from that of the Meacham circuit largely by the fact that the circuit resistances degrade rather than enhance the effective value of crystal Q.

It is assumed that the tube is a pentode operating in class C, with the effective transconductance reduced to g_m' by bias resulting from grid current, and that the transformers are loss-free, have negligible leakage inductance, and are resonant with the associated plate and grid capacitances at the operating frequency. Fortunately, the effect of leakage inductances present in physical transformers is small and can be canceled by assigning an appropriate value to C_d. The useful load is represented as a resistor in shunt with the plate transformer; however, it will be shown that a tuned load circuit, magnetically coupled to the plate coil, has several important practical advantages. Finally, it is assumed that the holder capacitance, C_0, of the crystal is negligible or is compensated by methods described later.

Analysis of the conditions for oscillation is facilitated by reference to Fig. 9.1b, in which the crystal is replaced by its series resistance, and the useful load and grid-circuit losses are referred to the low side of the transformers.   It is convenient and desirable to introduce at this time the *Q degradation factor D*, which is the ratio of the intrinsic selectivity of the crystal to its selectivity in the circuit.   This parameter may be thought of as the inverse of the Q magnification factor of the Meacham bridge, and is useful in the analysis of many oscillator circuits.   In the present case it takes the form

$$D = (R_1 + R_2 + R_3)/R_1 = 1 + m + n. \tag{9.1}$$

Because the tube operates in class C with grid current, and because transit-time loading is important at the higher frequencies, the tube requires an appreciable driving power, which is represented by R_2 in Fig. 9.1b.   Because the plate load impedance represented by R_3 is limited by stability and other considerations, the power gain of the tube is always finite and may be rather low.   The equilibrium amplitude is established in the grid circuit; thus, it is appropriate to express the power in terms of the rms grid voltage.   On this basis, the grid driving power, useful power output, and power dissipated in the crystal are, respectively,

$$P_d = V_g^2/N_2^2 m R_1, \tag{9.2}$$

$$P_0 = V_g^2(1 + m)^2/N_2^2 m^2 n R_1, \tag{9.3}$$

and

$$P_c = V_g^2/N_2^2 m^2 R_1. \tag{9.4}$$

The power gain G of the tube is a convenient and important parameter; it is given by

$$G = (P_d + P_c + P_0)/P_d = 1 + 1/m + (1 + m)^2/mn. \tag{9.5}$$

In previous discussions it has been assumed that the power-handling capacity of the resonator was, or could readily be made, adequate.   In crystal oscillators this is rarely true, and the ratio of output to crystal power must be large if any considerable power output is to be obtained. In the present circuit this important ratio is

$$P_0/P_c = (1 + m)^2/n \doteq GD - G - D. \tag{9.6}$$

It is evidently increased by making m large and n small, and can be relatively large only if both G and D are considerably in excess of unity.

The foregoing relationships all assume that oscillation occurs at the series resonant frequency, a desirable condition. With this assumption we may show that the transconductance required for sustained oscillation, that is, unity loop gain is

$$g_m' = D/R_1 N_1 N_2 nm. \tag{9.7}$$

Other parameters of interest are the impedances faced by the plate and grid, which are, respectively,

$$R_p = N_1^2 R_1 (n + mn)/(1 + m + n), \tag{9.8}$$

and

$$R_g = N_2^2 R_1 (m + mn)/(1 + m + n). \tag{9.9}$$

9.2 Design considerations in the transformer-coupled oscillator

There are at least three important objectives which govern the design of this and other crystal oscillator circuits, namely: (1) good frequency stability; (2) large power output; and (3) ability to operate with crystals having substantially different frequencies. It will be shown that best frequency stability is achieved by obtaining appropriately low products DR_p and DR_g, that best power output requires increases of R_p and R_g at a sacrifice of frequency stability, and that operation with crystals varying over the widest possible band of frequencies requires that R_p and R_g be decreased, again at a sacrifice of frequency stability.

In Section 7.13, on the Meacham oscillator, it was shown that the variation of loop phase shift with respect to frequency is directly proportional to the effective Q of the resonator, and that the phase shift produced by an increment in plate or grid capacitance is directly proportional to the associated impedance. Therefore, consistent with any given crystal Q and tube transconductance, best frequency stability is obtained by proportioning the circuit so as to minimize the products of resistance and Q degradation. If we assume that the plate capacitance is k times more stable than the grid capacitance, we should set

$$R_p = kR_g. \tag{9.10}$$

The problem, then, is to minimize the product DR_p consistent with eq. 9.7. Combination of eqs. 9.1, 9.7, 9.8, and 9.9 with 9.10 yields

$$R_p D = (\sqrt{k/g_m'})(1 + m + n) \sqrt{(1 + m)(1 + n)/mn}. \tag{9.11}$$

From the symmetry of this relationship we see that the minimum value will occur only if $m = n$. With this substitution the derivative of eq.

9.11 is equal to zero, provided

$$m = n = \tfrac{1}{2}\sqrt{2}. \tag{9.12}$$

*That is, maximum frequency stability with respect to incremental varia-
tions of grid or plate capacitance exists if* $m = n$, $D = 1 + \sqrt{2}$ *and*
$N_1 = \sqrt{k}\, N_2$. Because eq. 9.12 corresponds to a low ratio (only 4.12)
of output to crystal power, it is often desirable to deviate from the
optimum conditions. Fortunately, the maximum is a broad one so
that a great increase in power ratio is obtained at a small sacrifice in
stability. For example, $R_p D$ is increased only 29 per cent by setting
$n = 0.3$ and $m = 1.5$, in which case $P_0/P_c \doteq 21$.

The frequency stability of the transformer-coupled oscillator with
respect to increments of grid (or plate) capacitance is readily determined from eqs. 7.76 and 7.80. Note that ϕ is smaller, not larger,
than θ. The resulting expression is

$$\frac{dC_g}{d\omega/\omega} = \frac{2Q}{\omega D R_g}. \tag{9.13}$$

The ability of the circuit to operate with crystals having different
frequencies depends mainly upon the phase shift introduced by the
plate and grid capacitances, hence upon R_p and R_g. Therefore, it is
desirable to make R_p and R_g as small as possible consistent with the
specified value of g_m'. Substitution of eqs. 9.1 and 9.7 in eqs. 9.8 and
9.9 yields

$$R_p = \frac{N_1}{N_2} \cdot \frac{1 + m}{m g_m'} \tag{9.14}$$

and

$$R_g = \frac{N_2}{N_1} \cdot \frac{1 + n}{n g_m'}. \tag{9.15}$$

These expressions have no minimum, but approach $1/g_m'$ as m and n
become large. Evidently, there is little profit in giving either m or
n a value in excess of 4, which degrades the frequency stability by a
factor slightly less than 2. When the grid and plate capacitances
are unequal the impedances should be adjusted so that the RC products, and hence the bandwidths, are approximately equal.

In the circuit of Fig. 9.1 the loop phase shift of the system, exclusive
of the crystal, departs rapidly from zero if the frequency deviates
from that to which the plate and grid circuit are tuned. However,
it is possible to make the loop phase shift quite small over a considerable frequency band by removing the physical load resistor and

coupling a suitably tuned load to the plate winding. The method is not applicable to the grid circuit because the conduction and capacitance of the grid are not separable. Therefore, it is often desirable to make the natural bandwidth of the grid circuit somewhat greater than that of the plate circuit; and it is sometimes possible to overcompensate the plate circuit.

The bandwidth over which the phase shift may be controlled is limited by the impedance level and capacitance of the plate circuit. The necessary design relationships may be derived directly[129] or by applying the band-pass transformation to the familiar shunt-peaked video interstage network. However, the following rules, based on that procedure, are sufficient in ordinary situations. (1) The total useful bandwidth ω_b is $3/(4R_pC_p)$. (2) The primary and secondary are both tuned to ω_0, the geometric mean of the useful band. (3) The secondary selectivity Q is $(3/4)\omega_0 R_p C_p$. (4) The primary to secondary coupling coefficient k is $1/\sqrt{1 + (4/3)Q^2}$. (5) The phase shift reaches 20°, and the gain rises about 2 db at the edges of the band. A useful bandwidth of 20 Mc may be obtained with the 6AK5 pentode in a carefully adjusted circuit.

Because the grid (or plate) transformer must produce a phase reversal, it is possible to balance the effects of grid-plate and crystal-holder capacitance. It is readily shown that the required relationship is

$$C_0 = N_1 N_2 C_{gp}. \tag{9.16}$$

Fortunately, this relationship is consistent with reasonable values of circuit parameters. When this condition is approximated the circuit has little tendency to generate spurious oscillations of any kind.

Alternatively, the effect of C_0 may be largely eliminated by antiresonating it at the operating frequency with a low-Q coil. Finally, this physical inductance may be eliminated by providing a suitable degree of magnetic coupling between plate and grid transformers.

Limiting ordinarily occurs in the conventional manner by rectification in the grid circuit. However, if the grid circuit impedance is made low in the interest of frequency stability or broad-band operation, the level of limiting may be too high for the crystal unit. This difficulty may sometimes be avoided by lowering the plate (not screen) voltage to a value near the knee of the pentode characteristic. The effective transconductance then decreases rapidly with increase of amplitude so that limiting occurs ever though the grid is never driven to cutoff.

A numerical example may prove helpful. Let us assume a 70-Mc crystal having a series resistance $R_1 = 100$ ohms. A 6AK5 pentode having its effective transconductance reduced to 2000 from the nominal value of 5000 micromhos is suitable. The input and output capacitances are about equal, but the grid circuit capacitance is considerably the less stable. Therefore, as a compromise between stability and wide-band operation, let us set $k = 2$ in eq. 9.10. The choices $n = 0.3$ and $m = 1.5$, corresponding to $P_0/P_c = 21$, also represent a reasonable compromise between stability and power output. The foregoing assumptions yield as the operating conditions: $R_p = 1900$, $R_g = 950$, $R_3 = 30$, $R_2 = 150$ ohms; $N_1 = 8.42$ and $N_2 = 3.70$.

Assuming $Q = 10,000$, an increment of 1 $\mu\mu$f in the grid capacitance or $\frac{1}{2}$ $\mu\mu$f in the plate capacitance will lower the frequency by 58 ppm. If limiting occurs at 3 rms grid volts, the power output and the crystal power are, respectively, 61 and 2.92 mw. A supply voltage of 75 for screen and plate is approximately correct. The plate load should be provided by inductive coupling. The grid impedance will be at least partially provided by rectification and transit-time effects; but additional conductance may be required. The effects of crystal-holder and grid-plate capacitance are balanced if C_0 and C_{gp} have the reasonable values 7.5 and 0.24 $\mu\mu$f. For a more detailed treatment of high-frequency oscillators the reader is referred to a report prepared for the Signal Corps by the author.[84]

9.3 The C.I. meter circuit

The circuit of Fig. 9.2 was developed for the measurement of the effective series resistance of crystal units in an arrangement called the

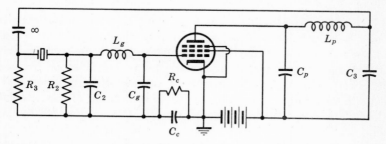

FIG. 9.2. The C.I. meter circuit.

"crystal impedance meter." The measurement is based upon a substitution procedure in which the frequency and amplitude of oscillation are unchanged when the crystal is replaced by a resistance or specified resistance-capacitance combination. Other oscillator circuits may also be used for this purpose, but the present circuit is particularly suitable because the tuned circuits remove the harmonic currents which might otherwise flow through the substitution resistor and thereby produce error. Conversely, the present circuit is useful for applications other than measurement.

The circuit may be viewed as a transformer-coupled oscillator in which the required impedance transformations and phase reversal are provided by a pair of quarter-wave artificial transmission lines connected in tandem. Moreover, R_2 and R_3 are normally so low that C_2 and C_3 have negligible effect and may be omitted.

It is well known that a quarter-wave loss-free transmission line has the property of impedance inversion. Therefore, high values of plate and grid impedance are associated with low values of R_3 and R_2. Moreover, *the impedances faced by the crystal are very low provided the*

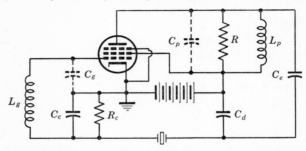

FIG. 9.3. Alternative form of transformer-coupled oscillator.

impedances of grid and plate are very high. It is in this one respect that the present circuit differs most significantly from the transformer-coupled circuit.

The load resistor R_3 has a value of about 10 ohms in typical situations. Because such a resistance is rarely identifiable with a useful load, we are led to examine other arrangements. Usually, it is desired to drive another vacuum tube serving as an amplifier or frequency multiplier. Although it is possible to connect the amplifier grid to the oscillator plate, it is undesirable to do so because of the associated Q degradation and increased capacitance. It is preferable to use a second artificial line, which develops a suitable grid-driving voltage by series resonance, joining the lines at the terminals of C_3. Appropriately interpreted, the equations developed in connection with the transformer-coupled oscillator apply also to the C.I. meter circuit.

Another useful variation of the transformer-coupled oscillator is shown in Fig. 9.3. The phase relationships correspond to those of Fig. 9.1, the required reversal being produced by resonance of L_g with C_c and C_g. The voltage delivered to the crystal is reduced by the potentiometer action of C_e and C_d. The principal advantage of this circuit over Fig. 9.1 is that no tapped coils are required. The disadvantage is that the resulting system is somewhat less flexible and stable. The equations previously developed apply reasonably accurately provided the equivalent transformer ratios are taken as

$$N_1 \doteq C_d/(C_d + C_e) \quad \text{and} \quad N_2 \doteq C_c/(C_c + C_g). \tag{9.17}$$

9.4 The grounded-grid circuit

A very simple series-mode circuit is due to Butler[51] and shown in Fig. 9.4. It may be thought of as a special form of transformer-coupled oscillator in which no phase reversal is necessary and one transformer may be omitted. Although operable at ordinary frequencies, this

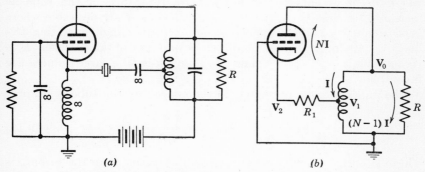

FIG. 9.4. Grounded-grid series-mode oscillator: (a) schematic and (b) equivalent circuit.

circuit is rarely employed except at relatively high frequencies and in conjunction with overtone crystals.

The tube may be thought of as a grounded-grid, class C amplifier, and as such delivers a plate current which is equal to the current injected at the cathode. Desirable operation, therefore, requires that a considerable fraction of the total plate current flow through the load resistor R, and that this loss be compensated by the current step-up ratio of the autotransformer. As is well known, the impedance presented to the crystal by the cathode is nearly the reciprocal of the effective transconductance—a few hundred ohms in typical tubes. The circuit therefore operates quite well with crystals having series resistances as high as a thousand ohms. Limiting occurs, as in other class C oscillators, as a result of the bias developed by rectification in the grid circuit. However, an additional tendency to limit arises from the fact that grid current is necessarily robbed from that delivered to the plate.

To analyze the circuit, we assume that the cathode-to-ground capacitance is small or tuned out by the cathode choke, that the direct plate-to-cathode capacitance is negligible, that the plate transformer has negligible leakage inductance, and that the plate circuit is tuned to the frequency at which the crystal is series resonant. The transformer is assumed to be ideal, with a turns ratio of N, and the effects of grid current are neglected. With these idealizations, which are reasonably approximated in practice, the conditions for sustained oscillation may be written

$$R = \frac{N^2(r_p' + R_1 + \mu R_1)}{(N - 1)(\mu + 1 - N)}, \tag{9.18}$$

where r_p' represents the effective plate resistance of the tube as increased by class C operation. Low values of R are desirable where good frequency stability must be obtained at a high operating frequency, but larger values of power output are obtained when R is comparable to r_p'. Low values of r_p' and R_1 and a large value μ are favorable.

The impedance R_k presented to the crystal by the tube is simply

$$R_k = \frac{V_2}{NI} = \frac{r_p'}{\mu + 1} + \frac{(N - 1)R}{(\mu + 1)N}. \tag{9.19}$$

The first term, which is often considerably larger than the second, is nearly equal to the reciprocal of the effective transconductance.

The impedance R_2 presented to the other terminal of the crystal is obtained by taking the parallel combination of the load impedance and the effective plate resistance of the tube, as modified by the turns ratio of the transformer. The exact value involves a complicated expression that is not justified in practice, because the value is closely bounded by the relations

$$\frac{Rr_p'}{N^2(R + r_p')} < R_2 < \frac{R}{N^2}. \tag{9.20}$$

It is ordinarily possible and desirable to make R_2 substantially smaller than R_1 or R_k.

The crystal Q degradation factor is

$$D = \frac{R_1 + R_k + R_2}{R_1} \doteq 1 + \frac{R_k}{R_1}. \tag{9.21}$$

The most serious limitation of this circuit is that the power gain of a grounded-grid amplifier cannot exceed the amplification factor of the tube. Therefore, it is hard to obtain a large ratio of output to crystal power without seriously degrading the frequency stability. It is readily shown that the approximate form of eq. 9.6 also applies to the grounded-grid circuit. Thus, we see that values of G in excess of ten and values of D around three are required to obtain a favorable ratio of output to crystal power. However, the frequency stability is degraded by increase of either parameter, so that a compromise is necessary.

In spite of this limitation, the grounded-grid circuit is capable of excellent frequency stability because the plate capacitance is relatively stable, the cathode impedance very low, and the crystal Q not unduly degraded. Ordinarily, the impedance faced by the cathode is so low that frequency instability due to variation of the cathode capacitance is relatively unimportant. When this is true, best frequency stability is obtained by proportioning the circuit so as to minimize the DR_p product. No detailed analysis is offered; however, results obtained in connection with the transformer-coupled oscillator indicate that the value is not critical and good results are obtained if $D = 3$. Provided μ is relatively large, it is readily shown from eq. 9.18 that R reaches a minimum when $N = 2$. This condition is conducive to frequency stability and broad-band operation on a crystal-substitution basis.

Under some circumstances the impedance R_k presented by the tube is either too high or too low for suitable operation with the available crystal. In this case an additional impedance transformation at the cathode is desirable. This is most conveniently obtained by substituting a suitable tightly coupled autotransformer for the cathode choke, the total inductance antiresonating the cathode capacitance. A significant improvement in operation may sometimes be obtained in this way.

The band over which operation is obtained by crystal substitution is greatly increased if the load is suitably tuned and inductively coupled to the plate coil. The resulting bandwidth is comparable with that of the transformer-coupled circuit because the advantage of one transformer is compensated by the higher impedance level which it must have. Also, crystal compensation may be achieved by shunting a coil across the crystal or by providing magnetic coupling between the plate and cathode coils.

A numerical example, based on the 6J4 triode, serves to illustrate these points. The normal value of $\mu = 55$ is preserved, but the plate resistance is increased from the nominal value of 5000 to 11,000 ohms by class C operation. A crystal resistance of 50 ohms at 50 Mc is fairly typical. Choosing a turns ratio $N = 9$, we have $R = 1660$ and $R_k = 222$ ohms; also, $D \doteq 5.4$ and $G = 5.9$. The ratio of output to crystal power is thus 20.6. Assuming that the effective value of crystal current is 5 ma, the output and crystal power are, respectively, 26 and 1.25 mw.

9.5 The cathode-coupled oscillator

The cathode-coupled circuit of Fig. 9.5 is popular because of its economy of parts, ease of adjustment, and excellent performance. One tube, T_1 serves as a cathode follower to drive the crystal from a low impedance without the use of a physical transformer. The other tube, T_2, serves as a grounded-grid amplifier. The tuned circuit in the plate lead of T_2 serves to select the general frequency of operation if the crystal is capable of oscillating in several different modes; with this single limitation the crystal has almost complete control over the frequency. Limiting usually occurs by rectification at the grid of the cathode follower.

A considerable power output at the operating frequency or at one of its lower harmonics may be taken from the tuned circuit in the plate of T_1. The shielding effect of the suppressor and screen grids is such that the tuning and impedance level of this circuit have little effect upon the oscillation; and it is therefore possible to choose these elements for maximum output.

A triode may be substituted for pentode T_2 with little or no loss of performance because the control grid is grounded. And a triode is entirely satisfactory as a cathode follower provided the load circuit is omitted. In fact, a triode may, with some care, be used for the cathode follower even when the load circuit is used, provided the latter is tuned to a harmonic of the operating frequency and does not have too high an impedance. Triodes are favored principally because of the compactness achieved by the use of a dual tube.

Details to be considered in the design of this oscillator are indicated in Fig. 9.5b. The entire system will operate at zero phase shift and hence at the natural frequency of the series arm of the crystal, provided

$$1/\omega_0^2 = L_c C_0 = L_k C_{k2} = L_{p2} C_{p2} \qquad (9.22)$$

and provided the capacitances of the cathode follower are related on the basis of a resistance-capacitance voltage divider. The internal impedance of T_1 is nearly equal to $1/g_{m1}$, and the load impedance is substantially equal to $R_1 + 1/g_{m2}$. Therefore, there will be no phase shift, provided

$$g_{m1}(R_1 + 1/g_{m2}) = C_{k1}/C_{gk1}. \qquad (9.23)$$

Limiting still occurs in the grid circuit of T_1, and suitable values of resistance and capacitance are indicated. The cathode bias of both

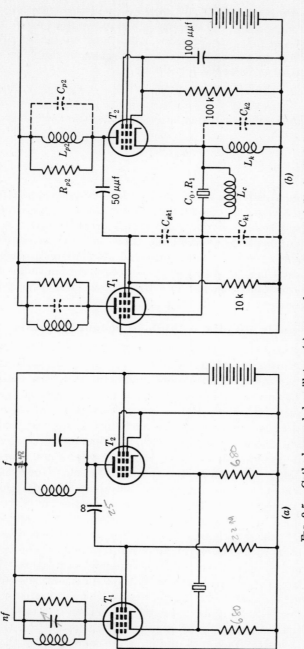

FIG. 9.5. Cathode-coupled oscillator: (a) general arrangement and (b) detailed design.

tubes has been removed by the presence of the compensating coils, so that it is appropriate to bias T_2 by means of a grid leak and condenser as indicated. Under these conditions the same alternating current flows in both tubes. Denoting this current by I, we find that the grid voltage of T_1 is given by

$$V_{g1} = IR_{p2}. \tag{9.24}$$

By the cathode follower principle of eq. 9.23, the cathode voltage of T_1 is

$$V_{k1} = \frac{V_{g1}(R_1 + 1/g_{m2})}{R_1 + 1/g_{m1} + 1/g_{m2}}. \tag{9.25}$$

The principal advantage of the cathode-coupled oscillator is its simplicity; the principal disadvantage is that two tubes are required to obtain the performance given by one tube in other circuits. Moreover, the cathode impedance of available tubes is upwards of 100 ohms; therefore the circuit does not perform well with low-resistance crystals. In most situations a one-tube oscillator followed by a buffer amplifier will exceed the power output and frequency stability of a cathode-coupled oscillator.

9.6 Series-mode circuits for high-impedance crystals

Circuits given by Heegner[134] and suitable for use with high-impedance crystals are shown in Fig. 9.6. They differ principally in the manner in which the required phase relationship is obtained. In both circuits the sum of R_g and R_L should be made as small as practical in the interest of frequency stability. Both circuits will oscillate at the frequency of the tuned circuit if the crystal is short-circuited or replaced with a corresponding resistance. Also, both will operate successfully if the tuned circuit is omitted, provided the loop gain is not excessive and the crystal has a small value of shunt capacitance. However, there is a marked tendency to produce relaxation oscillations, for the circuits correspond respectively to the van der Pol and the multivibrator.

The modified form of Fig. 9.6a shown in Fig. 9.7 is useful up to frequencies in the neighborhood of 150 Mc. It is described in some detail because it illustrates clearly an important principle, applicable with some modification to most high-frequency oscillators. We first assume that the crystal is replaced by a fixed capacitance equal to its shunt capacitance, and that C_0 represents the total effective capacitance from screen to suppressor. We further assume that C_2 and C_3 represent total capacitances to ground and that the three circuits are tuned to the crystal frequency and have the same value of Q. Subject

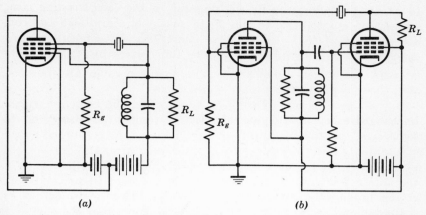

FIG. 9.6. Series-mode crystal oscillators: (a) transitron form and (b) feedback form.

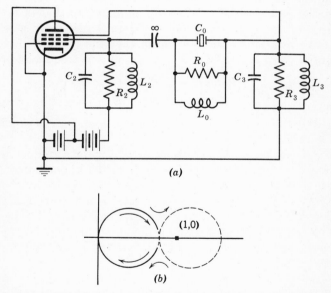

FIG. 9.7. Compensated transitron series-mode oscillator: (a) schematic and (b) Nyquist plot.

to these assumptions, the coupling and suppressor circuits act as a compensated voltage divider having no phase shift and a constant voltage ratio.

The total impedance presented to the screen grid is a simple multiple of the impedance of each circuit, and the Nyquist plot for the system is a true circle as shown by the solid line of Fig. 9.7b. It is readily shown that the diameter of this circle is given by

$$|\mu\beta|_0 = g_m R_2 R_3 / (R_0 + R_2 + R_3). \tag{9.26}$$

To avoid uncontrolled oscillations, the resistance values are chosen so that the diameter is somewhat less than one.

If the crystal is now restored to the system, the behavior will be unchanged except at frequencies near the resonant frequency of the series arm. At the resonant frequency, however, R_0 is shunted by the substantially lower resistance R_1 of the crystal arm, and the Nyquist plot is modified by the subsidiary circle shown dotted in Fig. 9.7b. Oscillation will occur at or very near the resonant frequency of the crystal because the modified Nyquist plot encircles the critical point.

Reexamination of the preceding material shows that the operation will not be adversely affected if the three antiresonant circuits differ somewhat in Q. In particular, the tuning of either the screen *or* suppressor circuit may be very broad compared to that of the others with no effect upon the shape of the Nyquist plot. By a relatively simple differentiation it may be shown that the Nyquist plot, in the absence of R_1, will cross the real axis at only one frequency provided

$$C_0 \leq \frac{R_2 R_3}{R_0} \left(\frac{C_2}{R_0} + \frac{C_2}{R_3} + \frac{C_3}{R_0} + \frac{C_3}{R_2} \right). \tag{9.27}$$

That is, spurious oscillations will not occur if eq. 9.27 is satisfied and if eq. 9.26 is less than unity.

As an illustration let us design an oscillator for a frequency of 159 Mc, using an overtone crystal having a holder capacitance of 5 $\mu\mu$f and a series resistance of 1000 ohms. The most suitable available tube is the 6AS6, which has a suppressor-to-screen transconductance of 1600 micromhos. Assuming that the irreducible circuit capacitances are $C_2 = C_3 = 10$ $\mu\mu$f and that C_0 is increased to 10 $\mu\mu$f by the screen-to-suppressor capacitance, we find that eq. 9.27 is satisfied if $R_2 = R_3$ and $R_0 \leq 2.73 R_2$.

Providing a 3-db margin against undesired oscillation, we have from eq. 9.26, $R_2 = R_3 = 2090$ ohms and $R_0 = 5700$ ohms. At the crystal frequency, however, R_0 and R_1 are effectively in parallel, and the loop transmission determined from eq. 9.25 is 1.39, a value which offers reasonable margin. The required inductances are 0.1 μh each.

9.7 The Pierce circuit

The crystal oscillators previously described have in common the property that the crystal is employed as a series-resonant element having a relatively low impedance.   Such oscillators are finding increasing use because they operate over a very wide range of frequencies and because they possess excellent frequency stability, which is due, at least in part, to the fact that the crystal is little affected by increments in shunt capacitance.   The great majority of crystal oscillators, however, employ the crystal in effective antiresonance with an external capacitance called the *load capacitance*.   This is referred to as operation in the *parallel mode*.   The following paragraphs describe several important parallel-mode oscillators.

Figure 9.8 shows a circuit, now generally referred to as the Pierce crystal oscillator, which is characterized by extreme simplicity and economy of parts.   It has the desirable properties that it will operate

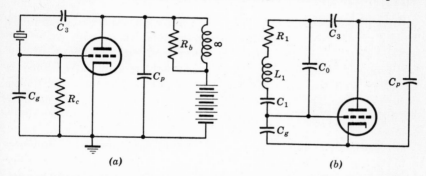

(a)   (b)

FIG. 9.8.   The Pierce circuit: (a) schematic and (b) idealization for analysis.

under the control of crystals having widely different frequencies, and that no output is produced if the crystal is absent or defective.   These features are particularly important in military apparatus, where operating frequencies must be changed quickly and with a minimum of adjustments.

In a typical Pierce oscillator C_3 has a negligible reactance and is provided to isolate the crystal from the plate voltage; the grid leak resistance R_c is of the order of 100,000 ohms; and C_g and C_p are of the order of 50 $\mu\mu$f each.   The use of a low-resistance coil in parallel with the load resistor is appropriate when a considerable power output is required.   When a very small amplitude of oscillation is tolerable or desirable the choke may be omitted; and best frequency stability is obtained by retaining the coil and removing the load resistor.

Analysis is facilitated by noting that the circuit reduces to the familiar Colpitts configuration if the crystal and C_3 are replaced by a coil; therefore, the equations developed in Chapter 8 are applicable. Oscillation occurs at the frequency at which the crystal is antiresonant with C_g and C_p in series; and the tank or resonator impedance is simply the Performance Index (PI) of the crystal in conjunction with this capacitance.

If C_g and C_p are equally stable, the frequency stability is greatest when $C_g = C_p$. However, C_g is usually the less stable, and should therefore be padded to several times C_p. This increase of the excitation ratio leads to an increased amplitude and power output which may cause excessive heating of the crystal. The reader who desires additional information about this circuit is referred to the work of Boella,[35] Fair,[90] Koga,[176] Terry,[308] Wheeler,[340] and Wright.[350]

9.8 Frequency stability of the Pierce circuit

The frequency stability of the Pierce circuit with respect to increments of plate or grid capacitance may be determined by an extension of the analysis developed in Chapter 8 in connection with the Clapp circuit. The analysis assumes that the direct plate-to-grid capacitance is negligible, that the plate resistance is very high, that no useful power output is taken, and that losses in the grid circuit are negligible; these assumptions are well approximated by a pentode in an appropriate circuit.

The previous chapter shows that C_3 does not affect the frequency stability (of the Clapp circuit), provided the inductance is suitably chosen; however, C_3 does provide a very useful means of impedance transformation. In the present case, when a quartz crystal is substituted for a physical coil, C_3 serves a similar function, but its importance is increased by the fact that a given crystal must face its specified load capacitance C_x in order to operate at its rated frequency. Because the equivalent inductance of the crystal is thus fixed, C_3 provides the only convenient means of adjusting the impedance level for best operation.

We see that Figs. 8.11 and 9.8b are equivalent provided the impedance of the crystal at its operating frequency is represented by R_e in series with $X_e = \omega L_e$. Following the method formerly used, let us investigate the frequency deviation produced by an arbitrary increment in C_g (or C_p), finally introducing the transconductance requirements to determine the optimum relationship between C_g, C_p, and C_3.

The frequency increment is calculated on the basis of the reactive elements only. The work is facilitated by obtaining an expression for the effective capacitance facing the crystal terminals and combining this with an appropriate expression for the frequency change produced by an increment in this load capacitance. From Fig. 9.8b we see that the load capacitance faced by the crystal is given by

$$1/C_x = 1/C_g + 1/C_p + 1/C_3. \tag{9.28}$$

The increment in C_x produced by an increment in C_g may be written

$$1/(C_x + \delta C_x) = 1/(C_g + \delta C_g) + 1/C_p + 1/C_3. \tag{9.29}$$

Taking advantage of the fact that the increments are small, we have by division

$$\delta C_x/C_x \doteq (\delta C_g/C_g) \cdot (C_x/C_g). \tag{9.30}$$

Repeating the substitutions of eq. 8.33,

$$C_g = hC_p = kC_3, \tag{9.31}$$

we have the useful relation

$$C_g = C_x(1 + h + k). \tag{9.32}$$

Therefore, we have

$$\delta C_x = \delta C_g/(1 + h + k)^2. \tag{9.33}$$

Again referring to Fig. 9.8, we see that oscillation will occur at the frequency represented by

$$\omega^2 L_1 = 1/C_1 + 1/(C_0 + C_x). \tag{9.34}$$

The frequency increment produced by a small change in C_x becomes

$$\omega^2(1 + \delta\omega/\omega)^2 L_1 \doteq \frac{1}{C_1} + \frac{1}{C_0 + C_x + \delta C_x} = \frac{C_1 + C_0 + C_x + \delta C_x}{C_1(C_0 + C_x + \delta C_x)}. \tag{9.35}$$

Using eq. 9.34 and neglecting second-order terms because the increment is small, we have

$$\frac{\delta\omega}{\omega} = \frac{-C_1\delta C_x}{2(C_0 + C_x)(C_1 + C_0 + C_x)}. \tag{9.36}$$

Introducing eq. 9.33 to eliminate δC_x, we obtain the important result

$$\frac{\delta\omega}{\omega} = \frac{-C_1\delta C_g}{2(1 + h + k)^2(C_0 + C_x)(C_1 + C_0 + C_x)}. \tag{9.37}$$

We see that a small value of C_1 and large values of h, k, and C_x are desirable in the interest of frequency stability. The extent to which these variables may be controlled is now determined by introducing the conductance terms.

To obtain a relationship between the effective series resistance R_e and the internal resistance R_1 of the crystal, we equate the admittances.

$$\frac{1}{R_e + jX_e} = j\omega C_0 + \frac{1}{R_1 + j\omega L_1 + 1/j\omega C_1}. \tag{9.38}$$

Introducing the inherent selectivity and capacitance ratio of the crystal

$$Q = \omega L_1/R_1 \quad \text{and} \quad r = C_0/C_1, \tag{9.39}$$

we have

$$\frac{R_e - jX_e}{R_e{}^2 + X_e{}^2} = j\omega r C_1 + \frac{\omega C_1/Q + j\omega C_1(1 - \omega^2 L_1 C_1)}{(1 - \omega^2 L_1 C_1)^2 + 1/Q^2}. \tag{9.40}$$

Taking the real parts, and neglecting $R_e{}^2$ and $1/Q^2$ in comparison to the associated terms, we have

$$\frac{R_e}{X_e{}^2} = \frac{\omega C_1}{Q(1 - \omega^2 L_1 C_1)^2}. \tag{9.41}$$

With use of eq. 9.33 to eliminate the equivalent reactance, we have

$$R_e = \frac{(C_x + rC_1)^2}{Q\omega C_1 C_x{}^2}. \tag{9.42}$$

Combination of eqs. 8.39, 8.40, and 8.41 with eq. 9.42 yields as the conditions for oscillation

$$g_m{}' = \frac{R_e \omega^2 C_g{}^2}{h} = R_e \omega^2 C_x{}^2 \frac{(1 + h + k)^2}{h}. \tag{9.43}$$

Elimination of R_e between eqs. 9.42 and 9.43 yields with eq. 9.36 the frequency stability

$$\frac{\delta\omega}{\omega} = -\frac{\omega\delta C_g}{2Qhg_m{}'} \cdot \frac{(C_0 + C_x)}{(C_1 + C_0 + C_x)} \tag{9.44}$$

In a typical crystal, C_1 is very small compared to $C_0 + C_x$; hence the last term may be taken as unity, and the expression is identical with eq. 8.44 developed for the Clapp and Colpitts circuits. Therefore, we are led to suspect that the relationship is quite basic and applies to a variety of situations.

It is interesting to note that the capacitance ratios r, h, and k all disappear in the final result, which is therefore applicable to the conventional Pierce circuit in which C_3 has negligible reactance.

9.9 Power output and crystal dissipation in the Pierce oscillator

A practical oscillator is often required to deliver an appreciable power output; however, the frequency stability is degraded if the load substantially affects the conditions of oscillation or if the crystal is driven too hard. It is therefore appropriate to investigate the equations which govern these relationships.

The effective plate-to-grid conductance provided by the crystal, which may be obtained from eqs. 8.31 and 9.43, is

$$G_m = R_e\omega^2 C_x{}^2 \cdot \frac{(1 + h + k)^2}{(1 + h)^2}. \tag{9.45}$$

Therefore, we may represent the power loss in the crystal by

$$P_c = V_g{}^2(1 + h)^2 G_m = V_g{}^2 R_e\omega^2 C_x{}^2(1 + h + k)^2, \tag{9.46}$$

where V_g is the rms value of the alternating grid voltage.

A useful power output is obtained by adding an effective plate-to-ground conductance G_p and increasing the effective transconductance in conformity with eq. 8.31 to maintain oscillation. The useful power output is evidently

$$P_0 = h^2 V_g{}^2 G_p. \tag{9.47}$$

The important ratio of power output to crystal power is thus given by

$$\frac{P_0}{P_c} = \frac{h^2 G_p}{R_e\omega^2 C_x{}^2(1 + h + k)^2}. \tag{9.48}$$

It is increased by increase of the excitation ratio h and by decrease of the capacitance ratio k, the load capacitance C_x, the crystal resistance R_e, and the frequency. However, the product $\omega^2 R_e$ is nearly independent of frequency in typical crystals; and C_x is seldom under the control of the circuit designer. Because the value of G_p which may be used is seriously limited by available transconductance, the power ratio is limited in practical circuits to values in the neighborhood of ten.

Additional insight into the operation of the Pierce oscillator is obtained by introducing the power gain and Q degradation factors. The tube driving power, neglected in the preceding discussion, is given by

$$P_d = V_g{}^2 G_g, \tag{9.49}$$

and the power gain is as before

$$G = 1 + P_0/P_d + P_c/P_d. \tag{9.50}$$

That the effective Q of the crystal is degraded by plate and grid conductances is easily seen by rendering the tube inactive; the extent of this degradation is

$$D = 1 + P_0/P_c + P_d/P_c. \tag{9.51}$$

Therefore, even if P_d is small, a considerable ratio of output to crystal power is obtainable only if the effective Q of the crystal is greatly degraded.

9.10 Illustrative design of Pierce oscillator

Let us design a crystal oscillator employing the 6SJ7 pentode (nominal $g_m = 1600$) and a CR-18/U (military) crystal unit at 3.0 Mc. The crystal chosen has the small temperature coefficient characteristic of the AT cut, and is designed to operate into a load capacitance C_x of 32 $\mu\mu$f. It has a maximum effective series resistance R_e of 175 ohms. Assuming that C_3 has negligible reactance, and that an excitation ratio $h = 3$ is to be used, we may determine from eq. 9.43 the operating transconductance which is 339 micromhos. (This value is appropriate to the chosen tube; however, had R_e been smaller or the nominal transconductance larger, it would have been desirable to assign a finite value to C_3.) Consistent with eq. 9.32, we have $C_g = 128$ $\mu\mu$f and $C_p = 42.7$ $\mu\mu$f. The design is completed by providing a high-impedance plate choke coil and suitable grid leak and condenser. Inspection of eq. 8.31 shows that a plate conductance of one micromho and a grid conductance of 9 micromhos will each add 3 micromhos to the transconductance required for oscillation. These values exist if the plate choke has an inductance of 2.5 mh with a Q of about 20 and if the grid leak has a resistance of 330,000 ohms. A grid condenser of about 100 $\mu\mu$f capacitance is suitable.

In the event that an appreciable power output is required, we must add a useful load G_p. The choice of 100 micromhos for the load increases the transconductance requirements by 300 micromhos to a total of 639. Assuming that the amplitude is 5 rms grid volts, the crystal power is 25.4 mw, and the power output is 22.5 mw. Only by using a higher transconductance tube or a lower resistance crystal may we obtain a larger ratio of output to crystal power.

9.11 The Miller circuit

The circuit shown in Fig. 9.9 is commonly designated the Miller crystal oscillator. It has the advantages that one terminal of the crystal is directly grounded, that the crystal is isolated from the plate voltage, and that very few parts are required. In fact, the circuit will ordinarily operate on the basis of grid-plate capacitance even if no physical condenser C is supplied.

As in the Pierce circuit, the crystal operates at a frequency to which its reactance is positive. Thus the circuit corresponds to the form of the familiar Hartley oscillator in which no mutual inductance is

employed. Like the Pierce circuit, it has the desirable feature that
no output is produced in the absence of a suitable crystal.   However,
it is unlike the Pierce in that the plate inductance must be readjusted
if a crystal of substantially different frequency is substituted.   This is
a fairly serious practical drawback, because the frequency as well as
the frequency stability and general operating condition of the tube
are affected by the adjustment of the plate inductance.   In practice,
the plate inductance is usually replaced by an inductance in parallel
with a variable capacitance.   The effective inductance is thus considerably larger than the actual value, and is readily adjusted by the
capacitance.   This arrangement possesses the additional advantage
that the capacitor offers a low-impedance path to harmonic currents,
thus considerably improving the wave form produced.   Moreover, it

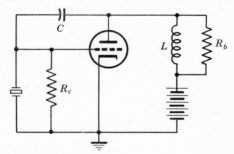

FIG. 9.9.   The Miller circuit

makes it possible to operate crystals on a mechanical overtone.   Crystals tend to oscillate at their fundamental frequency when placed in
the Pierce circuit because the fundamental mode usually produces a
higher performance index than do the overtone modes.

The conditions for oscillation are the same as those already developed in Chapter 8 for the Colpitts circuit.   Consistent with the notation of that chapter, let G_g and G_p account for losses in the grid and
plate circuits, respectively, and let the equivalent inductance of the
crystal be L_e, conforming with the expression

$$\omega^2 = 1/C_x L_e. \tag{9.52}$$

Provided circuit losses are not excessive, oscillation occurs at the series
resonant frequency of L, C and L_e, represented by

$$\omega^2 = 1/C(L + L_e). \tag{9.53}$$

The excitation ratio is, as usual,

$$h = V_p/V_g = L/L_e. \tag{9.54}$$

These equations may be combined to obtain the useful relationship

$$C = C_x/(1 + h). \tag{9.55}$$

Because there is no direct plate to grid conductance, eq. 8.31 reduces to

$$g_m' = hG_p + G_g/h. \tag{9.56}$$

It is seen that the required transconductance may be made very small by increasing h, provided G_p is very small; and for fixed values of G_p and G_g the required transconductance reaches a minimum if h is such that the last two terms of eq. 9.56 are equal.

The power relationships in the Miller oscillator are considerably more favorable than in the Pierce because the crystal is subjected to only the alternating grid voltage. Assuming the coil losses are negligible and the dynamic plate resistance is high, we may write for the output power

$$P_0 = V_p{}^2 G_p. \tag{9.57}$$

The power lost in the crystal, neglecting grid circuit losses, is

$$P_c = V_g{}^2 G_g. \tag{9.58}$$

Taking the ratio of these terms, with use of eq. 9.54, yields

$$P_0/P_c = h^2 G_p/G_g. \tag{9.59}$$

Under favorable conditions the power ratio may approach 100. This is desirable if a considerable power output is required.[68]

If the grid losses are not negligible they may be taken into account by representing the total grid conductance as the sum of the crystal and tube conductance

$$G_g = G_c + G_d. \tag{9.60}$$

The power loss in the crystal is now

$$P_c = V_g{}^2 G_c. \tag{9.61}$$

The effective Q of the crystal is degraded by the factor

$$D \doteq 1 + G_d/G_c, \tag{9.62}$$

where the effect of the plate circuit losses is neglected, as it usually may be. With these substitutions it is easy to show that the ratio of output to crystal power takes the familiar form

$$P_0/P_c \doteq GD - G - D. \tag{9.63}$$

9.12 Frequency stability of the Miller circuit

The frequency stability of the Miller circuit with respect to capacitance variations may be investigated by methods similar to those used for the Pierce circuit. However, the analysis is more complicated because the grid-cathode, grid-plate, and plate-cathode capacitances affect the frequency in quite different ways.

The grid-cathode capacitance is treated most simply because it is directly in parallel with the crystal, forming a part of the load capacitance; therefore, an increment δC_g is an increment δC_x in the load capacitance, and eq. 9.36 is directly applicable.

To determine the effect of variations in the grid-plate capacitance we combine eqs. 9.52 and 9.53, obtaining

$$C_{x} = C/(1 - \omega^2 LC). \tag{9.64}$$

Differentiation yields

$$\delta C_x = \frac{(1 - \omega^2 LC)\delta C + \omega^2 LC \delta C}{(1 - \omega^2 LC)^2} = \frac{C_x{}^2}{C^2}\,\delta C, \tag{9.65}$$

where differentials in ω are neglected in comparison to the others. Combination with eq. 9.36 and 9.55 yields

$$\frac{\delta\omega}{\omega} = \frac{-C_1(1 + h)^2 \delta C}{2(C_0 + C_x)^2}, \tag{9.66}$$

where C_1 is neglected in comparison to C_0. Unfortunately, the use of a large excitation ratio, although conducive to a large output, is unfavorable to frequency stability.

The frequency deviation associated with a change in L is obtained by differentiating eq. 9.64 with respect to that variable

$$\delta C_x = \frac{\omega^2 C^2 \delta L}{(1 - \omega^2 LC)^2}. \tag{9.67}$$

Combined with eq. 9.36 and 9.64 this gives

$$\frac{\delta\omega}{\omega} = \frac{-C_1 C_x{}^2 \omega^2 \delta L}{2(C_0 + C_x)^2} = \frac{-h C_x C_1 \delta L}{2L(C_0 + C_x)^2}. \tag{9.68}$$

A detailed analysis of the effect of an incremental plate-to-ground capacitance is somewhat tedious. However, by analogy with the Colpitts circuit, we anticipate that the frequency deviation will be h^2 times larger than that produced by an equal capacitance increment in the grid circuit.

9.13 Impedance-inverting circuits

It is well known that any loss-free network which produces a phase shift of 90° has the property of impedance inversion. That is, the input impedance increases when the terminating impedance decreases and vice versa. This property is readily demonstrated in terms of the artificial line of Fig. 9.10a. At an appropriate frequency ω_0, the characteristic impedance of the line may be represented by

$$Z_0 = \omega_0 L = 1/\omega_0 C. \tag{9.69}$$

At this frequency the input impedance is

$$Z_{in} = Z_0{}^2/Z. \tag{9.70}$$

The correctness of this formula is easily verified, and is evident for $Z = 0$ and $Z = \infty$.

The property of impedance inversion may be applied to crystal oscillators by identifying the terminal impedance with a quartz

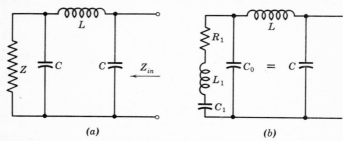

(a)   (b)

FIG. 9.10. Impedance-inverting networks: (a) quarter-wave artificial line and (b) line with crystal.

crystal unit as shown in Fig. 9.10b. It is assumed that the crystal holder capacitance constitutes one of the line capacitances, and that the line inductance is adjusted to produce 90° phase shift at the resonant frequency of the crystal. At this particular frequency the reactances of the series arm cancel, and the input impedance is given by 9.70, where $Z = R_1$. At a slightly higher frequency the series arm of the crystal is inductive, and its impedance is considerably increased. Therefore, the input impedance is lowered and rendered capacitive. Because of the large value of Q, the entire resonance of the series arm occurs in so small a frequency interval that the parameters of the artificial line may be considered constant. *Thus, the artificial line inverts a series resonance into an effective antiresonance.* Moreover, if Z_0 is substantially larger than R_1, as it should be, the impedance level is considerably increased.

It is usually desirable to add a resistor equal to Z_0 across the crystal terminals. This has no serious effect upon the crystal response, and avoids a large antiresonant impedance which would otherwise occur at $\omega = \sqrt{2}\,\omega_0$ due to the elements of the line itself. Finally, the other line capacitor C may be identified with the input capacitance of the vacuum tube. If, as often happens, the tube and crystal capacitances are nearly equal, the visible system reduces to a single inductor, usually associated with a damping resistor.

The question immediately arises as to what should be done when the tube and crystal capacitances are unequal. In turn, we inquire whether the line viewpoint is fundamental or whether other element values are useful. These questions may be answered, but the analysis, is too long to justify inclusion. The main result is that the line viewpoint, although not essential, is very convenient, and that any considerable deviation from the parameters so determined is undesirable. Where some deviation is necessary we should adjust L to resonate with C at or very near ω_0; variations in C_0 from the nominal value are unimportant because C_0 is shunted by the relatively low impedance R_1.

9.14 Impedance-inverting oscillators

The impedance-inverting networks described in the previous section permit a crystal to develop an effective antiresonant impedance at the frequency of resonance of the series arm. They are, therefore, usable in any circuit, such as the Pierce or the Miller, which requires anti-resonant conditions for operation. They are, however, also useful in several other circuits. In the C.I. meter circuit, for example, the impedance transformations between the tube and the crystal are made by means of impedance-inverting quarter-wave sections. These arrangements are not restricted to the fundamental mode of the crystal and, in fact, work very well with third and fifth overtone crystals.

A simple circuit which uses an impedance-inverting network on a two-terminal basis is shown in Fig. 9.11. The artificial line, consisting of the inductance L and the two equal capacitances C, has a characteristic impedance equal to the terminating resistor R. This impedance level is made somewhat lower than the minimum value of negative resistance produced by the tube so that parasitic oscillations will not be produced by the line. The series resonant resistance R_1 of the crystal is substantially smaller than R so that the tube will face a relatively high impedance at the series resonant frequency, and oscillation will result. As previously noted, the tube and crystal may provide part or all of the design capacitances C. Moreover, the behavior is not greatly affected if the crystal-shunting capacitance differs somewhat from C.

The present circuit is simple to adjust and is capable of excellent frequency stability, but is characterized by relatively low values of efficiency and power output. It appears probable that a substantial increase in power output or a useful power output at harmonic frequencies could be obtained by adding an electron-coupled load in the plate circuit and by increasing the plate voltage.

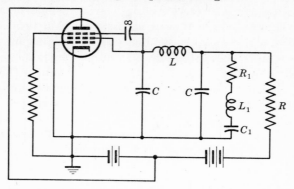

Fig. 9.11.   Impedance-inverting transitron oscillator.

9.15 Electron coupling

Electron coupling is sometimes used in crystal oscillators for the same reasons that it is used in other circuits, that is, to render the frequency independent of the load and to give frequency multiplication.   In addition, it facilitates the generation of a large power output without overheating the crystal.   Any crystal oscillator which operates satisfactorily with a triode may be converted to electron coupling by arranging the elements so that the plate is by-passed to ground.   A pentode with plate load and by-passed screen is then substituted. Alternatively, the cathode and suppressor may be grounded and the screen used as oscillator plate.

The electron-coupled form of Miller oscillator, shown in Fig. 9.12, and commonly designated the tri-tet, is capable of delivering a large power output with good frequency stability.   In a well-shielded pentode having the suppressor suitably by-passed (not connected to the cathode) the plate circuit is isolated from the oscillator circuit to a very high degree; and the load circuit may be tuned to the fundamental or a harmonic frequency without affecting the operation.   In less well-shielded tubes the effect of plate tuning may be great enough to damage the crystal, so that it is customary to restrict the output to harmonics of the crystal frequency.   The capacitance between the control and screen grids is often appropriate to oscillation, but may need to be increased in some cases.   The parameters should be chosen so that the alternating voltage on the grid is considerably in excess of twice that on the cathode, and is sufficient to produce class C operation

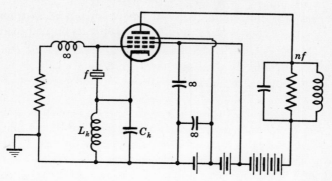

FIG. 9.12.   The tri-tet oscillator.   The cathode circuit is tuned to a frequency above that of the crystal so as to be inductive.

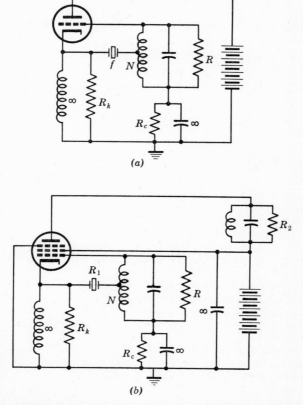

FIG. 9.13.   Grounded-plate oscillators: (a) with triode and (b) with pentode.

without exceeding the crystal rating. The electron-coupled Pierce circuit yields comparable results and is somewhat simpler to adjust.

At higher frequencies a variant of the grounded-grid series-mode oscillator is convenient; a suitable arrangement appears in Fig. 9.13. A large fraction of the alternating cathode current passes through R_k, the remainder being transmitted through the crystal to drive the grid. Good operation results if the grid circuit impedance is a few thousand ohms, if the impedance presented to the crystal by the transformer is approximately equal to R_1, and if R_k is adjusted for class C operation. The plate circuit is thoroughly isolated from the crystal and may be adjusted for a relatively large power output at either fundamental or a harmonic frequency. The circuit may be analyzed by methods similar to those used in Section 9.4.

It is emphasized that electron coupling does not violate the GD-G-D relationship established in connection with the Miller and transformer-coupled oscillators. In no case is the ratio of output to crystal power greater than that obtainable from the same tube in an appropriate transformer-coupled oscillator. However, electron coupling *does* minimize frequency changes due to susceptances in the load circuit and *does* facilitate harmonic operation. Moreover, it simplifies the problem of obtaining the necessary power and impedance relationship in practical oscillators.

PROBLEMS

9.1. Derive eqs. 9.7, 9.8, and 9.9.

9.2. Derive eq. 9.12 and defend the assumptions made in its derivation.

9.3. Verify eq. 9.16.

9.4. Calculate the performance of a transformer-coupled pentode crystal oscillator differing from the numerical example in section 9.2 only in that $k = 1$ and $m = n = 3$.

9-5. The C.I. meter circuit is to operate at 50 Mc with a pentode having an effective transconductance of 2000 micromhos and a crystal having a resistance of 70 ohms and a Q of 10,000. Using eq. 9.69, calculate element values and frequency stability with respect to an increment of grid-circuit capacitance.

9.6. Derive eq. 9.23.

9.7. A cathode-coupled oscillator is to employ a 100-ohm crystal with two 6J4 triodes. In Fig. 9.5b the cathode choke is replaced by a 100-ohm resistor. Calculate a tank impedance for T_2 which will cause T_2 to operate in class A with a transconductance of 10,000 micromhos and T_1 in class B (5000 μmhos). Discuss the way in which limiting occurs and the resulting operation.

9.8. Derive eq. 9.27, using the low-pass (inductance-free) analogue.

9.9. Calculate the frequency change produced by a one-micromicrofarad increment of grid capacitance in the oscillator of Section 9.10.

9.10. A particular pentode as a transitron produces a minimum negative resistance of 4000 ohms. Design an impedance-inverting oscillator, using this tube with a 5-Mc crystal having a series resistance of 100 ohms.

10

INTERMITTENT BEHAVIOR

It is well known that harmonic oscillators of all sorts may generate intermittent rather than continuous oscillations. This behavior is desired in the superregenerative receiver, and in a few other special applications, but is ordinarily a nuisance to be avoided. Intermittent operation may arise in almost any kind of oscillator, but it is observed most frequently in microwave triode oscillators and in linear oscillators designed for a high degree of amplitude stability. The occurrence of the effect is known to depend upon the relative proportions of the various circuit elements, particularly those controlling the time constant of the limiter. Therefore, we must look to the proportions rather than the configuration of an oscillator for an understanding of the phenomenon.

The general nature of the problem is conveniently discussed in terms of the tuned plate oscillator described in Chapter 8 (Section 1). With suitable element values this arrangement is capable of producing highly stable harmonic oscillations of reasonably sinusoidal form. As shown in Chapter 12, however, the same configuration with different element values can operate as a blocking oscillator and is then capable of producing well-defined pulses of quite nonsinusoidal wave form. Finally, with a still different set of values, this configuration is capable of generating intermittent oscillations having the general characteristics shown in Fig. 10.1. Ordinarily, but not necessarily, the tube is completely cut off for a large fraction of the cycle; only in exceptional cases does the oscillation envelope approximate a sinusoid.

Because the same system is capable of three distinct kinds of behavior or "states," it is clear that the performance must be representable by some sort of triple-point diagram, as indicated in Fig. 10.2. Our knowledge of this matter is very meager, but the diagram is useful in a qualitative way. On the basis of the principal roots of the system, we have already identified in Chapter 2 the boundary designated (1) between harmonic and relaxation oscillations. The following paragraphs will define the boundary designated (2) between harmonic and intermittent oscillations. Little is now known of the boundary between relaxation and intermittent behavior or, in fact, of the region near the center of the diagram; and it is for this reason that only a portion of the first and second boundaries is drawn heavy.

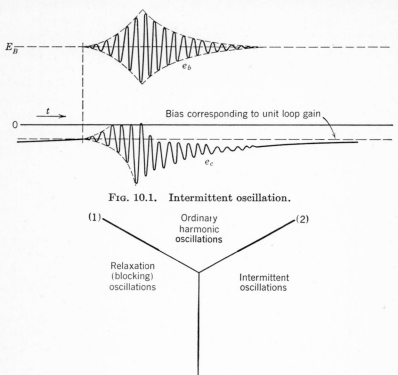

FIG. 10.1.   Intermittent oscillation.

FIG. 10.2.   Diagram relating behavior of a tuned plate oscillator to the element values.

Fortunately, practical circuits ordinarily operate at regions remote from these boundaries.

10.1 Direct approach to intermittent operation

In simple oscillators it is possible to obtain a useful and essentially correct picture of intermittent behavior in terms of the exponential decay of a signal.   Suppose that the tuned plate oscillator of Fig. 10.3 is operating in a class C manner, and that the assumed operating condition is to be tested for stability.   In principle, we should assume that the amplitude of oscillation is suddenly decreased by an incremental amount and determine whether this increment increases or decreases with time. The assumed operating condition is stable only if the deviation decreases.*

In practice, it is sufficient, and far more convenient, to assume that one pulse of plate current is artificially removed from the system. Both the alternating grid voltage and the grid bias decrease exponentially with time, at rates which depend upon the properties of the tuned circuit and of the grid bias system, respectively. Depending upon the relation between these two rates, the following pulse of plate current may be larger or smaller than normal. Intermittent operation will not occur if the pulse is of normal size or larger, and will

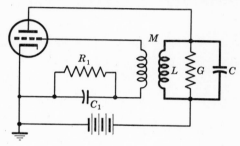

FIG. 10.3.   Tuned plate oscillator.

occur if it is appreciably smaller than normal, although the exact condition for stability is not readily defined.

The idea described in the foregoing paragraph is illustrated in Fig. 10.4. Following an assumed steady state, one pulse of plate current is omitted. The grid bias now decays in a manner described by the equation

$$v_c = V_c e^{-t/R_1 C_1}. \tag{10.1}$$

If, as is usually the case, the fractional decay per cycle is small, we may use the approximation

$$\log (1 + x) \doteq x \tag{10.2}$$

to obtain for the bias change during one cycle

$$\delta v_c = -V_c/f R_1 C_1. \tag{10.3}$$

The alternating grid voltage decays in a similar manner because of losses in the tuned circuit. As shown in Chapter 2, the change in the

* The problem has been studied from a somewhat different viewpoint by van Slooten[327, 328] and Gladwin.[112]

peak alternating grid voltage during one cycle is

$$\delta v_g = -V_g \pi / Q \qquad (10.4)$$

where Q is the operating selectivity of the tuned circuit. It is clear that the following pulse of plate current will be unchanged if these two voltage increments are equal. Therefore, the system will not operate intermittently if

$$V_c / f R_1 C_1 \geq V_g \pi / Q. \qquad (10.5)$$

In a self-biased oscillator the bias is never larger than the peak alternating grid voltage, and is often nearly equal to it. Using this

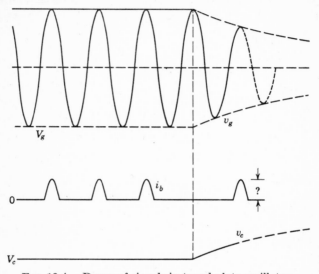

FIG. 10.4.   Decay of signals in tuned plate oscillator.

approximate equality, we obtain a simpler though slightly optimistic relationship for stability

$$Q \geq \pi f R_1 C_1. \qquad (10.6)$$

If, for example $f = 10^6$, $R_1 = 10^5$, and $Q = 100$, instability will occur only if C_1 exceeds $1000/\pi = 318$ $\mu\mu$f. The difficulty with microwave oscillators is apparent from a second example. Using $f = 10^9$, $R_1 = 10^3$, and $Q = 100$, we anticipate instability if C_1 exceeds 31.8 $\mu\mu$f. A larger value of grid leak is very desirable in the interest of obtaining a reasonable bias, and is obtainable only if Q can be raised, because C_1 cannot be appreciably decreased without also reducing its effectiveness in delivering the oscillation signal to the grid of the tube. It should be noted, moreover, that the grid bias is substantially smaller than the grid signal under these conditions so that the value of C_1 required for stability is considerably smaller than that indicated by eq. 10.6.

The direct approach just described applies to all sorts of oscillators in which the loop gain is expressible in terms of the bias applied to some electrode of a vacuum tube. However, the method is inconvenient where several distinct time constants are present; and it is completely inapplicable to thermistor-controlled oscillators.

10.2 Stability in automatic output control systems

The transitron oscillator of Fig. 10.5 serves to illustrate a simple though incomplete criterion for stability. Let us suppose that the

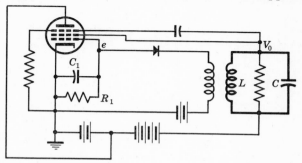

FIG. 10.5.   Transitron oscillator with simple automatic output control.

first grid is disconnected from the bias resistor R_1 and is supplied by a variable direct voltage v. The voltage e across R_1 is then observed as a measure of the amplitude of the desired oscillation. Depending upon whether or not the tube operates about an inflection point of its equivalent negative resistance characteristic, the amplitude represented by e may take the continuous or discontinuous forms shown in Fig. 10.6.

If the characteristic is continuous, as shown by the heavy line, then the automatic output control system will be stable no matter how large the amplitude stability is made, provided the control system responds at a sufficiently slow rate. This is evidently a sufficient but not a necessary condition.   However, it is directly useful in a number of situations, and serves as a guide toward the design of stable systems even when more elaborate criteria are employed.

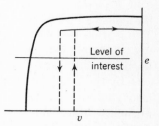

FIG. 10.6. Response of automatic output control oscillator to slow variation of bias.

10.3 Llewellyn's criterion

The ideas developed in the preceding sections may be expressed in a more formal and exact way by means of Llewellyn's criterion, as given in Chapter 5. The procedure depends upon the fact that in every electronically limited oscillator, a direct voltage or current dependent upon the amplitude of oscillation is found at some point in the circuit. In the desired operating condition this direct voltage or current is constant, whereas it becomes pulsating or alternating if intermittent operation occurs. The problem, therefore, reduces to one of determining if these unwanted alternating voltages or currents will spontaneously occur. That is, the problem reduces to the normal one of testing for simple stability of a system, with suitable care to restrict the test to points where the desired oscillation is not observed.

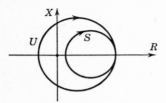   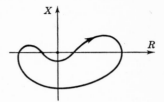

FIG. 10.7.   Stability plot for Llewellyn's criterion.

FIG. 10.8.   Conditional stability in terms of Llewellyn's criterion.

The test may be applied to the tuned plate oscillator of Fig. 10.3 by connecting a zero-resistance alternator directly in series with the grid leak R_1. The impedance seen by this alternator at various frequencies is observed and plotted in polar form as shown in Fig. 10.7. The system is stable if the plot for increasing positive real frequencies does not encircle the origin in the clockwise direction. Stable and unstable cases are shown. At very low frequencies the resistance seen by the generator is nearly equal to R_1 because limiting in the oscillator produces a nearly constant bias voltage. At very high frequencies the resistance is also equal to R_1 because C_1 is an effective short circuit. At intermediate frequencies the voltage developed across C produces amplitude modulation which reacts upon the bias by the action of the tuned circuit. The combined phase shifts produce a component of negative resistance which may exceed R_1.

In practice, Llewellyn's criterion is equivalent to the statement that a pure negative resistance must not be observed in the bias system at any real frequency. The two statements differ only in the case of conditional stability, illustrated in Fig. 10.8 but virtually never observed. Moreover, Llewellyn's criterion is not usually applicable on an experimental basis because it requires the action of the complete system. If intermittent oscillation is possible it will probably occur so as to make the test both futile and impossible. On an analytic basis, however, this criterion is valuable because it permits calculation of the behavior of a proposed system and points the way to modifications which will avoid any indicated instability.

A somewhat more favorable example of the application of Llewellyn's test is offered by the circuit of Fig. 10.5. Again, it is convenient to assume that the test oscillator is connected in series with the bias resistor R_1. And again the impedance seen at very low and at very high frequencies is equal to R_1 because of amplitude controlling feedback and the action of C_1, respectively. At intermediate frequencies the voltage across C_1 lags the applied voltage. The oscillation amplitude in the tuned circuit still further lags this bias voltage so that the rectified current may well be more than 90° out of phase with the test voltage. The resulting plot has the same general shape as that of Fig. 10.8. The following sections show how to calculate the behavior of this system and show also that the system is absolutely stable for all values of the parameters.

10.4 A Time-variable system

The question as to whether or not a particular oscillator will operate intermittently may be approached through a study of a simple system involving a time-variable conductance, as shown in Fig. 10.9. We

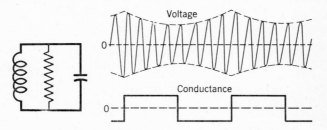

Fig. 10.9. Behavior of time-variable circuit.

assume that the conductance is alternately positive and negative, of equal value and for equal periods. An oscillation, if started by external means, will persist at a constant average amplitude exponentially increasing and decreasing as indicated. The oscillation may be thought of as amplitude modulated, with maximum amplitude at the instant of conductance reversal. Moreover, the degree of modulation increases with the value of the conductance used and the duration of the period of its reversal.

A similar situation exists if the conductance is varied sinusoidally rather than in a square-wave manner about zero. Following the analysis presented by Arguimbau[15] on pages 324 ff. of his book, we assume that the voltage wave may be represented by the equation

$$v = v_0 \ (1 + m \cos qt) \cos \omega t, \tag{10.7}$$

where ω is the natural frequency of the tuned circuit, q is the modulation frequency, and m is the modulation fraction, which must be less than one for sinusoidal modulation, and is here assumed to be very small compared to one. Let us investigate the conductance variation

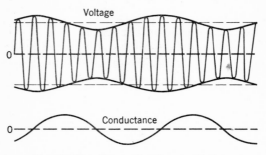

FIG. 10.10.   Sinusoidal time variation.

which would produce such a wave. From Chapter 2 we know that the amplitude of free oscillations of a parallel circuit decay according to the equation

$$da/a = -g \ dt/2C, \tag{10.8}$$

where a represents the instantaneous amplitude and g the instantaneous conductance. From eq. 10.7 we obtain by differentiation

$$da/a = -mq \sin qt \ dt. \tag{10.9}$$

Combining terms yields

$$g = 2mqC \sin qt. \tag{10.10}$$

This conductance variation is plotted together with the assumed voltage wave in Fig. 10.10. It is seen that the modulation envelope leads the conductance variation by 90° in phase, and that for a given modulation index the conductance is directly proportional to the capacitance and the modulating frequency. Expressed in another way, m cannot remain small as q approaches zero no matter how small q is.

10.5 Use of Nyquist's criterion

The ideas just developed are directly applicable to the problem of self-modulation in the transitron oscillator with the modified automatic output control shown in Fig. 10.11.   The key relationship is Nyquist's criterion, described in Chapter 5, which is applied to the bias system. If the system is free from self-modulation, there will be no alternating voltage on the inner grid of the tube or in the associated elements. Therefore, we may open the gain control loop at the grid, or at any other point which is free from alternating current in the desired operating condition, and apply Nyquist's test.   The system will be unstable in the sense that alternating voltages corresponding to self-modulation

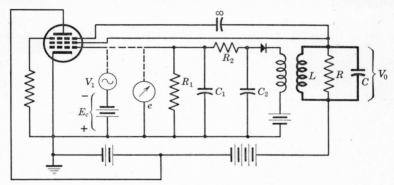

Fig. 10.11.   Modified automatic output control oscillator.

will be generated in the final system if and only if the Nyquist plot encircles the critical point, $(1, 0)$.

The application of the test is indicated by the dotted lines.   The auxiliary bias source E_c, has such a value that the negative conductance of the tube exactly balances the positive conductance of the system. It is assumed that the oscillation in the plate circuit has the desired amplitude, in which case the direct voltage developed across the bias resistor R_1 is equal to E_c.   Subject to these conditions a very small alternating test voltage V_1, of variable frequency is injected in series with E_c.   As shown in the previous pages, the oscillation at the desired frequency ω will be amplitude modulated at the test frequency q. Rectification in the bias diode reproduces the modulation signal, which is modified in amplitude and phase by the action of the RC filter and returned to the test detector.

If we imagine conducting this test, we find that at low frequencies the oscillation envelope is very large compared to V_1 and leads it by $90°$.   The rectifier polarity is such that the alternating voltage at e

is positve when the envelope is a maximum. Therefore, we may say that, as the test frequency approaches zero, the loop gain approaches infinity at a phase angle of 90° lead. As the test frequency is increased, the modulation index in the tuned circuit steadily decreases. Moreover, the filter in the bias system produces attenuation and phase shift, which in the present case cannot exceed 180°. The corresponding Nyquist plot of e/V_1 is shown in Fig. 10.12a. Evidently the system is unstable. If, however, the filter section composed of R_2 and C_2 were removed, the Nyquist plot would take the form shown in Fig. 10.12b, and the system would be absolutely stable regardless of element values.

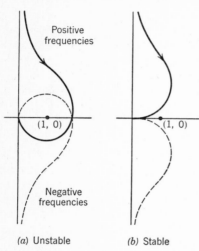

Positive frequencies

Negative frequencies

(1, 0)

(1, 0)

(a) Unstable   (b) Stable

Fig. 10.12. Nyquist plot for bias voltage.

Let us explore the requirement for stability of the complete system of Fig. 10.11. It is assumed that a negative voltage increment V_1 applied to the first grid modifies the effective conductance of the tuned circuit by an increment g. That is,

$$g = k_1V_1. \qquad (10.11)$$

Then, when an alternating test signal is used, the plate voltage wave has the general form given by eq. 10.7. Because the fractional modulation is restricted to small values, the control system acts as a linear rectifier, so that the signal delivered to the resistance-capacitance filter is directly proportional to the output voltage and to the fractional modulation. The effect of the filter is most readily treated by assuming that the two sections have equal time constants, are effectively in tandem, and do not have appreciable interaction. Converting from trigonometric to exponential form, we may write

$$e = k_2mV_0/(1 + jqC_1R_1)^2 \qquad (10.12)$$

where k_2 is a factor which depends upon the transformer ratio and rectifier action. Eliminating g between eqs. 10.10 and 10.11 with proper consideration of the phase angle yields

$$k_1V_1 = -j2mqC. \qquad (10.13)$$

Finally, eliminating m yields as an expression for the complete Nyquist diagram the equality

$$e/V_1 = jk_1k_2V_0/2qC(1 + jqC_1R_1)^2. \qquad (10.14)$$

The Nyquist diagram will intersect the positive real axis at a frequency such that

$$1 = qC_1R_1 \qquad (10.15)$$

and will pass through the point $(1, 0)$ provided that

$$k_1k_2V_0 = 4qC = 4C/C_1R_1. \qquad (10.16)$$

Values of the $k_1k_2V_0$ product larger than given by eq. 10.16 produce instability.

A large $k_1k_2V_0$ product, which is desirable in the interest of amplitude stability, may be obtained only by increasing C or by decreasing R_1 or C_1. Increase of C with a given tube is evidently possible only by increasing the Q of the tank circuit. Reduction in C_1 and R_1 increases the speed of the control system[221] and is desirable, but only to the extent that it does not degrade the filtering action of these elements, which must be preserved in order to maintain frequency stability.

10.6 Example of stability calculation

To illustrate the method, let us calculate the stability condition for a transitron oscillator using the 6SJ7 triode at a frequency of 1.59 Mc ($\omega = 10^7$). The tube readily produces a negative conductance of 200 micromhos. Therefore, we assume that the coil and bias system produce a positive conductance of 200 micromhos. If the effective Q of the passive tank is 100, we may find $C = 2000 \ \mu\mu f$ from the relationship

$$\omega C = Qg_0. \qquad (10.17)$$

With typical plate and screen biases the desired operating point will be found for $E_c = -2$ volts, and k_1 will be in the order of 50×10^{-6} mho per volt. The other parameter in a typical circuit is $k_2 = 1$; if we assume the reasonable values $C_1 = 1000 \ \mu\mu f$ and $V_0 = 10$ volts, we have for marginal stability $R_1 = 16,000$ ohms.

A substantially smaller value would be advisable in a practical design in the interest of providing a margin of safety. Moreover, in the interest of lowering the loading applied to the tuned circuit through the diode, it is desirable to make R_1 substantially larger than R_2 and to adjust C_1 accordingly.

10.7 Extension of Nyquist's criterion

The foregoing analysis is satisfactory for the study of two-terminal (negative resistance) oscillators and may be extended to treat all sorts of circuits in which the effective resistance or transconductance may be expressed in terms of a bias voltage.   In fact, it is the only known method for studying the tendency toward self-modulation in two-terminal oscillators.   However, the analysis is somewhat cumbersome in some cases, and is completely inapplicable to thermistor-controlled oscillators.   Moreover, it is completely impractical from the experimental viewpoint because it assumes that the average level of oscillation will remain constant at the desired value throughout the test.

An analysis which is free from these defects and which applies to all types of feedback oscillators is based upon an extension of Nyquist's criterion.[82]   It is assumed that the criterion is applicable, not only to a simple voltage or current, but also to envelope functions.   Subject to this assumption, it may be used to determine whether or not a modulation envelope of some sort will be generated.

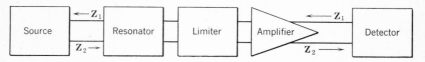

FIG. 10.13.   Test for self-modulation.

The test or analysis is conducted in terms of Fig. 10.13.   The normal oscillating loop is opened and a source and receiver are inserted, with appropriate precaution as to matching impedances.   The source is then adjusted to such an amplitude and frequency that the voltage delivered to the detector is exactly equal in magnitude and phase to that supplied.   This is evidently the desired operating condition, the stability of which is to be tested.   The required test is obtained by superimposing a very small amplitude modulation of variable frequency upon the source voltage, and observing the transmission of the envelope of this modulation.

If, at some frequency, the output envelope is in phase with and larger than that supplied we anticipate that the system will generate self-modulation at or near this frequency.   More exactly, *self-modulation is to be anticipated if the polar plot of envelope transmission encircles the point (1, 0).*

The experimental execution of this test would doubtless be quite difficult and is not recommended.   But, unlike the previously described tests, it is basically possible because the system under test is absolutely stable, and is therefore responsive to measurement.   As with the other tests, however, the principal application is one of analysis as an aid to design.

The use of this extended criterion is nicely illustrated in terms of the lamp bridge oscillator, shown in Chapter 7 as Fig. 7.4. It is assumed that the lamp bridge is symmetrical and operates at a loss in the order of 40 db, and that the input and output transformers are tightly coupled and have equal values of working Q. Here, as in many analyses, it is convenient to open the loop at the plate terminal of the tube. The modulation transmitted from the plate to the lamp bridge will be reduced and shifted in phase by the selectivity of the tuned circuit. This is shown in Fig. 10.14, which is reduced to polar form in Fig. 10.15a. Evidently this effect will be compounded by the selectivity of the identical grid filter.

The behavior of the lamp bridge requires special study. It is clear, however, from the discussion of Chapter 7 that modulation of very

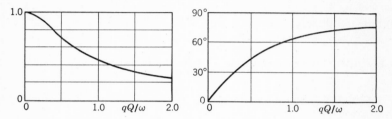

FIG. 10.14.   Envelope transmission of a single tuned circuit.

low frequency will be reversed in phase and greatly magnified, because this is the basic property of a good limiter.   Moreover, for sufficiently high modulating frequencies the thermal inertia of the lamps will be such that the input and output waves are similar, and no change of the modulation envelope will occur.   At intermediate frequencies the situation is more complicated.   The heat supplied is partly stored in the thermal capacity of the filament, partly dissipated by conduction and radiation.   Because the fractional modulation is small, however, we may neglect nonlinear effects and consider only linear terms in heat loss and storage.   On this basis, we know that the lamps reach their maximum resistance somewhat later than the current envelope reaches its maximum, so that the envelope phase is shifted forward.   From these considerations we would anticipate the behavior shown in Fig. 10.15b, and confirmed by experimental measurements.   The frequency scale is very approximate, but gives the correct order of magnitude for typical switchboard lamps such as the A1.

The envelope Nyquist diagram is constructed by combining the data of Fig. 10.15b with the square of that of Fig. 10.15a.   However, it is necessary to assign a value to the frequency parameter ω/Q before proceeding, because the shape as well as the frequency scale of the final plot depend upon this ratio. The results of two choices of this parameter are shown in Fig. 10.15c. As in the previous examples, stability is favored by increasing the selectivity of the tuned circuit or the speed of the limiter circuit.

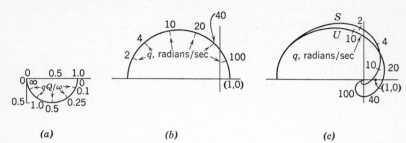

(a)   (b)   (c)

FIG. 10.15.   (a) Transmission of filter; (b) transmission of bridge; and (c) Nyquist diagrams showing stability if $\omega/Q = 5$ and instability if $\omega/Q = 50$.

10.8 Application of the tuned plate oscillator

The tuned plate oscillator has already received extensive treatment in earlier sections. It is therefore chosen as a second example of the application of the extended Nyquist criterion. In terms of Fig. 10.3 it is assumed for the analysis that the plate lead is opened and an

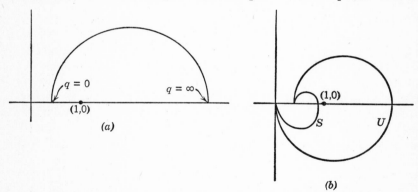

FIG. 10.16.   (a) Envelope transmission of a grid-leak-biased class C amplifier and (b) envelope Nyquist diagram.

equivalent load is substituted. In terms of the current delivered, the plate and grid envelope voltages behave as shown in Fig. 10.15a, where Q is the actual selectivity of the plate circuit including plate and grid conductances. The variation of the bias voltage may be taken account of by considering the tube as a class C amplifier. It is well known that the output of a typical class C amplifier increases only slightly when the steady input is increased a moderate amount. Therefore, at low frequencies the envelope is reduced and not reversed in phase. At very high modulating frequencies the bias is unable to follow the amplitude, and the envelope is amplified because a small fractional increase in grid voltage produces a large fractional increase in plate current. The behavior at intermediate frequencies is shown in the semicircle of Fig. 10.16a.

The complete Nyquist diagram is obtained by combining Figs. 10.15a and 10.16a with suitable attention to the frequency scales. The values of ω/Q used formerly in Fig. 10.15c are used to obtain the two curves, one stable the other unstable, in Fig. 10.16b.

10.9 Behavior of system roots

The preliminary discussion given in Section 10.1 is worthy of further study because it provides a relationship between intermittent behavior and the characteristic roots of the system equation. Subject to the assumption that the grid bias is equal to the peak alternating grid voltage, the criterion developed as eq. 10.6 is expressible as

$$1/R_1C_1 = \alpha_1 \geq \alpha_2 = \pi f/Q. \tag{10.18}$$

That is, the decay rate of the bias system must be as great as that of the tuned circuit. Or, in terms of the complex plane, the single real root associated with the bias system must lie to the left of the conjugate roots associated with the resonator to avoid generation of intermittent oscillations.

The situation just described suggests that the addition of the transconductance of the tube shifts the three roots equally to the right. If the conjugate roots reach the axis first, the system generates continuous waves. If the single root reaches the axis first, a behavior related to relaxation oscillation occurs, and intermittent waves are produced.

An additional feature of this analysis is that it gives at least some information as to the relationship between intermittent and relaxation oscillation. Consistent with the analysis of Section 8.20, which ignored the grid-circuit time constant, the tuned plate circuit will generate relaxation rather than harmonic oscillations if the transconductance exceeds a minimum value given by the equation

$$g_mM/L - G \geq 2\sqrt{C/L}. \tag{10.19}$$

In terms of the natural frequency and effective Q of the tuned circuit t his is equivalent to the expression

$$g_m \geq \frac{1 + 2Q}{Q\omega_0 M} \geq \frac{2}{\omega_0 M} \text{ if } Q \gg 1, \tag{10.20}$$

where the latter form is an approximation valid for large values of Q. A comparison of eq. 10.20 with eq. 10.18, which also assumes a reasonably high Q, shows no contradiction. Therefore, we may conclude that a system which simultaneously satisfies these relationships as equalities corresponds to the triple point of Fig. 10.2; continuous harmonic oscillations will be generated if g_m and the product $R_1 C_1$ are below the critical values; intermittent harmonic oscillations will be generated if g_m is below and $R_1 C_1$ is above the critical value; and relaxation oscillations will be generated if g_m is above the critical value.

In practice, the situation is not so simple as the preceding paragraph implies, and it is doubtful whether a good experimental check of these predictions would be obtained. The principal difficulty is associated with the fact that the various results are based upon linear equations. These equations give good approximations to the behavior of the system for some ranges of the variables, but are subject to serious error in the present case. Notably, the effective Q of the resonator and the effective decay rate of the bias circuit are both greatly affected by grid current.

10.10 Suppression of intermittent oscillation

The preceding sections have been principally concerned with methods for predicting whether or not a given system will oscillate intermittently. That is, the viewpoint has been one of analysis. In the present section we shall consider the more difficult problem of synthesis, that is, designing systems which are free from intermittent behavior.

The procedure to be followed is based upon the extended Nyquist criterion and upon methods developed in connection with feedback amplifiers. It has been shown by Bode[34] on pages 303 ff. of his book that in minimum phase shift systems there is a unique relationship between attenuation and phase shift. This principle is directly applicable to the present problem, because the networks in question are almost always of the minimum phase shift type.

In terms of the extended Nyquist plot, the envelope transmission for the system of interest always has a phase shift of 180° at zero frequency. Ordinarily this is associated with a considerable gain or amplification. The problem, therefore, is to reduce this gain to zero in such a way that the phase shift does not change by as much as 180°. *The idealized attenuation and phase shift of a full section of prototype low-pass filter represent the limiting behavior. If the attenuation is increased (or gain reduced) more slowly with respect to frequency the phase shift will be correspondingly decreased, and a positive margin for stability established.*

The use of this cutoff characteristic is well illustrated by an example in connection with the Meacham oscillator. The analysis of the

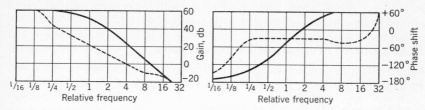

FIG. 10.17.   Envelope characteristics of a Meacham oscillator.

Meacham oscillator is complicated by the fact that the lamp bridge serves as both resonator and limiter, and that the thermal properties of the lamp are neither well known nor readily expressible in terms of an equivalent circuit. Let us suppose, however, that the envelope behavior of a particular Meacham oscillator has the form shown by the

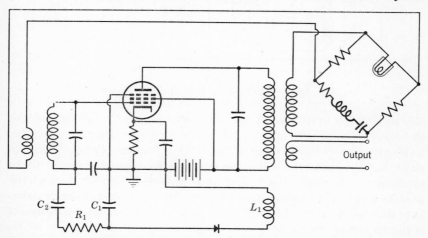

FIG. 10.18.   Meacham oscillator with auxiliary control.

solid line in Fig. 10.17. Intermittent operation is indicated, because the phase shift exceeds 180° at the frequency of zero loop gain. Such behavior would be avoided if the characteristics could be modified to the form shown by the dotted lines.

The indicated change may not be accomplished by modifying the bridge, because this would jeopardize the frequency stability of the system. It may, however, be obtained by the addition of an auxiliary control circuit as shown in Fig. 10.18. The added elements, consisting of the diode, L_1, R_1, C_1, and C_2, come into play only if there is a tendency toward intermittent operation, and do not affect the desired behavior of the frequency stabilizing bridge. Because they are subject to no other restriction, they are readily proportioned so as to obtain the desired modification of the envelope behavior.

10.11 Control of intermittent oscillation

Under certain circumstances it is desirable to produce self-modulation. In a signal generator, for example, the amplitude of oscillation is usu-

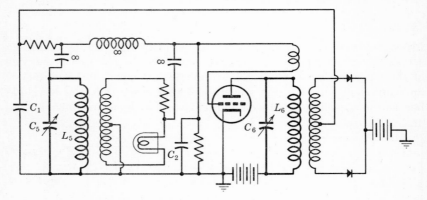

Fig. 10.19. A self-modulating linear oscillator.

ally modulated in a more or less sinusoidal manner. Let us consider the possibility of generating such a wave in a single vacuum tube. Evidently the Nyquist diagram and the envelope Nyquist diagram must both encircle the critical point if a modulated wave is to be produced. Moreover, the system must provide means for limiting the general amplitude of oscillation and the degree of modulation if desirable results are to be obtained. A circuit which provides such means is shown in Fig. 10.19.

The basic circuit is a tuned plate oscillator in which the operating frequency is set by C_6 and L_6, and limiting is accomplished by means of the back-biased balanced rectifier. The elements in the bias system are such that envelope instability will be produced at a modulating frequency corresponding to C_5 and L_5. As self-modulation is produced and increases in amplitude, the tungsten lamp heats and tends to balance the bridge circuit, thus reducing the envelope gain at this frequency.   Accordingly, it is possible to obtain a substantially sinusoidal wave modulated in a sinusoidal manner from a single tube.

10.12 Summary

Several different criteria for the presence or absence of intermittent operation in various types of oscillators have been presented.   None is applicable to every possible type of oscillator, but the extended Nyquist criterion appears to be most convenient and generally flexible. It has the advantages that the degree of amplitude stability is directly represented by the plot, and that conventional feedback ideas and formulas are directly applicable.   Moreover, it applies to all types of oscillators which may be represented as feedback systems, and therefore includes the transitron class.

It should be noted that in all the analyses we assume that the resonator Q is at least moderately high.   This underlying assumption is clear in the direct approach but is somewhat concealed in the others. In the case of the extended Nyquist method it enters by the assumption that the response of a tuned circuit is symmetrical on a linear frequency scale, as shown in Fig. 10.14, so that upper and lower sidebands are treated in a similar manner.   If this is not true, the lower sideband may reach zero frequency before the loop transmission is negligible, and marked distortion of the envelope occurs.

The several criteria are convenient as a method of predicting and calculating intermittent behavior in various oscillators, but are more useful as a guide to designing or modifying systems so as to avoid such behavior.

PROBLEMS

10.1. A Hartley oscillator operates at 3 Mc with an effective Q of 27.   If the grid leak resistance is 20,000 ohms, how large a grid condenser may be used without producing intermittent oscillation?

10.2. Show how to apply the analysis of Section 10.1 to the transformer-coupled pentode crystal oscillator.

10.3. Calculate curves corresponding to Fig. 10.9 for a frequency of 2 Mc, provided the effective Q varies from $+82$ to -82 at a 200 kc rate.

10.4. A particular lamp has a thermal time constant of 0.10 second when operated with 50-ohm resistors in a bridge which is nearly enough balanced so the input is twenty times the output voltage.   Calculate the curve corresponding to Fig. 10.15b.

10.5. Show how to apply the analysis of Section 10.7 to the Colpitts oscillator.

10.6. Show how to apply the analysis of Section 10.7 to the transformer-coupled pentode crystal oscillator.

11

OPERATION AT
HIGH-POWER LEVELS

11.1 Introduction

The foregoing chapters have been mainly concerned with general principles which apply with equal validity to oscillators operating at any frequency or power level. This chapter is devoted to a discussion of the special problems which arise when the power output is relatively large but the frequency is low enough to be consistent with lumped circuit techniques. However, a few problems peculiar to high-frequency applications are discussed in the closing section. A particularly clear discussion of the effects of electron transit time is given by Sloane and James.[287]

There are several reasons for giving the present topic separate treatment, all related to the fact that tubes and components suitable for high-power operation are both bulky and expensive. Accordingly, these parts are ordinarily operated at conditions much closer to the breakdown point than is common in low-power systems. It is therefore necessary to design with considerable care. Efficiency is important, both because of the cost of primary power and because it is difficult to dissipate the heat produced by wasted power. Since excessive heat is the greatest enemy of tubes and other components, this is a matter of primary concern. Moreover, oscillators used in industrial applications are subject to rough handling, operation by untrained people, and exposure to dust and moisture. Accordingly, they will perform in a satisfactory manner only if the construction is rugged, and if adequate precautions are taken to avoid damage by improper operation.

High-power oscillators are used in several applications, notably dielectric and induction heating, [18, 41] diathermy, and in connection with cyclotrons. The economic importance of these applications is already large and is growing rapidly. A discussion of some of these

246

applications, especially at the higher frequencies, is given by Marcum and Kinn.[204]

There is, of course, no sharp line between low and high power. However, the following discussion is generally pertinent to oscillators in which the applied voltage exceeds 1000 volts or the power generated is in excess of 100 watts.

In most heating applications the characteristics of the load change drastically during the process. In such cases it is impossible to maintain an optimum load impedance at all times, and the coupling system is necessarily a rather rough compromise. The operating frequency has a marked tendency to vary during the process, and this variation can be used as an aid in impedance matching if it is permissible from other considerations.

At the present time the industrial application of high-frequency heating may be divided into two district categories. Metals, which are good conductors, are heated by magnetic induction, and the process is referred to as induction heating. Other materials, which act as dielectrics, are heated by placing them in an electric field produced between metal conductors, and the process is referred to as dielectric heating.

11.2 Choice of circuit

The frequency range, type of vacuum tube, and application will ordinarily exclude certain circuit configurations as unsuitable. It is necessary to choose between several remaining circuits of more or less equal merits, but the choice can normally be made rather easily. The simplest possible circuit is desirable in the interest of economy and compactness. These considerations, although applicable in other situations, are especially important here because of the expense and bulk of components suitable for operation at high-power levels. For the safety of operating personnel it is very desirable that there should be no direct voltage between the main tuned circuit and ground. Finally, the tuned circuit should include a capacitance directly between the plate and cathode. Such a condenser produces a low impedance for the high-frequency components present in the short pulses of plate current which must exist if high efficiency is to be obtained. A serious loss in efficiency may result if this precaution is ignored.

Circuits possessing some or all of these desirable properties are illustrated and discussed in the following paragraphs. Meters for observing the direct plate voltage and grid and plate direct currents are indicated, because they are often essential. The shunt-fed Colpitts oscillator of Fig. 11.1 is widely used because it is sufficiently flexible to meet most requirements and because the coil requires no tap. The tuning condensers C_g and C_p must be of low-loss construction and adequate to support the alternating grid and plate voltages, respectively. They are not subjected to direct voltage. The blocking condensers C_c and C_b must also be of low-loss construction and must withstand the direct grid and plate voltages. They should have sufficient capacitance so that they support no appreciable alternating voltages; that is, they should have upwards of ten times the capacitance of the tuning condensers. The by-pass condenser C_d is desirable when the grid choke coil L_c does not have a suitably large impedance.

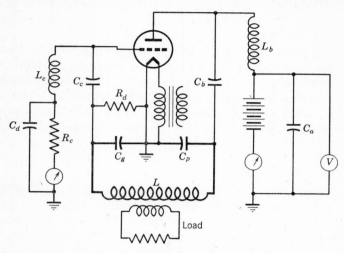

FIG. 11.1.   Shunt-fed Colpitts oscillator.

If L_c is inadequate and C_d is omitted, there may be a considerable loss of a-c power in the grid leak R_c. Because the direct grid voltage is rarely high, it is often cheaper to add the condenser than to improve the coil. Similar comments apply to the plate circuit condenser C_a, but in this case the investment is not trivial because of the high voltage involved; however, a capacitance at this point is ordinarily necessary as part of the power supply filter, and it can often be made to serve this additional purpose. The resistor R_d serves only to preclude the accumulation of undesired static charge on the coil L; it may, therefore, have a relatively high resistance.

Figure 11.2 shows a series-fed form of the tuned plate oscillator. It does not require a plate choke coil or grid tuning condenser. On the other hand, it does require inductive coupling to the main coil, and may sacrifice some efficiency because of the impedance presented by the associated leakage inductance to pulses of grid current. The well-insulated filament transformer does not ordinarily present any particular problem.

Symmetrical (push-pull) arrangements are often used because they permit the use of smaller tubes for a given power output, and because they yield convenient mechanical arrangements. Symmetry favors efficient operation and economy of parts, and somewhat reduces the tendency to produce parasitic oscillations, discussed later in this

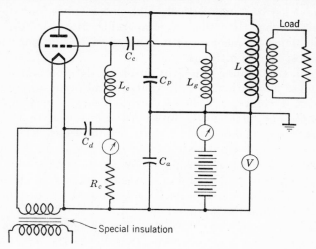

Fig. 11.2. Series-fed tuned plate oscillator.

chapter. Symmetrical versions of nearly all the standard oscillator circuits are readily devised.

11.3 Operating conditions of the tube

The vacuum tube (or tubes) represents one of the major investments in a high-power system. Moreover, it has the shortest operating life, and ordinarily accounts for most of the power loss. It is, therefore, appropriate to examine its operation with some care. The cost of large tubes is such that the interest on this investment is a relatively large item in total operating cost. Unless primary power is unusually expensive, therefore, it is most economical to operate the tube so as to obtain the greatest possible power output consistent with satisfactory life. The adjustment which gives maximum plate circuit efficiency usually reduces the power output by too large an amount to be permissible. The reader is referred to the excellent analysis of Frommer,[105] who assumes that the tube is operated at the maximum power output consistent with its rating.   Methods for making detailed calculations of current waves, power output, and efficiency from experimental characteristics of a given vacuum tube have been presented by Prince,[245] Everitt,[88] Sarbacher,[266, 267] and Chaffee and Kimball,[54] and will not be duplicated here.

High-vacuum triodes having amplification factors in the range of 8 to 50 are used almost to the exclusion of all other types in the generation of large amounts of power.   Advances in the construction of tetrodes have led to some relatively high-power tubes, but the cost is substantially higher than that of comparable triodes.   Tetrodes are used at the higher frequencies, or in other special situations where the additional cost can be justified.

The tube manufacturer ordinarily furnishes data on maximum safe values of plate dissipation, grid dissipation, and plate-supply voltage. The problem, therefore, is to choose the grid bias, alternating plate and grid voltages, and plate load impedance which lead to the largest possible power output consistent with these limitations.   The problem differs from that of designing a class C amplifier only in that the grid driving power, which must be supplied by the output, should be made as small as possible, and that the chosen operating condition must satisfy the conditions of stability.   Otherwise, the actual operating point will differ from the intended one.

The most characteristic feature of high-efficiency operation is that the plate current must flow in short pulses during the intervals when the plate-to-cathode voltage is much smaller than the supply voltage. The required large values of current are obtainable only if the grid is driven far positive during these intervals.   An important problem which arises from such operation is that of secondary emission of electrons from the grid and plate.   Secondary emission from the plate is rarely serious, because the electrons liberated from the plate must return to it unless the grid is more positive.   The characteristics of modern tubes are such that excessive driving power and loss of output are observed before the grid voltage exceeds the minimum plate voltage.

11.4 Grid emission

A far greater hazard is presented by secondary emission from the grid. Some secondary emission is produced in all known materials when they are bombarded by electrons having velocities corresponding to voltages in the approximate range of 10 to 500 volts.   Because the plate voltage is greater than the grid voltage during the interval of interest, many of these electrons leave the grid and are captured by the plate.   Secondary emission in moderation is an asset, because it decreases the grid current and increases the plate current so as to improve plate circuit efficiency and somewhat decrease grid losses. Thus, if it could be adequately controlled, secondary emission from the grid would be a useful asset. The grid loss does not decrease as much as might be anticipated, however, because the electrons which leave the grid have lower velocities, and hence lower energies, than those which strike it.

In practice it is impossible to exert a good control over secondary emission, and it is necessary to suppress the phenomenon as much as possible. The tube manufacturer does this by a careful choice of the material used for the grid and by a special treatment given the

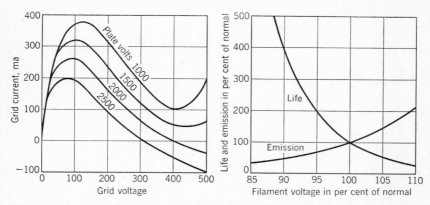

FIG. 11.3. Typical grid characteristics of tube having secondary emission.

FIG. 11.4. Effect of filament voltage upon the emission and life of a pure tungsten filament.

surface of this material; the user must do his part by a suitable choice of operating conditions. The most important factor in controlling this difficulty is the effective plate load conductance. If the conductance is made too large, the alternating plate voltage is reduced and a much larger fraction of the secondary electrons released by the grid is captured by the plate. Secondary emission exerts an appreciable influence, even in conservative operation, by sharpening the pulse of plate current and correspondingly broadening the grid current pulse. Figure 11.3 indicates that this should occur, for the curves show that the grid current is likely to pass through a maximum as the grid voltage increases and the plate voltage decreases in the normal cycle.

If uncontrolled, secondary emission at the grid may lead to the destructive phenomenon of *blocking*. If an excessive load (conductance) is applied to an operating oscillator, the grid current may be negative over a sufficient portion of the cycle to reverse the total average current. When this occurs, the bias produced by the grid leak is reversed and the grid and plate currents rise together to values which will destroy the tube unless a protective device opens the plate circuit in a very short time. It should be noted that the phenomonon is completely unrelated to intermittent operation, discussed in the previous chapter, or to the operation of the blocking oscillator of the following chapter. Improvements in vacuum tubes have made blocking much less of a hazard than it was at earlier times, but the problem is fundamental in nature and will probably never be completely solved.

11.5 Cathode limitations

The maximum instantaeous current which may be drawn is also limited by the properties of the cathode. Depending upon the construction, several different effects may occur. If the cathode is a pure tungsten filament the current will be sharply limited so that the total cathode current wave will have a flat top. The tube is not injured if this occurs, and a slight increase in the filament voltage may provide the required current at a corresponding decrease in operating life. The relationship between life, emission, and voltage is shown in Fig. 11.4. It is rarely necessary or desirable to exceed the rated filament voltage, and it is often desirable to operate at a substantially reduced voltage because of the increased life expectancy.

The thoriated tungsten filament behaves in quite a different way. The operating temperature is such that evaporation of tungsten does not control the useful life of the tube, which ends by depletion of the supply of thorium in the outer layers of the filament. The migration of thorium from the interior to the surface of the filament is a rather critical process, which is upset if the temperature is either too high or too low. Moreover, the emission is rapidly reduced if the current exceeds the normal emission, and is not always capable of restoration. For these reasons it is necessary to operate such tubes within the specified tolerances of the nominal heater voltage and to design the circuit for a peak instantaneous current which is not more than half the normal emission. The oxide-coated cathode is not ordinarily found in high-power tubes. However, it too must be operated as nearly as possible to the rated temperature.

High-power oscillators which must operate where line voltage fluctuations are extreme should be provided with some sort of automatic voltage regulator for the filament circuits. The additional investment is small in terms of the saving effected through increase of tube life and reduction of maintenance problems. Useful practical rules for extending the life of high-power tubes are given by Dailey.[69]

11.6 Parasitic oscillations

High-power, medium-frequency oscillators are particularly subject to trouble from parasitic or spurious oscillations, although the difficulty is by no means unknown in other systems. In its most common form, the undesired oscillation has a frequency much higher than the desired one and is intermittent in character. Once, or possibly twice, during the desired operating cycle the conditions of the vacuum tube are favorable to the parasitic oscillation, which because of its high frequency is able to build up to a considerable amplitude and execute many cycles before the conditions change sufficiently to end it.

At least three distinct mechanisms tend to cause such oscillations. In the first, the tube operates as a normal regenerative triode. The resonant circuit consists of the parasitic inductances and capacitances of the internal and external leads to the tube, whereas the coil and condenser which were intended to be the tank elements serve as a power coupling filter. Oscillations of this nature are sensitive to the geometry of both plate and grid leads, and to the surface resistance of the conductors. Two separate pulses of oscillation are likely to occur during each cycle of the desired wave because conditions to the parasite are most favorable when the grid voltage is slightly negative but the plate current is still rather high.

The second mechanism for producing oscillation is the dynatron action of the positive grid. Under more or less typical operating conditions, the incremental resistance of the grid can be negative, as shown in Fig. 11.3. Oscillations will therefore occur if the grid circuit, with respect to the cathode and plate, presents a sufficiently high antiresonant impedance. This can readily occur, especially if the grid lead is relatively long. The oscillations are sensitive to the geometry of the grid lead, but may be affected by other connections because the effective path returns to both the cathode and the plate.

Finally, electron transit time may result in Barkhausen oscillations if the grid is positive with respect to both cathode and plate. Barkhausen oscillations rarely occur as parasites unless the tube is a tetrode or pentode, in which case the electrons tend to oscillate with respect to the screen grid. Wave forms typical of parasitic oscillation are shown in Fig. 11.5.

Parasitic oscillations should be anticipated in any new system.[107] They tend to produce excessive heating of the tube, reduced power output, and a general instability of voltages and currents. With some experience, we may recognize their presence by noting changes in the average grid current when a dielectric rod or probe is moved about in the region of the grid and plate terminals of the tube. This is possible because the high-frequency parasitic oscillations are much more sensitive to an added dielectric than are the desired oscillations.

The suppression of parasitic oscillations is a difficult problem, and no general solution exists; each case must be treated individually. However, an early diagnosis of the difficulty and an appreciation of the general mechanism are very helpful in effecting a cure. A wavemeter, or other indicator, to show the presence and frequency of the oscillations, together with a rectifier and oscilloscope to determine the envelope wave shape, are very helpful in determining the nature of the parasite and any progress toward its suppression.

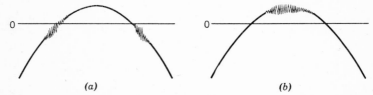

FIG. 11.5.   Parasitic oscillations on grid voltage waves due to: (a) grid-plate feedback and (b) dynatron action of grid.

Under some circumstances the resonator formed by the parasitic reactances of the plate and grid leads is sufficiently favorable so that unwanted oscillations occur to the exclusion of the desired frequency. This situation is not common and is readily recognized by the absence of output at or near the intended frequency. Modification of the circuit to produce the desired output may or may not lead to the periodic parasitic effects previously discussed.

Intermittent operation, as discussed in Chapter 10, is rarely found in high-power systems because the operating frequencies are such that there is little difficulty in making the time constant of the grid bias system sufficiently short. However, the possibility of intermittent operation exists and should be considered whenever a new system is being designed or an abnormal effect is observed.

11.7 Resonator loading

In high-power oscillators, as in others, it is desirable to employ a resonator with the highest practical inherent Q. High efficiency and a large power output are then obtained by lowering the working Q by means of a relatively heavy loading. The situation may be studied by

Fig. 11.6a, in which it is assumed that g represents the irreducible loss of the coil, and that G represents the useful load. Losses in the condenser are nearly always negligible, but may be accounted for in g if necessary. The unloaded selectivity of the resonator is assumed to be given as a basic design parameter, and should be as high as possible. It is represented by the equation

$$Q_0 = \omega_0 C/g = 1/g\omega_0 L. \qquad (11.1)$$

The loaded or working Q takes account of the useful load and is lower than Q_0. It is given by

$$Q = \omega_0 C/(g + G) = 1/\omega_0 L(g + G). \qquad (11.2)$$

The operating frequency is assumed to be prescribed and is expressed by the standard equation

$$\omega_0{}^2 = 1/LC. \qquad (11.3)$$

The useful power output P_0, is readily expressed in terms of the rms plate voltage V by

$$P_0 = GV^2. \qquad (11.4)$$

The ratio of P_0 to the total power produced by the tube may be called the resonator or circuit efficiency η_c and is given by

$$\eta_c = G/(G + g). \qquad (11.5)$$

Evidently, the resonator efficiency steadily increases as G is made large compared to g. However, the sum $(G + g)$ should remain constant to provide proper loading for the tube, as observed by Osborne[231] and discussed in Section 11.3. Therefore, G may be increased only by decreasing g, which by eq. 11.1 requires a decrease in C and an increase in L. The frequency stability is evidently degraded by a reduction of the effective Q of the resonator, and the efficiency of the tube is affected in a complicated manner. Some information on this subject is given by the following analysis, which is based on the work of Offner.[230] However, it is shown later that an increase in effective Q does not necessarily increase tube efficiency, and that an optimum value probably exists.

The analysis is referred to Fig. 11.6b, which shows the plate voltage wave form of a class C oscillator or amplifier. Because of the decrement inherent in a heavily damped circuit, the plate voltage is higher at the instant when conduction begins than it would otherwise be. Therefore, the efficiency with which the tube converts power from direct to alternating current decreases with decrease of the working Q. Consistent with the analysis of Chapter 2 the alternating voltage across the tuned circuit will increase during one cycle by the amount

$$\ln \frac{V - \delta V}{V} = -\frac{\pi}{Q}. \tag{11.6}$$

Because δV is small compared to V in all cases of interest, we may use the approximation formula to obtain

$$\delta V/V = \pi/Q. \tag{11.7}$$

The calculation of the magnitude of this effect is facilitated by assuming that the plate current flows in *short* rectangular pulses, as shown. On this basis the actual plate voltage will follow a linear transition between the smaller and larger sinusoidal waves as indicated.

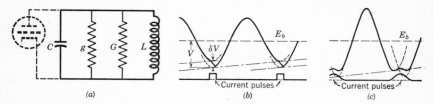

FIG. 11.6. (a) Parallel representation of resonator, (b) effect of decrement with short pulses, and (c) effect of detuning with rounded pulses.

For a given plate current wave, the efficiency is directly proportional to V. Therefore, the tube efficiency η_t is decreased by the ratio

$$\delta\eta_t = \pi/2Q, \tag{11.8}$$

where the factor 2 is introduced to account for the averaging which takes place as the voltage difference is linearly decreased by the constant plate current which flows during each pulse. Evidently, plate current does not flow in rectangular pulses. However, if the pulses are short, their shape is immaterial, as may be seen by reference to the familiar problem of charging a condenser from a constant-voltage source. In both cases half the available energy is lost regardless of how the operation is conducted.

Assuming that the tube operates under fixed conditions, with very short current pulses the largest useful output will correspond to the maximum of the product $\eta_c\eta_t = \eta$. Using eqs. 11.2, 11.5, and 11.8, we have

$$\eta = (1 - \pi/2Q)(Q_0 - Q)\eta_\infty/Q_0, \tag{11.9}$$

where η_∞ is the tube efficiency for an infinite value of Q. Setting the derivative with respect to Q equal to zero to obtain the maximum total efficiency yields

$$Q_0\pi = 2Q^2 \quad \text{or} \quad Q = \sqrt{\pi Q_0/2}. \tag{11.10}$$

In practice, the pulses of plate current are rarely short compared to the total period, and the results of the foregoing analysis are misleading. The situation is illustrated in Fig. 11.6c, in which the resonator is tuned to a frequency somewhat higher than the operating frequency. Under the assumed conditions the plate voltage remains nearly constant at a low value during the interval of conduction, *and the efficiency is actually higher than it would be if the resonator Q were infinite.*

A re-examination of the situation indicates that the important parameters are the impedance of the tube, the frequency, and the capacitance of the resonator. It makes little difference to the present topic whether the load is directly or inductively coupled. Experimental work tends to confirm this conclusion. A considerable accumulation of data indicates that a working Q in the neighborhood of 15 gives good results in most practical situations.

11.8 Resonator design

Oscillators intended for induction heating of metals ordinarily operate in the frequency range of 200 to 550 kc. For such oscillators a suitable resonator consists of a capacitance of the order of 500 $\mu\mu$f and an inductance of the order of 50 μh. The capacitance is ordinarily provided in a mica condenser, which is mounted in a substantial case and constructed to withstand the considerable values of voltage and current to which it is subjected. The inductance ordinarily takes the form of a single-layer solenoid. The conductor which makes up the winding is often tubular for cooling.

Oscillators intended for dielectric heating usually operate in the frequency range of 2 to 25 Mc. Especially at the upper end of this range, the use of lumped circuits becomes difficult, and resonators based upon distributed circuits, such as transmission lines, are often used. Cyclotrons, which operate in this frequency range, ordinarily employ the load circuit, which is constructed as a resonant transmission line, as the resonator. The arrangement used in typical cyclotrons is of considerable interest, and is discussed more fully toward the end of the chapter. Oscillators intended for diathermy ordinarily operate in the neighborhood of 25 Mc, and differ from those used for dielectric heating principally in that their power output is relatively small.

In addition to the electrical characteristics described in the previous section, the resonator of a high-power oscillator must possess several other properties. Ordinarily, the construction involves a number of compromises between theory and practice. As shown in the preceding paragraphs, a large value of Q is desirable from every possible standpoint. However, the mechanical construction must be such that the inductance and Q are stable in spite of any dirt and rough handling to which the unit may be subjected. Because considerable heat is dissipated in the coil in spite of its high Q, it is desirable to provide cooling so that the resistance and loss will not be further increased by excessive temperature. Ordinarily, the desired cooling is most conveniently effected by winding the coil from metal tubing and circulating cooling water through it.

It is readily shown from skin effect formulas[339, 342] that for a given outer diameter at a given high frequency the resistance of a tubular conductor reaches a minimum when the wall thickness t given by

$$t = 1.6/\sqrt{\pi f \mu \sigma} \text{ meters,} \qquad (11.11)$$

where MKS units are used throughout. For copper at 30°C the corresponding expression is

$$t \doteq 4/\sqrt{f} \text{ inches.} \qquad (11.12)$$

When this relationship is satisfied, the resistance is about 90 per cent of that of a solid rod having the same outer diameter. It is rarely practical to use this formula directly because the walls are too thin; however, Teare and Schatz[304] show that substantially the same resistance is obtained if the interior of the tube is partially or entirely filled with iron. Therefore, a desirable 10 per cent increase in Q may be obtained by making the tank coil of copper-plated steel tubing rather than of solid tubing. At the frequencies of present interest it is entirely practical to produce plating controlled to the desired thickness. An additional Q increase of 3 per cent may be secured by using silver rather than copper for the plating.

11.9 Coupling circuits

It is rarely practical to attach the load directly to the main tank circuit because the load impedance is unsuitable for direct application to the tube. The impedance of metals is quite low, and has an inductive component, so that a voltage step-down and capacitive phase correction is suitable. The impedance of dielectric materials, such as wood, is relatively high and is associated with a capacitive reactance. Therefore, a voltage step-up and inductive phase correction is required. Because the two problems are quite different they are discussed separately. The problems associated with induction heating appear to have received the more complete analysis and are discussed first.

The factors which govern the choice of frequency and the general problem of induction heating are ably discussed by Kinn.[170] He favors the shunt-fed tuned plate oscillator, which is shown in conjunction with several load circuits in Fig. 11.7. In this connection it should be noted that it is often desirable to heat several objects simultaneously with a given oscillator. It is therefore practical to connect the load circuits in series or parallel as best suits the individual situation.

Ordinarily, the circulating current in the main coil is too small to produce the desired result. When this is true, a capacitor of fairly

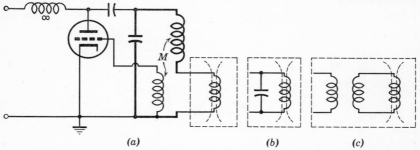

(a)   *(b)*   *(c)*

FIG. 11.7. Simplified tuned plate oscillator with various load arrangements: (*a*) series connection of load, (*b*) partly tuned load, and (*c*) current transformer to load.

small voltage rating, as shown in Fig. 11.7*b*, can be added to obtain a considerable increase in current. However, instability will occur if the added capacitance is too large, because the tuned system will develop two resonant frequencies, as discussed in Chapter 18. The use of a closely coupled transformer, as shown in Fig. 11.7*c*, to produce the required current step-down is ordinarily preferable.

The problem of coupling the load circuit to the tank circuit has been investigated by Roberds.[264] He favors the use of a transformer coupled to the entire tank coil, and he presents a construction which is stable and efficient. In a typical model the primary consists of a single-layer solenoid of twenty turns of $\frac{1}{4}$-inch copper tubing having a diameter of 6 inches and a length of 8 inches. The secondary is a single turn in the form of a sheet of copper about 9 inches wide and 21 inches long wrapped around the solenoid, but spaced from it by about $\frac{3}{8}$ inch and having a gap, as shown in Fig. 11.8. To provide cooling, water is circulated through the primary and through copper tubes soldered to the secondary, thus avoiding the increased losses which would occur if the temperature and resistance were allowed to rise. The primary inductance is about 6 μh, which is suitable for application in a typical system at a frequency of about 5 Mc. A relatively high coupling coefficient of the order of 75 per cent can be obtained in this way.

A major problem in practical systems is obtaining sufficiently low values of contact resistance. Welded or soldered joints of large cross section and suitable shape should be used wherever possible. Mechanical joints are to be avoided, but where used should provide

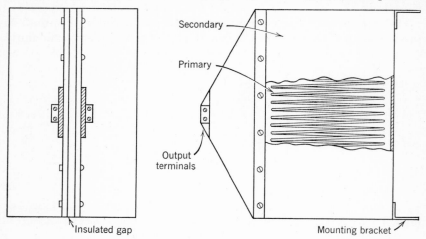

Fig. 11.8.   Coupling transformer for induction heating.

high contact pressure over a large area. A numerical example may serve to emphasize the point. In the transformer just described the primary reactance at 5 Mc is about 180 ohms. The secondary reactance is about 400 $[= (20)^2]$ times smaller or about $\frac{1}{2}$ ohm. To produce a selectivity of 100, the total resistance of the secondary must not exceed 0.005 ohm! Evidently the resistance of a single joint should be small compared to this total.

An additional practical problem is the inductance of the leads which connect the load coil to the secondary of the main transformer. This inductance serves to reduce the effective coupling coefficient of the system, thus destroying much of the advantage gained in the special transformer construction. This difficulty is alleviated by reducing the length of the leads and extending the copper sheet which forms the secondary to provide most of the lead length required. The use of a parallel capacitor as close as possible to the work is recommended as a last resort. Additional information on the practical design of coupling systems is given by Brown[40] and Mittelman,[212] and pertinent analytic relations are advanced by Kunz.[178]

The problems of securing an adequate impedance match for dielectric heating appears to be somewhat simpler than those associated with induction heating. Two facts contribute to this situation. First, the general impedance level of the dielectric load is much more nearly equal to the optimum load for the tube than is that produced in induction heating. Second, and perhaps more important, the properties of the load are very different from those of the electrodes. Therefore, it is relatively easy to obtain high efficiency in the energy-transfer process.

The principal difficulty experienced in dielectric heating is associated with the large and essentially parallel electrodes which are commonly used. The required high voltage can be maintained across the resulting substantial capacitance only by provision of a large circulating current. When such a system is coupled to the main tank circuit there is a marked tendency toward frequency instability, especially if a transmission line of any appreciable length is interposed. More is said of this problem in Chapter 18. A good general discussion of dielectric heating is given by Winlund.[348]

11.10 Interference

Regardless of the purpose for which it was designed, a high-power oscillator will radiate a considerable amount of power and thus cause radio interference unless adequate precautions are taken. The production of such interference is illegal as well as antisocial and must be avoided. Two avenues are open to the designer, but neither is especially attractive. One possibility is to choose a frequency within the rather few and very narrow bands* allocated to industrial and diathermy applications; in this case the overall frequency stability must be extremely high. This requirement is so severe that it is virtually necessary to employ a quartz crystal, either as the reference element in an automatic frequency control system or in a low-power oscillator followed by amplifiers, which may also be frequency multipliers. The use of automatic frequency control is discussed in Chapter 17, and its application to radio-frequency heating has been described by Rambo.[250] The use of a crystal oscillator followed by amplifiers is described by Norton.[226]

The alternate procedure, which must be employed if these frequencies are not used, is to provide sufficient shielding and filtering so that the radiation is negligible. Such shielding and filtering must be

* At this time the bands open to industry are 13.6525 to 13.6675, 27.185 to 27.455 and 40.95 to 41.00 Mc.

effective over a substantial band of frequencies in order to suppress the relatively strong harmonics which are produced in high-efficiency operation, but this rarely adds any considerable problem.   Moreover, Klingaman and Williams[174] observe that radiation is rarely a problem in induction heating units operating at frequencies below 400 kc. This favorable situation occurs because the load circuit, although exposed, is very small compared to the wavelength; and coupling circuits which give high efficiency of power transfer automatically discriminate against harmonics.   Therefore, at frequencies below about 400 kc, we may anticipate freedom from interference if the oscillator unit is enclosed in a well-fitted metal cabinet, and if the parts are laid out so that power leads are not unnecessarily coupled to the oscillating circuit.   In this connection it is interesting to note that a significant improvement in efficiency is observed if a thin copper lining is added to an iron cabinet.   The superior conductivity of copper reduces the losses which exist when the fields produced by the oscillatory circuit are confined by shielding.

11.11 Shielding

The gravest interference problem is experienced in dielectric heating applications where frequencies upwards of 2 Mc have proved to be most useful.   The difficulty is aggravated by the facts that the load circuit is ordinarily a large parallel-plate condenser operating at high voltage and that the ability of a given conductor to radiate increases with frequency.   Still further, the interwinding capacitance of power transformers provides a relatively low impedance path at these frequencies, so that radiation from power supply leads is also troublesome. Shielding and filtering are necessary unless the frequency is restricted to one of the assigned bands.

In a high-power, high-frequency installation the total attenuation to be provided by the combined action of shielding and power line filtering may be as high as 100 db.   Such a large attenuation can be obtained only if care is given to the design and construction.   Whenever possible, the entire system should be treated as an integral unit. Even a thin piece of metal sheet or screen wire is adequate to prevent direct penetration of the field.   The problem, therefore, is entirely one of apertures.[127]   A very narrow slit will produce a large leak if its length is at all great.   Therefore, all seams or door edges must make contact throughout their length.

The situation corresponds in virtually every detail to that of building a shielded room in which sensitive receivers may be tested in proximity to high-power sources of interference.   The only differences are that for dielectric heating a much larger amount of power must be handled through the power line filters, and a factory production line must pass through part of the shielded enclosure. In general, it is found that a double shield of copper or bronze screen wire (fly screen) or of the coarser hardware cloth provides the most practical arrangement. The two shields are separated by several inches and as far as possible are electrically isolated. Water pipes, signal or lighting circuits, or other conductors should not be allowed to pass through the enclosure if any other arrangement is possible because they serve as a transmission line to couple the interior to the exterior space. Necessary piping may be bonded to one or both screens, and circuits may be shielded or filtered. Construction details which may prove helpful are given by Swan.[303]

Doors or other openings are to be avoided as far as possible because they present a difficult problem of contacts. Metal weather stripping has been used with reasonable success, but it is difficult to secure and maintain the required continuity of electrical contact in a busy installation. In some situations, doors may be avoided by using relatively small shielded tunnels which extend from the main enclosure. Unfortunately, as shown by Linder,[190] the attenuation rate is rather low, about 10 db for each unit length equal to the widest dimension of the opening.

11.12 Cyclotron oscillators

The cyclotron, devised by E. O. Lawrence, has proved a very important tool for atomic research. A basic part of the cyclotron is a source of radio frequency applied to the semicircular cavities generally referred to as the "dees." In contemporary instruments, the dees are excited with a potential of about 10 kv at a frequency near 10 Mc. Because the dees have an area of many square feet, and a consequent capacitance of several hundred $\mu\mu f$, a large circulating current and considerable power input is required to produce the desired voltage. Moreover, many cyclotrons employ a frequency-modulated excitation in order to supply still larger values of energy to the particles being accelerated. Frequency modulation is effective because it compensates for the effects of the relativistic increase of particle mass associated with high velocity, but considerably complicates the electrical design.

In early cyclotrons the dees were excited symmetrically with respect to ground by attaching them to the ends of a balanced transmission line as indicated in Fig. 11.9a. This arrangement has certain advantages, but is difficult to shield; and unless the system is appropriately shielded excessive energy losses result from radiation and from eddy currents in the magnet poles. The unbalanced system shown in Fig. 11.9*b* is favored because the fields are completely confined, and a favorable current distribution results. The structure is a form of cavity resonator and is closely related to a coaxial section, short-circuited at one end and open-circuited but shielded at the other. By using copper throughout, and by distributing the current over a large surface area, it is possible to obtain values of Q well in excess of 1000; this is a very desirable situation, because large values of Q are associated with low driving power requirements.

Because the evacuated dee structure constitutes a resonator having characteristics superior to those readily achieved in other ways, it is

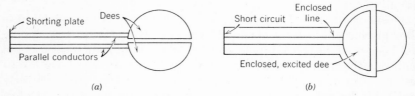

FIG. 11.9.   Cyclotron dees excited by equivalent quarter-wave lines: (*a*) open symmetrical structure and (*b*) enclosed unsymmetrical arrangement.

ordinarily used as the principal resonator of the driving oscillator, which is coupled to it by means of loops or similar devices. The circuit arrangement may be identified roughly with the Meissner oscillator of Chapter 8, but it corresponds much more closely to the grid-separation arrangement used in microwave oscillators.

PROBLEMS

11.1. In induction heating of a nonmagnetic metal the efficiency of power transfer from the coil to the load depends on the conductivity ratio of the coil and load metals.   Prove that the efficiency cannot exceed 50 per cent if the metals are alike.

11.2. Distinguish between intermittent oscillation, true blocking, and the action of the blocking oscillator of Chapter 12.

11.3. Sketch schematic diagrams illustrating how several different kinds of parasitic oscillations can be produced, and state rough criteria for the presence or absence of such oscillations.

11.4. Sketch apparatus and circuits suitable for the detection and identification of parasitic oscillations.

11.5. Review and criticize the development leading up to eq. 11.10, and the associated discussion of Fig. 11.6*c*.

11.6. Discuss the problem of shielding a 100-kw oscillator which drives a 25-Mc dielectric heating press which is 5 × 10 feet in area.

11.7. Execute a rough design for a 15 Mc oscillator to develop a voltage of 8 kv across an unbalanced cyclotron dee system having a Q of 800 and an equivalent capacitance of 200 $\mu\mu$f.

12

PRACTICAL RELAXATION
OSCILLATORS

The preceding chapters have shown that a particular circuit configuration may produce either relaxation or harmonic oscillations, depending only upon the relative magnitudes of the parameters. Moreover, the behavior of the system varies continuously and smoothly through the transition region. It may appear somewhat artificial, therefore, to discuss relaxation oscillators as a separate topic. The justification for this procedure stems from the fact that practical circuits virtually never operate in the region of transition between relaxation and harmonic oscillations. Circuits which are intended to produce sinusoidal waves ordinarily have an intrinsic Q larger than 10, corresponding in the notation of Chapter 3 to $\epsilon < 0.2$. On the other hand, systems designed to produce distorted waves characteristic of relaxation oscillations ordinarily are excessively overdamped, corresponding to $\epsilon > 20$. Because of the wide variation in the parameters, the behavior of corresponding configurations is so different that a shift of viewpoint is virtually necessary.

The following sections are devoted to a discussion and analysis of the more familiar and useful relaxation oscillators, including the multivibrator, blocking oscillator, and several sweep circuits. Consistent with the purpose of the book, the discussion has been limited to circuits which produce sustained oscillations without application of an external signal. Many interesting and important circuits, such as the Phantastron[64, 197] and the flip-flop, which require an external triggering voltage, have therefore been omitted. The Eccles-Jordan trigger circuit is closely related to the multivibrator. It is discussed in connection with its use for frequency division in Chapter 13. A very complete account of such circuits, as well as true relaxation oscillators, is given by Puckle[248] and by Chance[57] et al. The interested reader is referred to these books.

12.1 The gas tube oscillator

Of relaxation oscillators, none is simpler in configuration than that shown in Fig. 12.1* The explanation of its operation is also simple, provided we do not pry too closely into the internal mechanism of conduction within the tube itself. The gas tube is of the cold-cathode glow-discharge type, either an ordinary neon lamp (without associated resistor), or preferably one of the more uniform diodes designed as voltage regulators. Such tubes are characterized by the fact that they conduct an entirely negligible current until the terminal voltage exceeds a particular value, V_1, called the striking voltage, which is sufficient to produce ionization leading to conduction. Then, the terminal voltage drops abruptly to a second value, V_2, appreciably

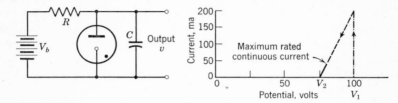

FIG. 12.1.   Gas tube oscillator.   FIG.   12.2.   Static   characteristic   of
VR75.

lower than V_1. The equilibrium conditions depend upon the resistance of the test circuit. The characteristics of a typical VR75, observed under static conditions, are shown in Fig. 12.2.

The behavior of the circuit of Fig. 12.1 may now be discussed, subject to several assumptions: that the dynamic characteristic is the same as the static characteristics, that V_b is substantially larger than V_1, that R is of the order of a megohm, and that C is of the order of 1000 $\mu\mu f$. When the circuit is energized at $t = 0$ the voltage v rises from zero toward V_b along a simple exponential curve, as indicated in Fig. 12.3. When the striking voltage is reached, ions form in the gas tube and the condenser begins to discharge. Because the tube is directly connected to the condenser, there can be no instantaneous change of the tube terminal voltage. Accordingly, by Fig. 12.2, the current will rise to a value of about 200 ma as rapidly as cumulative ionization will permit, ordinarily a small fraction of a microsecond.† This large current discharges the condenser very

---

* The standard I.R.E. symbol used to represent the gas diode is somewhat misleading in that the cathode, represented by the small circle, is actually a large cylinder whereas the anode is a slender rod.

† Such a large current would, if continued, heat the cathode to the point of

rapidly and itself decreases as the condenser voltage approaches V_2. The discharge ends when the current drops to a small fraction of a milliampere, which is inadequate to maintain ionization. The ionization virtually disappears within a few microseconds; and the gas tube remains nonconducting until the current through R again charges the condenser to a voltage V_1, at which time another discharge begins and the cycle is repeated.

In practice, the operation differs in several details from that just described. First, because of residual self-inductance in the circuit, the discharge current does not rise to such a large value as previously indicated, and correspondingly persists until the condenser is discharged to a voltage below V_2. More important, as shown by Reich,[257] the dynamic characteristic of a glow tube is not the same as the static

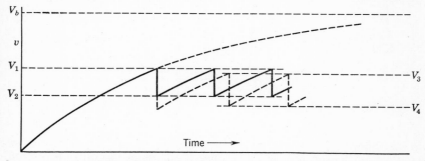

FIG. 12.3.   Wave form generated by gas tube oscillator.

characteristic. The high degree of ionization established during the early part of the discharge persists long enough to allow the condenser to discharge to a voltage V_4, considerably less than V_2. Finally, sufficient ionization may persist through the charging interval to reduce the striking voltage V_1 to a lower value V_3. The wave form which results when these effects are considered is shown by the dotted line of Fig. 12.3. It has a longer period and a greater amplitude than the other but is very similar in shape. Note that the first discharge cycle is barely distinguishable from all which follow, a characteristic property of extreme relaxation oscillations.

In its present form the circuit is of little practical importance, but it forms the basis of the thyratron oscillator described in Section 12.4 and widely used as the sweep circuit in oscilloscopes. Moreover, it

thermionic emission, thereby changing the discharge from a glow to an arc. However, because of the small amount of energy stored in the condenser, the discharge ends before the arc phenomenon sets in.

serves to illustrate a number of basic concepts which are useful in the analysis of more complicated systems.

12.2 The saw-tooth wave

For obvious reasons, the wave shape generated by the gas tube oscillator is referred to as a saw tooth. Because the voltage variation is approximately linear with time throughout a large fraction of the total period, such a wave is suitable as a *sweep* or *time base* for instruments such as the cathode ray oscilloscope. The properties of the wave shown in Fig. 12.4 will be discussed from this viewpoint.

The total time or *period, T,* of the recurrent wave is divided into two parts, the *period of trace, t_1,* and the *period of flyback, t_2.* Ordinarily, the period of flyback should be made as small as possible in

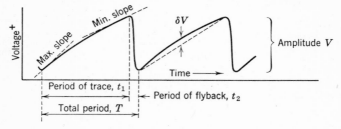

.Fig. 12.4.   Imperfect positive saw-tooth wave.

comparison to the period T, because it serves no useful purpose and often confuses the image produced on the oscilloscope screen. The *amplitude, V,* is clearly a peak-to-peak voltage. It must therefore be equal to 2 $\sqrt{2}$ times the rms value of a sine wave which will produce a trace of equal length on an oscilloscope screen.

The wave of Fig. 12.4 is designated *positive* because the slope of the useful trace is positive. The positive polarity is easiest to generate in practice because of the direction of conduction in ordinary electron tubes. The slope during the useful period of the wave should ideally be constant so as to produce a uniform velocity of the oscilloscope beam. Since a constant slope is a property of a straight line, this property is referred to as *linearity.* The degree of nonlinearity is expressed by the number of per cent which the minimum slope falls below the maximum slope in the useful region. The nonlinearity of Fig. 12.4 is 50 per cent because the initial slope is unity and the final slope is only one-half. A nonlinearity of 5 per cent is tolerable in nearly all applications.

The degree of linearity of the useful period may be expressed in an alternative manner, which is sometimes more convenient. This is referred to as the *displacement error* by Puckle[248] and is illustrated in the second cycle of Fig. 12.4.   It is defined as the greatest fractional departure between the actual wave and an ideal wave which coincides with it at beginning and end.   That is, the displacement error, D is given by the equation

$$D = \delta V / V. \tag{12.1}$$

For reasonable degrees of curvature the greatest departure is indistinguishable from the departure at the middle of the trace.   Other useful information concerning the properties of, saw-tooth waves is given by von Ardenne.[333]

The ideal saw-tooth wave is characterized by a rise which is linear with time, a flyback time, which is negligible, and successive cycles which are identical.   The waves generated by practical oscillators differ from this ideal not only because of nonlinearity and finite flyback time but also because successive cycles differ in amplitude and period.   This difference between successive cycles is commonly referred to by the inelegant term *jitter*, which is used here in the absence of an acceptable substitute.   Because jitter is usually of a random nature, it must be treated by statistical methods such as those used in the treatment of electrical *noise;* however, the deviations of period and of amplitude will each have some sort of average or rms value.   Logically, the average jitter in period and amplitude should be expressed as fractions of the average total period and amplitude.   In practice, however, jitter is usually expressed in absolute units of time or voltage.

12.3 The wave produced by the gas tube circuit

The gas tube circuit can produce a wave which approaches the ideal saw tooth in that the flyback time is short compared to the trace, and the degrees of nonlinearity and jitter are small.   The calculations are relatively simple, because the tube is inactive during the trace interval. Figures 12.1 and 12.3 show that in the steady state the output voltage during each trace is described by the equation

$$v = V_b \{1 - e^{-(t_0+t)/RC}\}. \tag{12.2}$$

For any single trace we may choose the time origin so that $v = V_4$ at $t = 0$.   Then by substituting the time t_1 at which $v = V_3$, we may find as the relationship between the circuit parameters and the trace period

$$t_1 = R\,C \cdot \ln\left(\frac{V_b - V_4}{V_b - V_3}\right). \tag{12.3}$$

The time of flyback is not readily calculated exactly. However, the condenser charging current cannot exceed V_b/R and is therefore limited to a few hundred microamperes, whereas the discharge current was shown to be of the order of one hundred milliamperes. Because the same net charge is transferred in charge and discharge, it follows that the trace time, t_1, is about one thousand times as long as the flyback time t_2.

The nonlinearity of the trace is readily found by using the fact that the slope is directly proportional to $(V_b - v)$. Thus we have

$$N = \frac{(V_b - V_4) - (V_b - V_3)}{(V_b - V_4)} = \frac{V}{V_b - V_4}. \tag{12.4}$$

By expanding eq. 12.3 in series and neglecting higher order terms, we have as an approximation useful when the nonlinearity is small,

$$N \doteq t_1/RC. \tag{12.5}$$

It is clear that nonlinearity is reduced by making V_b large compared to V and V_4.

The displacement error is found by substituting $t = t_1/2$ in eq. 12.2 and comparing the value with $\frac{1}{2}(V_3 + V_4)$. The result is somewhat complicated in its general form, but takes the simple form

$$D \doteq N/8, \tag{12.6}$$

provided the nonlinearity is small enough to justify the series expansion leading to eq. 12.5.

As a numerical example let $V_b = 300$, $V_3 = 90$, and $V_4 = 60$ volts. Then, by eqs. 12.5 and 12.6 the nonlinearity and displacement error are, respectively, 0.125 and 0.015.

Jitter is present principally because the breakdown voltage, V_3, is not stable. The breakdown voltage depends upon the number of ions present at that instant, and therefore varies with the amount of cosmic and other radiation. Operation of the gas tube in a generous supply of visible or ultraviolet light serves to reduce the jitter to a very small value.

12.4 The thyratron oscillator

The hot-cathode gas-filled triode or *thyratron* is substantially superior to the glow-discharge diode in respect to flexibility and internal resistance. Even a small tube, such as the 884, will conduct a momentary current of 300 ma with only 16 volts' drop; whereas the 2050 tetrode has the even more remarkable instantaneous rating of 10 amp. at 8 volts' drop. The deionization time of the 2050, however, is rather longer than that of the 884, and the behavior is more sensitive to ambient temperature. It will not, therefore, be considered further here.

Figure 12.5*b* shows a circuit which is widely used to generate a positive saw-tooth wave as a time base, or sweep, for cathode ray oscilloscopes. The general operation of this circuit is very similar to that of the gas tube oscillator described in Section 12.1. The differences are these. (1) The use of a hot cathode provides a steady source of current, greatly reducing the voltage drop in the tube. (2) The initiation of conduction is under grid control so that jitter is very small. (3) The control action of the grid provides a convenient means

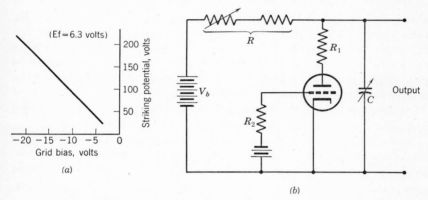

FIG. 12.5. Thyratron triode sweep: (*a*) control characteristic and (*b*) circuit.

for varying the period and amplitude of the wave and is therefore very useful in synchronizing the sweep with an externally injected voltage. The topic of synchronization is, however, deferred for a unified discussion in Chapter 13.

The manner in which the grid affects the breakdown or striking voltage in the 884 is shown in Fig. 12.5*a*. With this information and the equations already developed it is possible to design a sweep circuit to meet specified operating requirements.

12.5 Illustrative design of thyratron oscillator

Suppose that a saw tooth having a frequency of one kilocycle and a nonlinearity no greater than 20 per cent is to be generated with a type 884 gas triode. The first step is to choose a suitable value of grid bias. It is clear that a large bias will lead to a large output voltage but will also require a large value of V_b to produce reasonable linearity. A low bias, on the other hand, is likely to lead to excessive jitter. A bias of

10 volts corresponding in Fig. 12.3 to a starting voltage, V_3, of 96 volts is chosen as a reasonable compromise. Since the conduction takes place and ends at $V_4 = 16$ volts, the output voltage amplitude is fixed at $V = 96 - 16 = 80$ volts. By eq. 12.4 and the choice $N = 20$ per cent the supply voltage, V_b, is fixed at $V_b = 16 + (5 \times 80) = 416$ volts. The current-limiting resistor R_1 is fixed by V_3 and the fact that the current shall not exceed 300 ma to $R_1 = (96 - 16)/0.3 = 267$ ohms.

As previously shown, the ratio of trace to flyback time will be approximately equal to the ratio R/R_1. The choice of $R =$ one megohm, which is consistent with characteristics of the tube and common usage, leads to a desirably high ratio of trace to flyback time of about $t_1/t_2 = 10^6/267 = 3750$. The capacitance C is evaluated by means of eq. 12.3. Since a frequency of one kilocycle corresponds to a period of 0.001 second we have $C = 5000 \ \mu\mu\mathrm{f}$. The only remaining parameter to be determined is the grid resistor, R_2, which serves to protect the grid from excessive currents, and as an impedance for the injection of a synchronizing signal if one is used. A resistance of 100,000 ohms is consistent with good practice and meets the requirement that the grid current shall not exceed one milliampere.

The greatest frequency which can be generated with this circuit is about 50 kc because of the time required to deionize the thyratron. Frequencies as low as one cycle per minute may be obtained if great care is taken to prevent leakage internal and external to the condenser.

12.6 The van der Pol oscillator

A simple circuit which produces relaxation oscillations by means of a single high-vacuum pentode is shown in Fig. 12.6. It was originally devised by van der Pol[320] in 1926, and is of interest because several important practical circuits have been derived from it. The same configuration (with the addition of a shunting condenser C_2) has already been presented in Fig. 8.24, and its behavior as a harmonic oscillator is discussed in Section 8.19. The symbols and notation developed there are preserved; however, the relationship between the circuit parameters is modified here so as to obtain a large loop gain and thereby produce relaxation oscillations. Because the resulting behavior is highly nonlinear, it is impractical to analyze the system except in a qualitative way.

In terms of the equivalent circuit of Fig. 12.6, the threshold of oscillation was shown in Chapter 8 to correspond to

$$G = 1/R_2 + 1/R_1 + 1/r_p + C_2/C_1R_1, \tag{12.7}$$

where G is the suppressor-to-screen transconductance and r_p is the dynamic screen resistance. To obtain well-defined relaxation oscillations we should decrease C_2 and increase R_2 and R_1 so that the threshold of oscillation corresponds to a transconductance some ten times less than the actual value. The general nature of the oscillation cycle is determined by making the idealizing assumptions that C_2 is zero and that R_1 is very large compared to R_2.

Let us suppose that no voltage exists across R_1 so that the suppressor is at a potential V_c, and that a steady current flows through R_2 to the screen grid. If, from this reference, the screen current is assumed to increase slightly it requires that the screen voltage will

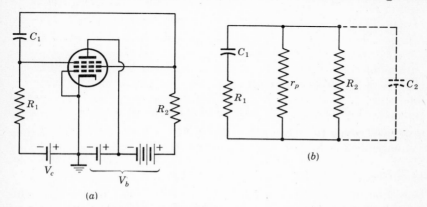

(a)

(b)

FIG. 12.6. Van der Pol relaxation oscillator: (a) circuit diagram and (b) equivalent circuit.

decrease and the suppressor voltage will be driven negative by the action of R_2 and C_1, respectively. Because the negative voltage on the suppressor diverts electrons from the plate to the screen, the action is cumulative, and a rapid transition takes place which ends only when the screen draws the entire cathode current and the suppressor is biased far beyond its cutoff value. An interval of relaxation now follows in which the suppressor bias decreases toward V_c by discharge of C_1, through R_1 and the parallel combination of R_2 and the screen grid.

When the suppressor bias has decreased sufficiently, plate current again flows and the screen current begins to drop. The resulting increase of screen voltage is again cumulative and the reverse transition takes place. The end of this transition finds the suppressor positive with respect to the cathode, the screen voltage considerably increased, and the plate current larger than the screen current. A second relaxation interval now follows, during which the suppressor again drifts towards the bias voltage V_c, the screen potential decreases, and the plate current decreases. This relaxation tends to be more rapid than the former because the considerable conductivity of the suppressor grid, which is now positive with respect to the cathode, is added to that of R_1.

The cycle is completed when the suppressor voltage returns to such a value that the suppressor-to-screen transconductance is sufficient to produce a net loop gain. The screen and suppressor voltages again change in the negative direction at an accelerating rate until the plate current is zero, and the suppressor is far negative. The wave forms

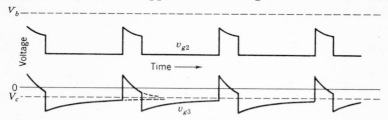

FIG. 12.7.   Voltage wave forms in van der Pol oscillator.

generated under these conditions are shown in Fig. 12.7, corresponding to experimental data of Page and Curtis.[234]

12.7 Analysis of the van der Pol circuit

It will be recalled from Chapter 4 that no genuinely practicable solution has been found for van der Pol's equation. Since the present circuit is somewhat more complicated, particularly in the volt-ampere characteristic, than that previously described, its analytic treatment will not be attempted. The following qualitative discussion, however, serves to describe the principal features of the oscillation.

The actual oscillation differs from the idealization just presented principally because of the effect of parasitic capacitances to ground. Since these are ordinarily small compared to C_1, they can be lumped into a single capacitance as shown by C_2 in Fig. 12.6. This parasitic capacitance slows down the transitions and somewhat rounds the corners of the wave, from the form indicated in Fig. 12.7.

Calculation of the amplitude and period of the wave which will be generated by a given system is rather difficult. However, the liberal use of approximations permits us to obtain results which represent the operation sufficiently accurately to be useful. The discussion is based upon Fig. 12.8, which shows the variation of screen-grid current with screen voltage for various values of suppressor voltage. The dotted curves represent the variation which the screen current would have if the suppressor and screen were varied so as to maintain their potential difference constant. A load line starting at V_b with a slope corresponding to R_2 is added.

Conditions which exist when the suppressor is biased beyond cutoff are represented by the point A, where the vertical displacement between A and the dotted load line represents the discharge current through C_1. As the suppressor bias decreases by relaxation of C_1 through R_1 a condition is reached at which plate current begins to flow, but the transconductance of the suppressor is inadequate to take control. The transconductance of the suppressor increases very rapidly in the interval represented by the arc AB until at B the loop

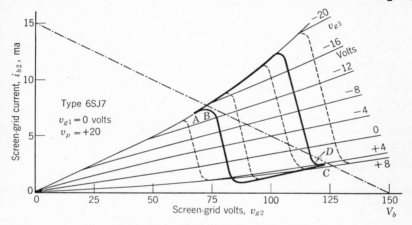

FIG. 12.8.   Operation of van der Pol oscillator.

gain is just unity. The transition now continues with cumulative acceleration along the line of a constant potential difference to point C, where the sum of the screen and suppressor currents meets the load line. In principle, the path for positive values of the suppressor deviates somewhat from that indicated, but the deviation is small because the charge which can accumulate in C_1 by the action of suppressor current during the transition is negligible.

This transition occurs at a nonuniform rate which is difficult to calculate or specify. However, the minimum possible time would be equal to that required for the current corresponding to point B to charge the stray capacitance C_2 to a voltage corresponding to the potential difference between B and C. If, for example, the current at B is 7 ma, the potential difference v between B and C is 50 volts, and C_2 is $10\mu\mu f$, then the minimum possible transition time is $t = q/i = 0.07\ \mu s$. A considerably longer interval is to be expected in practice.

A second period of relaxation from C to D now follows, during which the charge on C_1 increases by conduction through R_1 and the suppressor grid. The screen current increases somewhat as the suppressor current decreases and as the potential difference between the two increases. Nothing in the nature of a cutoff occurs, but over much of this interval the screen current is almost independent of the suppressor voltage. The duration of this relaxation period may, in principle, be computed from the knowledge of the initial and final voltages of the suppressor, and the currents which flow through R_1 and the suppressor. The suppressor voltage corresponding to point B is known from the curves, as is the transition voltage from B to C, so that the initial suppressor voltage is known (and is relatively high). The final suppressor voltage appears on the curves at D, and the suppressor current may be estimated from tube characteristics.

The relaxation interval ends when point D is reached. At D the loop gain is again exactly zero, and the reverse transition begins, again along a path of constant potential difference to point A. The rate and interval of this transition are also complicated, but the time required is longer than that previously calculated. The nature and duration of the final relaxation period are relatively simple. The suppressor grid is so negative that no plate current flows, and relaxation of its potential toward V_c occurs by current flow through C_1, R_1, and R_2. The initial value of suppressor potential is readily arrived at from knowledge of the suppressor voltage at D and the total transition voltage from D to A.

In practice, the calculations just indicated are rarely or never made because of the difficulty and uncertainty involved. However, they serve to clarify the operation of the device and to illustrate methods which are useful in the analysis of all relaxation oscillators.

12.8 A pentode sweep circuit

In the van der Pol oscillator just described the plate current flows in a series of nearly rectangular pulses, which may be made short compared to the interval if desired. Moreover, it is clear that the operation just described would not be affected if a *sufficiently small* impedance were placed in series with the plate lead. For example, a series of small negative pulses of voltage could be obtained by placing a resistor in series with the plate. If the resistor were replaced by a suitable parallel RC combination it is clear that a positive saw-tooth voltage wave could result from the integrating action of the combination. Such an arrangement is not very useful because of its small output, but it logically leads us to the next step in the development.

At about the same time Reich[258] and Fleming-Williams[95] independently devised saw-tooth generators having the circuit configuration of Fig. 12.9, which differs from Fig. 12.6 only in that the suppressor bias is zero, the plate voltage is increased, and the plate resistor and condenser are added. In this and several other circuits the operation is unaffected whether C_3 is returned to ground or to the positive end of the load resistor; however, the ground connection is usually preferred from mechanical and d-c considerations.

Although the circuit diagram of Fig. 12.9 is very similar to that of the van der Pol circuit just described, the operation is much more complicated. The additional time constant equal to R_3C_3, inherent in

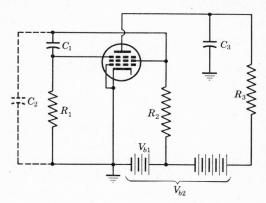

FIG. 12.9. Pentode sweep circuit.

the new system, affects the cycle because, for small values of the plate voltage, the screen current is affected by the plate voltage. In the operating cycle just described, the periods of relaxation and conduction are controlled by the parameters of the screen and suppressor circuits, whereas in the present circuit the desired mode is one in which the period is controlled by the parameters of the plate circuit.

To obtain the desired operation let C_1 be very large compared to C_3, which in turn should be large compared to the stray capacitance C_2. Moreover, let R_1 be at least as large as the load resistor R_3, which is likely to be somewhat larger than R_2. The operation is explained by assuming the desired state of affairs and then demonstrating its validity. We assume that the suppressor voltage is zero, the screen voltage is relatively high, and the plate and screen currents are high. Under these conditions the charge on C_3 is rapidly reduced toward zero because the current drawn by the tube is much larger than that flowing through R_3. This condition ends when the plate voltage falls to the knee of the pentode characteristic (usually about 50 volts), at which point the plate current decreases, the screen current increases, and the resulting drop of screen voltage acts through C_1 to cut off the plate current in a very short time.

In the next interval two different relaxation processes race for control. The charge on C_1 decreases through R_1 and R_2; and the charge on C_3 increases by the flow of current through R_3 and the B supply. However, because the time constant of the plate circuit has been made small compared to that of the suppressor circuit, the plate voltage rises to a considerable value before the suppressor bias decreases appreciably. If the screen resistor R_2 is suited to the characteristics of the tube, the plate voltage will reach a point at which the suppressor voltage no longer produces cutoff, and plate current will again flow. The current which goes to the plate is principally robbed from the screen so that the screen current decreases, the potentials increase, and the tube is driven into a condition of high conduction with the suppressor slightly positive, thus completing the cycle. An output of the order of 100 volts over a wide range of frequency is readily produced.

The linearity of the output can be made excellent if V_{b2} is large. Likewise, very short flyback times may be secured by using a large resistance for R_3 and by using a tube which draws relatively large currents. A tube having a large ratio of plate-to-screen current is desirable because it permits rapid discharge of C_3 without consuming excessive current during the remainder of the cycle.

Finally, the analysis indicates that the time constant of the suppressor circuit need not be greatly in excess of that of the plate circuit. In fact, partial relaxation of the suppressor bias is advantageous in timing the period. Stability at a fixed frequency, therefore, is improved by a proper proportioning of these two time constants. Where a widely variable period is desired the original conditions are preferable, because the period is then defined by and directly proportional to the plate circuit time constant.

12.9 Puckle's sweep

A circuit[247] which, with some refinements, can generate a saw-tooth wave of excellent linearity and short flyback time, is shown in Fig. 12.10. A carefully designed circuit using high transconductance tubes has produced saw-tooth waves having a fundamental frequency in excess of 5 Mc, and a flyback time approximately one-tenth of the period. The circuit is related to the multivibrator, but depends upon the principle of the cathode follower for its excellent performance.

It differs from the multivibrator in that the plate of one tube is connected directly to the grid of the other and that the period is fixed by a single resistance-capacitance combination in the cathode of T_1. The product C_2R_2 is large compared to the desired period.

The oscillation is explained by noting that throughout most of the cycle T_2 is at zero bias while T_1 is cut off. It is therefore necessary to make R_4 relatively large in order to avoid excessive current flow in T_2. An initial charge in C_1 leaks off gradually through the high resistance R_1 so that T_1 begins to conduct. The resulting potential drop which develops across R_3 is transferred to the grid of T_2 and causes a reduction of current in T_2. The resulting increase in the plate potential of T_2 and the grid potential of T_1 increases the conduction of T_1 and accelerates the first transition, which ends with T_2

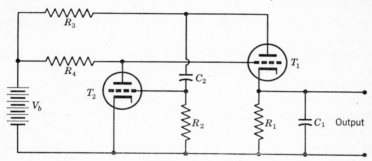

Fig. 12.10. Puckle's sweep.

biased far beyond cutoff and T_1 carrying a large current, the grid being returned to B^+ through R_4.

Provided the cathode of T_1 has adequate emission, as is usually the case, this condition will persist until C_1 is charged to a potential approaching V_b. As this potential is approached, the current through R_3 and R_4 decreases until the drop across R_3 is no longer sufficient to hold T_2 cutoff. The re-initiation of current flow in T_2 reverses the transition previously described and restores the system to the initial condition in which T_1 is cutoff and T_2 is conducting.

During the relatively short interval when T_1 is conducting, a considerable charge is placed upon C_1, increasing its voltage to a value approaching that of the supply. This charge must decrease by conduction through R_1 to a value such that the voltage across C_1 is comparable to the plate voltage of T_2 before T_1 can again conduct. Thus, a negative saw tooth is generated, the sweep period corresponding to the relaxation of R_1C_1 and the flyback corresponding to the conduction of T_1.

The flyback time can be made very short. At operating frequencies of about one kilocycle a flyback time of about one microsecond is typical; at higher frequencies it can be reduced to about $\frac{1}{50}$ μs. The linearity may be made reasonably good by proportioning the parameters so that the operating period is only a small fraction of the time constant R_1C_1. This may be achieved by choosing elements and plate voltages such that during the relaxation interval the grid-to-ground potential in T_1 is a fairly large fraction of the plate-to-ground potential.

This circuit has a number of desirable features. The output voltage is generated across a relatively large capacitance C_1, so that moderate capacitances in the load circuit do not degrade the wave shape and only slightly affect the frequency. Moreover, the output frequency can be varied between extremely wide limits simply by varying C_1. In practice, C_1 is ordinarily switched in steps of about 3 to 1, and smaller frequency intervals are obtained by variation of R_1. The amplitude of the output is fixed by the applied voltage and tube parameters; it is therefore nearly independent of the frequency.

Because the cathode of T_1 is not grounded but constitutes the output terminal, problems of cathode-to-heater potential arise. In most tubes this potential difference should never exceed 100 volts. Where large outputs are required it may be necessary to use a separate heater supply for this tube. And, as in other cathode followers, there is the possibility of hum in the output because of coupling between the heater and cathode. Somewhat similar to Puckle's sweep and useful in certain circumstances are the saw-tooth generators described by Cocking,[65] Malling,[202] and Sing.[284]

12.10 Refinements of Puckle's sweep

The linearity and high-frequency performance of the circuit just described leave much to be desired; they may be greatly improved by substituting a pentode for R_1 and another pentode for T_2. Because the plate current of a pentode is substantially independent of the plate voltage, the slope of the output voltage wave is nearly constant. Substitution of a pentode as T_2 minimizes the undesirable effects of grid-plate capacitance, thus decreasing the flyback time. Moreover, the suppressor grid of T_2 provides a convenient terminal for injection of a synchronizing voltage.

When frequencies in excess of a megacycle must be generated, the principal difficulty is in obtaining an adequately short flyback time and a satisfactory means of synchronization. Use of a pentode in place of R_1 is not necessary because the period must be short compared to R_1C_1, and tolerable linearity automatically results. The

necessary speed of operation is obtained by using high-transconduct-
ance pentodes for both T_1 and T_2 and by reducing all parasitic capacitances to the smallest possible values. Synchronization may be
achieved by injection of a signal on the *screen-grid* of T_1. This electrode is shielded by the first and third grids; therefore, the synchronizing voltage is not superimposed upon the output saw tooth by direct
capacitance coupling, as it is in most alternative arrangements.

12.11 The multivibrator

The symmetrical multivibrator, devised by Abraham and Block,[1] is
probably the best-known and most widely used form of relaxation

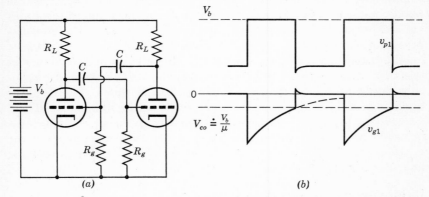

FIG. 12.11. Symmetrical multivibrator: (a) circuit, and (b) wave forms.

oscillator. The basic circuit, shown in Fig. 12.11a, has been modified
in a great number of ways by many workers and for a variety of purposes. Important applications include frequency multiplication,
frequency division, generation of square and other wave forms, and
timing functions. A useful summary of multivibrator information is
given by Mather.[207]

The arrangement corresponds to a two-stage resistance-capacitance
amplifier with output returned to the input. If we take account of
the parasitic capacitances to ground, it is easy to show that the Nyquist
plot has the form of a circle passing through the origin and centered on
the real axis. The large diameter and open frequency scale of the
circle immediately indicate that relaxation oscillations should occur.
As with most relaxation oscillators, the operating frequency bears no
simple relation to the frequency at which the Nyquist plot crosses the
real-frequency axis.

The oscillation is conveniently explained by assuming that both grid resistors have been shorted for a long time and that the short circuit is removed at time $t = 0$. By symmetry, both tubes are conducting equal and considerable values of plate current in an unstable equilibrium. If for any reason the plate current of one tube decreases slightly its plate potential increases, with a corresponding increase of the potential of the other grid. It is readily seen that the unbalance is cumulative and that it will continue until one tube is cut off and the other tube is conducting an abnormally large current. This state of affairs persists while the potentials of both grids relax toward zero. When the tube which was previously cut off is again able to conduct, it will drop the grid potential of the other tube, reversing the cumulative process just described. The intervals of transition are readily made very short, but are not zero. The duration of this interval is of considerable importance and is discussed later. The intervals of relaxation may be controlled between quite wide limits.

Figure 12.11b shows the wave forms of the grid and plate voltage in one tube of a symmetrical multivibrator; the wave form in the other tube is identical but displaced a half period in time. The negative excursions of grid and plate voltage are equal, as indicated. These curves are readily duplicated experimentally by using coupling condensers which are large compared to the parasitic capacitances of the circuits, grid leaks which are large compared to the plate resistors, and tubes having a relatively low value of μ.

12.12 Analysis of the multivibrator

Because its operation is inherently very nonlinear, and because many factors influence its behavior, the multivibrator defies exact and complete analysis. However, we can obtain a reasonably accurate picture of the operation by examining the several sections of the cycle. The present analysis follows the general approach of Kiebert and Inglis.[167] A somewhat more elaborate analysis is given by Webb and Becker.[337]

Because the resistance of a positive grid is low compared to that of a typical grid leak, the grid bias of the conducting tube is always very nearly zero when a transition begins. Correspondingly, the plate voltage is closely equal to the value determined from the static characteristic for zero bias with the given supply voltage and load resistor. In the other tube, the plate voltage is equal to the supply voltage, and the grid bias is equal to the cutoff value. We assume that the plate load resistors are small compared to the grid leaks.

Because the transition occurs in a very short time, it is possible to treat it as a switching operation. On this basis, the conditions which exist immediately thereafter can be calculated by the methods of ordinary transient theory. The blocking condensers are sufficiently large so that their charge cannot change appreciably during the transfer time; therefore, ordinary exponential relaxations must occur in the interval following the transition.

The analysis is based on Fig. 12.12. The ideal rectifier is included to represent the fact that the grid draws current only when positive. The symbol $\bar{r}_p$ represents the resistance which would draw the same current as the given tube with zero grid bias, whereas $\bar{r}_g$ is an average value of the resistance of the grid when positive under the conditions that the plate is fed from V_b through the load resistor.

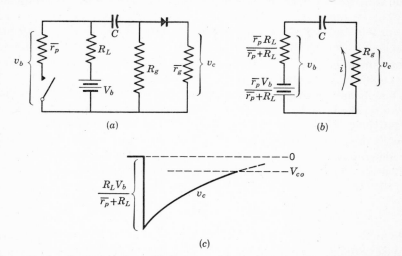

(a) (b)

(c)

FIG. 12.12. Analysis of multivibrator: (a) equivalent circuit; (b) Thévenin representation, and (c) wave form.

We first assume that the switch has been open for a long time. It is clear that no currents are flowing, that $v_c = 0$, that $v_b = V_b$, and that the voltage across C is also equal to V_b. When the switch is closed, v_b drops to a value lower than V_b, v_c assumes a negative value, and a discharge current begins to flow through C, R_g, and the parallel combination of $\bar{r}_p$ and R_L. No current flows in $\bar{r}_g$ because of the polarity of the discharge. The use of Thévenin's theorem leads to the modified equivalent circuit of Fig. 12.12b. Immediately following the closing of the switch, it is clear that v_c has the maximum negative value

$$v_{cm} = \frac{\bar{r}_p V_b}{\bar{r}_p + R_L} - V_b = -\frac{R_L V_b}{\bar{r}_p + R_L}. \tag{12.8}$$

Consistent with ordinary transient behavior, v_c relaxes exponentially toward zero with a time constant

$$T_0 = C\left(R_g + \frac{\bar{r}_p R_L}{\bar{r}_p + R_L}\right).$$

(12.9)

The half period of the generated wave may now be calculated, because the next transition will occur when the grid voltage v_c relaxes to the cutoff value

$$v_c = V_{co} \doteq V_b/\mu.$$

(12.10)

The total period T of the oscillation is then given by the equation

$$T = 2C\left(R_g + \frac{\bar{r}_p R_L}{\bar{r}_p + R_L}\right) \ln \frac{\mu R_L}{\bar{r}_p + R_L}.$$

(12.11)

Experiment confirms that this equation for the period is quite accurate if the effects of parasitic capacitance are negligible.

The behavior of the system during the remaining portion of the cycle is calculated by assuming that the switch is opened when eq. 12.10 is satisfied. The situation is shown in Fig. 12.13. The condenser current is now reversed and enlarged because $\bar{r}_g$, which is relatively low, becomes effective. The voltage which existed across the condenser when the switch was opened is given by the equation

$$v_1 = \frac{\bar{r}_p V_b}{\bar{r}_p + R_L} - V_{co}\left(1 + \frac{\bar{r}_p R_L}{R_g(\bar{r}_p + R_L)}\right),$$

(12.12)

where the first term represents the voltage which would ultimately have existed and the second term accounts for the voltages still existing across the resistors. Often part or all of the last term is negligible. Neglecting this term and the conductivity of R_g in comparison to $\bar{r}_g$, we see that the grid voltage immediately after the switch is opened has a maximum positive value

$$v_{cm}' = V_b\left(1 - \frac{\bar{r}_p}{\bar{r}_p + R_L}\right)\left(\frac{\bar{r}_g}{\bar{r}_g + R_L}\right) = \frac{V_b \bar{r}_g R_L}{(\bar{r}_p + R_L)(\bar{r}_g + R_L)}.$$

(12.13)

Because $\bar{r}_g$ is small, this voltage decays relatively rapidly with the exponential time constant

$$T_1 = C(\bar{r}_g + R_L).$$

(12.14)

Because T_1 is ordinarily a magnitude smaller than T_0 the relaxation goes through some ten time constants, and v_c becomes vanishingly small, as originally assumed.

Under the foregoing assumptions, the plate voltage wave would be rectangular and the grid wave a simple exponential. However, this is known to be incorrect; the discrepancy is removed by noting that the plate current increases and plate voltage decreases during the short interval when the grid is driven positive. The magnitude of this correction for the plate voltage wave is readily calculated, under the assumption of linearity, by use of eq. 12.13 with the effective amplification of the tube to obtain

$$v_p' = \frac{R_L \bar{r}_g V_b}{(\bar{r}_p + R_L)(\bar{r}_g + R_L)} \cdot \frac{\mu R_L}{\bar{r}_p + R_L}. \qquad (12.15)$$

However, this correction must be applied with caution, especially if the plate load resistor is high, because then the condition of linearity

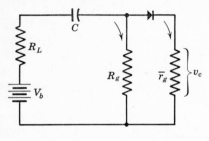

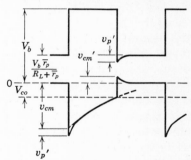

FIG. 12.13. Relaxation of positive grid.

FIG. 12.14. Details of multivibrator wave.

is violated and eq. 12.15 yields too large a result. The same correction, subject to the same caution, should be applied to eq. 12.8 to obtain a corrected maximum negative grid excursion. The periods and other amplitudes are little affected because of the rapidity with which the positive grid bias disappears. The detailed wave shape corresponding to these calculations is shown in Fig. 12.14.

12.13 Numerical example

A typical symmetrical multivibrator employs a pair of 6J5 triodes (or the equivalent duals 6SN7 or 6F8G) in a circuit having the parameters $R_L = 15,000$ ohms, $R_g = $ one megohm, $C = 1000$ $\mu\mu$f, and $V_b = 250$ volts. The chosen tube at the given voltage has the approximate values $\bar{r}_p = 10,000$ ohms, $\bar{r}_g = 1000$ ohms, and $\mu = 20$. By eq. 12.11 we have, as the total period, 5 milliseconds, representing a frequency of 200 cycles. The maximum negative and positive grid voltages are by eqs. 12.8 and 12.13 respectively $V_{cm} = -150$ volts and $V_{cm}' = +9.4$ volts. Applying the correction of eq. 12.15 we have

$V_p' = 104$ volts; however, this is absurd because it represents a negative plate voltage. Inspection of the actual rather than the idealized characteristics of the tube shows that the plate voltage will fall to a minimum of about 30. The time constants T_0 and T_1 are respectively 1.006 and 0.011 millisecond. That is, the time during which the grid is positive is indeed a very small portion of the total period.

12.14 Frequency stability of multivibrator

It is well known that the frequency of the multivibrator is not very stable, and that it is readily controlled by injection of an external signal. In almost every case, however, the *natural* frequency should be stable so that the response to a given influence is predictable. It is therefore important to examine the operation with a view to rendering the natural frequency constant. Because the resistance and capacitance values are quite stable, the problem is to proportion the circuit in such a way that the frequency is unaffected when the parameters of the tube change under the influence of applied voltage, aging, or replacement.

The equivalent plate resistance $\bar{r}_p$ is an extremely variable parameter, sensitive to aging, heater voltage, plate voltage, and interchange of tubes. It is therefore desirable to choose parameters such that the half period as given by eq. 12.11 is insensitive to $\bar{r}_p$. Inspection of the various terms shows that this result will be achieved if

$$R_L \gg \bar{r}_p \tag{12.16}$$

and

$$R_g \gg \bar{r}_p. \tag{12.17}$$

Moreover, the desired relationship between T_0 and T_1 requires that

$$R_g \gg R_L. \tag{12.18}$$

Because the value of R_g is limited by leakage currents within the tube and by the need to produce high frequencies with reasonable values of C, it is often necessary to make $\bar{r}_p$ quite low to satisfy eq. 12.16. Low-resistance tubes are therefore desirable from this viewpoint.

The amplification factor of a given tube is relatively insensitive to applied voltages and to aging, and different tubes of a given type differ less in this than in other parameters; however, the value of μ is not truly constant. Therefore, the ratio V_b/V_{co} in eq. 12.10 is not a constant, nor is its magnitude a matter of indifference. The preferred value of μ, which is closely equal to V_b/V_{co}, can be derived from eq. 12.11. Assuming that eqs. 12.16 and 12.18 are satisfied, we may write eq. 12.11 in the form

$$T = k \ln (V_b/V_{co}), \qquad (12.19)$$

where $k = 2CR_g$. The change of period which will result from a small variation in the cutoff voltage, which might result from a change in contact potential or emission velocity, is

$$dT = -k \frac{dV_{co}}{V_{co}}. \qquad (12.20)$$

The fractional change of period, which we wish to minimize, is

$$\frac{dT}{T} = - \frac{dV_{co}}{V_{co} \ln (V_b/V_{co})}. \qquad (12.21)$$

The desired minimum corresponds to a maximum of the previous denominator; differentiation yields as the optimum condition

$$V_b \doteq 2.71 V_{co} \quad \text{or} \quad \mu \doteq 2.71. \qquad (12.22)$$

That is, under the assumptions 12.16 and 12.18, the frequency is least affected by a prescribed change in V_{co} when $\mu = 2.71$. Such a low value of μ is consistent with obtaining the desired low values of r_p. Moreover the fractional change in μ from tube to tube is lower in low-μ than in high-μ tubes because it is less sensitive to the position of the grid with respect to cathode and plate. Because tubes having the desired characteristics are not commonly available, it is fortunate that the same result can be achieved with ordinary tubes by the simple circuit change, described in the following section.

12.15 Positive grid return

The poor frequency stability which is characteristic of high-μ triodes in the conventional multivibrator circuit is readily understood in terms of Fig. 12.15, which shows (curve a) that a small change in V_{co} will produce a large change in the period. A great improvement in stability would result if the voltage could be made to decrease linearly rather than exponentially with time. We are led immediately to the positive grid return as a means of approximating this objective.[*] The arrangement is shown in Fig. 12.16. It is seen that the grids now relax toward a voltage which is positive rather than zero and that the period is considerably shortened thereby. The successive steps in obtaining the original period with improved stability are represented

* The positive return was devised by the author in 1940 and was evidently invented still earlier by Bartelink.[21] It has probably been independently discovered by many other workers in the field.

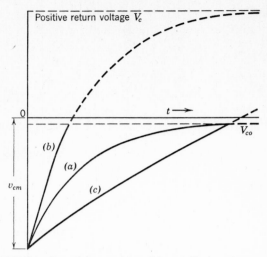

FIG. 12.15. Grid relaxation: (a) normal resistor and zero return voltage (b) same resistor and positive return voltage, and (c) higher resistor and positive return voltage.

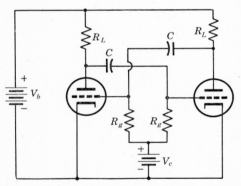

FIG. 12.16. Symmetrical multivibrator with positive grid return voltage.

by curves b and c in Fig. 12.15. Re-examination of the development of eq. 12.11 with use of eq. 12.8 shows that the total period is now given by

$$T = 2C\left[R_g + \frac{\bar{r}_p R_L}{\bar{r}_p + R_L}\right] \ln\left[\left(\frac{V_b R_L}{\bar{r}_p + R_L} + V_c\right)\left(\frac{1}{V_c + V_{co}}\right)\right]. \quad (12.23)$$

As before, frequency stability is favored by making $\bar{r}_p$ small. Paralleling the development of eq. 12.22, we conclude that for optimum frequency stability

$$V_b + V_c \doteq 2.71(V_{co} + V_c). \quad (12.24)$$

If, as is usually the case, V_{co} is negligible with respect to the other terms, the criterion for best frequency stability reduces to

$$V_b \doteq 1.71 V_c. \qquad (12.25)$$

However, the optimum is reasonably broad, and it is customary to let $V_b = V_c$. This is convenient and has the advantage that any drift occurs equally in both voltages. Moreover, when $V_b = V_c$, specified values of R_g and C lead to somewhat higher frequencies than correspond to eq. 12.25. The equation for the total period when $V_b = V_c$ becomes

$$T = 1.4 C R_g \quad \text{or, roughly,} \quad T \doteq \sqrt{2}\, C R_g. \qquad (12.26)$$

When suitable positive grid return is used and the impedance inequalities of eqs. 12.16 and 12.18 are observed, the frequency stability of the symmetrical multivibrator is reasonably good. Frequency variations due to aging and voltage changes are of the order of one per cent and those due to interchange of tubes are only a few per cent. Positive return of the grid leaks does not result in excessive currents or dissipation because of the large resistances used. The average grid current is usually only a fraction of a milliampere, and the plate current is little affected, the positive bias helping to make the effective plate resistance small. Thus, although the arrangement is startling at first glance, it is entirely consistent with conservative long-life operation of the tubes. The return of the grid leaks to an adjustable positive voltage provides a very convenient and practical way of varying the period of a multivibrator without affecting the symmetry or general form of the output wave. Data on this and other features of multivibrator behavior are given by Bertram.[32]

12.16 Transfer time in the multivibrator

As with the van der Pol and other relaxation oscillators, the rapidity of transfer from one tube to the other in the multivibrator is limited by parasitic capacitance. The complete behavior is very complicated, but it is possible to obtain a reasonable approximation by methods similar to those already described.* The analysis begins with examination of Fig. 12.17, which represents the multivibrator having positive grid return. Let us study the transition in which T_1 ceases to conduct and T_2 becomes conducting.

By assuming that both tubes have idealized cutoff characteristics and by limiting ourselves to the interval during which both tubes oper-

* An equivalent result is obtained by a comparable argument in *Waveforms*,[57] pages 174 ff.

ate in the linear negative-grid region, we may obtain a tractable equation. If the coupling capacitances are large compared to all others, their charge and potential difference cannot change during the transition.

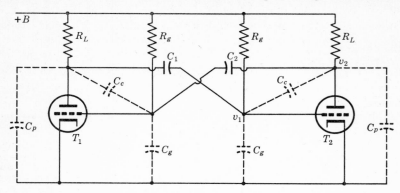

FIG. 12.17. Symmetrical multivibrator with stray capacitances.

Therefore, only two variable potentials need be considered. Let v_1 be the amount by which the second grid is more positive than the cutoff value and v_2 be the departure of the second plate from the initial (B^+) value. Use of p for d/dt and the substitutions

$$C_0 = C_g + C_p \tag{12.27}$$

and

$$C_m = 2C_c \tag{12.28}$$

yield as the differential equations for the system

$$pv_1(C_0 + C_m) + v_1(1/R_L + 1/r_p + 1/R_g)$$
$$- pv_2C_m + v_2g_m = 0 \tag{12.29}$$

and

$$pv_1C_m + v_1g_m + pv_2(C_0 + C_m)$$
$$+ v_2(1/R_L + 1/r_p + 1/R_g) = 0. \tag{12.30}$$

Elimination of the voltage variables and the additional substitution

$$G = 1/R_L + 1/r_p + 1/r_g \tag{12.31}$$

yields the system equation applicable during the transition

$$G + 2pC_m + pC_0 = g_m. \tag{12.32}$$

This equation has as the root which governs the rapidity of the transition

$$p = (g_m - G)/(C_0 + 2C_m). \tag{12.33}$$

The voltage variation during the transition may be calculated on the basis of a knowledge of v_1 and its rate of change at the beginning of the interval. From previous sections we know that at $t = 0$, $v_1 = V_{co}$ and

$$dv_1/dt \doteq (V_b + V_{co})/C_1R_g. \tag{12.34}$$

This equation takes account of the positive grid return but neglects the effect of plate and load resistances. Using eq. 12.33, we have

$$v_1 = v_0 + ae^{pt} \quad \text{and} \quad dv_1/dt = ape^{pt}. \tag{12.35}$$

Combination of the foregoing equation requires that $a = -v_0$ so that the variation of v_1 during the transition is described by

$$v_1 = \frac{(V_b + V_c)(C_0 + 2C_m)}{C_1R_g(g_m - G)} \left(-1 + e^{\left[\frac{(g_m - G)t}{C_0 + 2C_m} \right]} \right). \tag{12.36}$$

These conditions can hold only until $v_1 = V_{co}$ or until $v_2 = -V_{co}$, whichever occurs first. Because v_1 has an initial time derivative whereas v_2 has none, it appears that v_2 will not precede v_1; and consideration of the symmetry of the system urges that the two limits will be reached nearly simultaneously. The total transition time t_1 is then given by the equation

$$t_1 = \frac{C_0 + 2C_m}{g_m - G} \cdot \ln \left(\frac{V_{co}R_g(g_m - G)}{(V_b + V_{co})(C_0 + 2C_m)} \right), \tag{12.37}$$

where the initial value v_0 is neglected in comparison to V_{co}.

To illustrate the application of this equation we shall substitute parameters corresponding to the example already given. For a 6SN7 tube associated with typical socket and wiring, we have $r_p = 8000$ ohms, $g_m = 2500$ micromhos, $C_c = 4$, $C_p = 6$, $C_g = 8$, $C_0 = 14$, and $C_m = 8$ $\mu\mu$f. Corresponding to previous values, $G = 193$ micromhos; with $V_b = 250$ and $V_{co} = 16$ volts, eq. 12.37 yields $t_1 = 0.4$ μs. This result is in good agreement with experimental values, if in making such a comparison we recall that the majority of the actual transition occurs during the latter portion of this interval, as shown in Fig. 12.18. It should also be noted that the positive grid return speeds the transition somewhat by increasing the initial slope, but that this effect is small.

For most applications the *rate* of the transition is the important parameter. From eq. 12.33 it is seen that a large value of transconductance accompanied by a small value of total capacitance is desirable. Thus the figure of merit of a tube for this purpose is closely related to the figure of merit for video amplification. There is, however, a distinction of some importance. In video amplifiers the stage gain is greater than one, or no useful purpose would be served. Therefore, grid-to-plate capacitance is relatively important, and the performance of a given basic tube is improved by inserting a grounded screen between grid and plate to obtain a tetrode. In the multivibrator this is *not* true. Because each tube operates at unity gain during the transition, there is no profit in converting from a triode to a tetrode. For a plane-parallel tube, the removal of C_m by means of a grounded shield would at best increase both input and output capacitances by $C_m/2$ and leave eq. 12.33 unchanged. In practice, the total

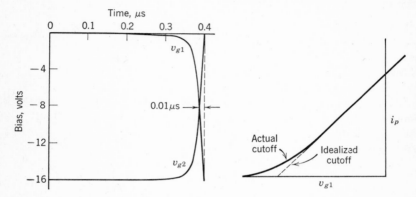

FIG. 12.18. Calculated wave forms during transition in multivibrator.

FIG. 12.19. Enlarged view of cutoff region.

capacitance would surely be somewhat increased and the transition slowed down. The use of pentodes is, however, sometimes desirable for other reasons, as discussed in a later section.

One additional feature of the transition should be mentioned. Because the cutoff in physical tubes is never sharp there is an additional interval to consider. In the tube which has been cut off, the plate current rises at first along a curve rather than as a sharp break, as shown in Fig. 12.19. Therefore, there is an interval during which the tube draws current but has a transconductance insufficient to produce unit loop gain. This interval evidently is short in time and provides a merging section between the two exponential curves already calculated. The effect is of importance only in connection with synchronization, as discussed in Chapter 13. In all cases a sharp cutoff is preferable to a remote one, and in some cases the difference is of vital importance.

12.17 Other symmetrical multivibrators

The multivibrator has been the subject of extensive development, and a large number of useful variations of the basic circuit have been devised. Some of the more important are described in this section.

Perhaps the simplest variation of the multivibrator is the substitution of pentodes for triodes. As previously mentioned, this does not in principle increase the ra-pidity of the transitions. How-ever, the extensive use of pen-todes in other applications has led to the development of tubes which are quite desirable in mul-tivibrators. Moreover, the knee region in the plate current char-acteristic is favorable to fre-quency stability in that the grid excursion is readily made almost equal to the applied plate voltage.

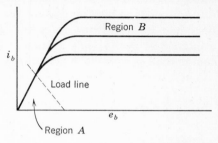

FIG. 12.20. Pentode characteristics.

Unfortunately, there is a marked tendency for the circuit to fail to oscillate when this is done. In this undesired stable condition, corresponding to Fig. 12.20, both grids are at zero bias and both plates are at a low voltage which is independent of the grid voltage. This condition, which is particularly

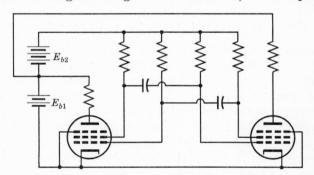

FIG. 12.21. Screen-coupled pentode multivibrator.

likely to occur with positive grid return, can be upset by a vigorous transient. However, the necessity of providing a starting impulse is so undesirable that this arrangement is rarely used.

An important variation of the pentode multivibrator is shown in Fig. 12.21. The feedback coupling is provided by the screen and control grids, and positive grid return is used in the interest of fre-quency stability. The output voltage may be taken from either or both plate circuits.   The desirable feature of this arrangement is that the output wave may be made remarkably square.   This useful behavior depends upon a property of pentodes which is illustrated in Fig. 12.20.   For low values of plate voltage the plate current depends principally upon the plate voltage and is virtually independent of screen and control grid voltages.   Therefore, the overshoot characteristic of the plate voltage wave of the triode is absent. Rounding of the leading edge of the wave form is avoided by limiting the plate load resistors to a low value, which in turn requires the use of a low plate supply voltage.   This arrangement is used in many commercial square-wave generators.

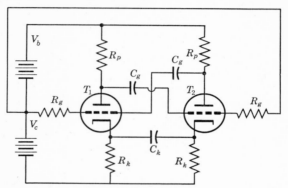

FIG. 12.22.   Symmetrical cathode-coupled multivibrator.

An important form of multivibrator depends for its action upon cathode coupling, as shown in Fig. 12.22.   An exceptional feature of this circuit is that the timing action occurs in the cathode circuit, and is independent of the grid leaks and coupling capacitors, which should be effectively infinite.   This is possible because there is no grid current, and desirable in the interest of allowing the cathode circuit to have complete control of the period, which then depends upon the coupling capacitor C and the plate and cathode resistors.   An advantage of this circuit is that relatively high frequencies may be produced with convenient values of the circuit parameters and without the loss of loop gain which is encountered in the conventional multivibrator.

The analysis is facilitated by assuming that the cathode resistors are large compared to the reciprocal of the transconductance ($R_k g_m \gg 1$). As previously stated, the grid leaks and condensers are assumed to be effectively infinite.   The plate load resistors are assumed to be equal and will presently be assigned a value somewhat smaller than the cathode resistors.   Each tube conducts an average current i_0; and during its active period carries a current which decreases in a nearly linear manner from $2i_0 + i_1$ to $2i_0 - i_1$. Typical wave forms are shown in Fig. 12.23.

The operating cycle may be explained by assuming that T_1, which previously carried a current $(2i_0 - i_1)$, has just ceased to conduct. Accordingly, the potential of the plate of T_1 and of the grid of T_2 is suddenly increased by an amount $(2i_0 - i_1)R_p$. Moreover, the cathode potential of T_2 increases by substantially this amount, as does the cathode potential of T_1 by the action of C_k. The potentials of the grid and cathode of T_2 now remain constant for an interval during which the cathode potential of T_1 relaxes toward zero by action of R_k and C_k.

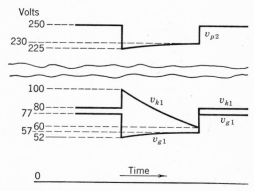

Fig. 12.23.   Wave forms in cathode-coupled multivibrator.

The discharge path includes C_k and R_k of T_1. Because the cathode potential of T_2 is nearly constant during this interval, the time constant of this relaxation is simply R_kC_k. Simultaneously, the potentials of the plate of T_2 and hence of the grid of T_1 increase, because the decrease in currents in R_p of T_2 and R_k of T_1 must be equal. The interval comes to an end when the grid and cathode potentials of T_1 reach the cutoff value; whereupon T_1 becomes conducting and T_2 is cut off.

The quantitative behavior of the cathode-coupled multivibrator may be approximated by a procedure similar to that used in conjunction with the ordinary multivibrator. During the time that a particular tube conducts, its grid potential and hence cathode potential are substantially constant. However, the cathode current, which equals the plate current, changes in an approximately linear manner in conformity with the relaxation of the cathode condenser. Let us represent the average current flowing through the cathode resistor of the conducting tube as i_0. Then, the total cathode (and plate) current decreases from $(2i_0 + i_1)$ to $(2i_0 - i_1)$ during the conduction interval. Therefore, in the nonconducting tube the cathode potential drops by $2i_1R_k$, and the grid potential increases by $2i_1R_p$, by action of the coupling condenser. Conduction will recommence when the sum of the above excursions is (approximately) equal to the sum of the transitions produced at the beginning of the cutoff interval. That is, when

$$2i_1(R_p + R_k) = i_1R_k + (2i_0 + i_1)R_p$$

or $$(12.38)$$

$$i_0/i_1 = (R_p + R_k)/2R_p.$$

Moreover, the period t of conduction by one tube is given approximately by the relation based upon relaxation of current in the cathode resistor of the cutoff tube

$$t = R_kC_k \ln\left(\frac{i_0 + i_1}{i_0 - i_1}\right) \doteq 2R_kC_k\,i_1/i_0, \qquad (13.39)$$

where the latter form is based on the series approximation valid if $i_1 \ll i_0$. The overall period, T, may be obtained by combining the previous equations to obtain

$$T = 2t = 8R_kC_kR_p/(R_k + R_p). \qquad (12.40)$$

The total period reduces simply to R_kC_k provided $R_k = 7R_p$, a relationship which is suitable for typical operation.

The operation of the circuit is illustrated by a numerical example, which corresponds to values indicated on Fig. 12.23. The tube is the 6SN7 dual triode, and the circuit parameters are $V_b = 250$ volts, $V_c = 67$ volts, $C_k = 1000\ \mu\mu\text{f}$, $R_k = 20{,}000$ ohms, and $R_p = 2800$ ohms ($R_k/7$ approximately). The values $i_0 = 4$ ma and $i_1 = 1$ ma lead to the potentials shown. Reference to the static characteristics of this tube show that a plate current of 9 ma ($2i_0 + i_1$) corresponds to a plate voltage of 145 volts and a negative bias of 3 volts. The plate current is reduced to 7 ma ($2i_0 - i_1$) at a plate voltage of 150 by about an additional volt of grid bias. The only serious discrepancy in the previous discussion arises from the assumption implicit in eq. 12.38 that the operating and cutoff biases are equal. Actually, the cutoff voltage in the present case is about 12 rather than 3 volts, and the period will be about 10 per cent shorter than indicated.

It will be noted that the full period corresponding to eq. 12.40 is only 20 microseconds, corresponding to a fundamental frequency of 50 kc, and that much shorter periods could be obtained without the use of unreasonable element values. The transition speed of this circuit has not been calculated; however, it is probably somewhat superior to that of the conventional multivibrator. In any event, the wave forms are not appreciably rounded because of the low impedance levels. Moreover, the frequency is insensitive to tube conditions because the grids are not driven positive and because a large amount of negative feedback is provided in the cathode circuit. For the same reason it is relatively easy to maintain equality between the conduction intervals of the two tubes. It is clear that the advantages of cathode coupling may be preserved when pentodes are used, and that very square output waves may still be obtained by the use of the form of plate clipping described in connection with Fig. 12.21.

12.18 Asymmetrical multivibrators

In the preceding sections we have assumed that the tubes and components are entirely symmetrical. Such a condition is never achieved exactly and is rarely approximated. However, the operation of the various circuits is not greatly affected unless the departure from symmetry is quite marked. The duration and magnitude of the voltages and currents at corresponding points are unequal, but the overall behavior is little affected. The principal effect from the practical standpoint is that for particular ratios of "off" and "on" time certain harmonics disappear from the output. For this reason it is unwise to attempt to use high-order harmonics from multivibrators. This topic is discussed more fully in Chapter 14.

For certain applications it is desirable to operate the multivibrator asymmetrically so that one tube draws current longer than the other.[93] In moderation, this effect is readily achieved in the standard circuit configuration by making one grid leak or condenser (or both) considerably larger than the other. However, as the degree of asymmetry is made large many problems arise. The basic difficulty is that the longer relaxation time must be prepared for during the shorter conduction period. This topic is discussed at length by Chance[57] (pages 179 ff. of his book) and will not be considered in detail here. In general, however, if a symmetrical multivibrator using fairly low values of grid leaks can be made to operate at the shorter of the two intervals, the desired operation is secured if one grid leak is increased to lengthen the corresponding conduction period. Increase of a coupling capacitance is *not* suitable because the initial charge as well as the discharge is upset. The cathode-coupled multivibrator of the previous section preserves much of its desirable behavior if rendered asymmetrical. Here too, however, some care must be given to the circuit proportions.

An inherently asymmetrical multivibrator is shown in Fig. 12.24. It is seen that the circuit would be stable and that both tubes would draw reasonable and nearly equal currents if R_g were shorted. The corresponding conditions of voltage and current approximate the average of the values which occur during operation. Use of Nyquist's test shows that the circuit is unstable. Application of a small positive voltage to the grid of T_1 would produce a nearly equal voltage rise at its cathode and hence at the cathode of T_2. The resulting loss of current in T_2 would produce a large positive voltage returned to the grid of T_1, through C.

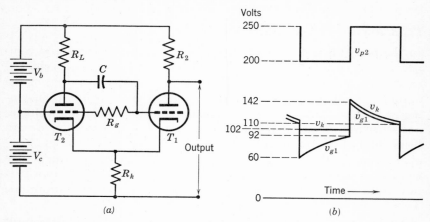

FIG. 12.24. Asymmetrical cathode-coupled multivibrator: (a) circuit and (b) wave forms.

Values suitable for operation with the 6SN7 dual triode are $R_g = 10^6$, $R_L = 10^4$, $R_k = 2 \times 10^4$ ohms, $C = 1000$ $\mu\mu$f, $V_b = 250$, and $V_c = 100$ volts. The operation is best understood in terms of the voltage waves of Fig. 12.24b. During one interval, the grid of T_1 is held negative by action of the plate circuit of T_2, which draws a constant current. The magnitude of this current is quite insensitive to the condition of the tube because of the marked stabilizing action of the large cathode resistor. When the grid has relaxed to about 92 volts, conduction in T_1 is resumed. The corresponding reduction of current in T_2 is regenerative through the plate circuit, and in a short time T_2 is completely cut off and the grid of T_1 is driven some 50 volts positive by the action of the coupling condenser. However, the grid of T_1 *does not* draw current during this interval because the cathode voltage rises very rapidly. During the next interval the grid relaxes downward toward V_c (100 volts). This timing period ends when the voltage equals about 110 volts, at which time tube T_2 begins to conduct and the grid is driven negative to 60 volts to commence the alternate timing interval.

In spite of the asymmetry of the connections, the conduction periods are almost identical. When T_2 is cut off, the relaxation is clearly that of C in series with R_g and R_L. When T_2 is conducting, the circuit is modified by the effective plate resistance, given by the formula

$$r_p' = r_p(1 + R_k g_m),\qquad(12.41)$$

which is 400,000 ohms in the present case, and since $R_g \gg R_L$ the effect is entirely negligible. Any asymmetry observed in the conduction intervals is due to inequality in the cutoff characteristics of the tubes.

The circuit is attractive because an output may be taken from a low-resistance R_2 in the plate lead of T_1, without affecting the operation and because the grid of T_2 is available for synchronization or other control. Finally, the voltage wave at the plate of T_2 is quite square and free from overshoot. Additional information concerning this and related circuits is given by Pullen,[249] Glegg,[114] and Newitt.[220]

12.19 The blocking oscillator

Figure 12.25 shows an important relaxation oscillator, now commonly referred to as the blocking oscillator. The configuration is virtually

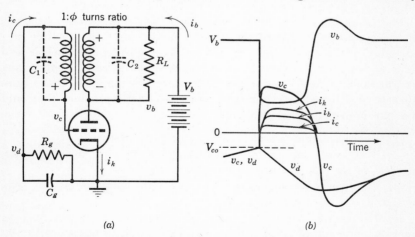

(a)   (b)

FIG. 12.25.   The blocking oscillator: (a) circuit and (b) typical wave forms.

identical with that of the tuned plate oscillator, previously described, but the operation is quite different because of the difference in the values of the parameters. In particular, the plate and grid windings are tightly coupled, usually by means of a laminated iron core.   The inductances are relatively large, and the capacitances are as small as possible.   An exceptional feature of the blocking oscillator is the large peak power which may be generated with a small tube.   A momentary power output of 100 watts from a tube such as the 6J5 is typical. Overheating does not occur because the plate current is zero during a very large fraction of the total time.   The circuit, which has received extensive development, appears first to have been devised by Vecchiacchi.[331]   Additional discussion and analysis is given by Last[183] and Benjamin.[29]

Slightly idealized wave forms representing the conduction interval in a typical blocking oscillator are shown in Fig. 12.25b.   The plate voltage drops to a small fraction of the supply value, the grid is driven to a large positive voltage, and large plate and grid currents flow. During the interval of conduction the grid-to-plate transconductance is very low and the grid loses control of the plate current; conduction ceases where the grid regains control.   This usually occurs when the charge accumulated in C_g by the large grid current is sufficient to bias the system so that the grid is no longer more positive than the plate. At the end of the conduction interval the tube remains cut off for a considerable relaxation period while the charge stored in C_g leaks off through R_g.   In typical circuits the conduction and relaxation periods are about one microsecond and one millisecond, respectively.

The operation of the blocking oscillator is complicated.   Analysis of the operation is difficult because of nonlinearity in the tube and probably in the transformer as well.   The empirical approach is also difficult because it is very hard to isolate and control the important parameters.   However, the following statements appear to be adequately established by experience.   In all cases it is assumed that only one parameter is varied at a time.

(1) The relaxation period is directly proportional to R_g.

(2) Both the conduction and relaxation periods increase with increase of C_g, but not proportionally.

(3) The conduction period increases with increase of the self-inductance of the transformer.

(4) More core material is required if the output power or conduction period is increased; otherwise saturation interferes with the operation.

(5) The conduction period will be shortened if the cathode emission of the tube is sufficiently reduced by lowering the heater voltage.

(6) Damping must be provided by means of a load resistor or by

core losses; otherwise the conduction interval is followed by violent oscillations.

(7) The steepness of the voltage waves is controlled by parasitic capacitances in the tube and transformer, and by leakage.

Pulse voltages of a kilovolt or more at power levels of several kilowatts may be obtained by using a transmitting tube such as the 829 in a blocking oscillator. Such an arrangement is greatly favored in compact low-power radar systems because of the resulting high efficiency and economy of parts.

12.20 Analysis of the blocking oscillator

In Chapter 7, it was shown that relaxation oscillations will occur in the circuit of Fig. 12.26, provided

$$\mu M > r_p(2\sqrt{L_2 C} + L_2/R + L_2/r_p). \tag{12.42}$$

This information is applicable, because we may identify Fig. 12.26 with the blocking oscillator of Fig. 12.25. Subject to the assumption of unity coupling, we have $M = L_2/\phi$, where ϕ is the turns ratio of the transformer. Moreover, the total effective capacitance is given by $C = C_2 + C_1/\phi^2$. Eliminating M in eq. 12.42 yields as the condition for relaxation oscillation

$$\mu > \phi(1 + r_p/R + 2r_p\sqrt{C/L_2}). \tag{12.43}$$

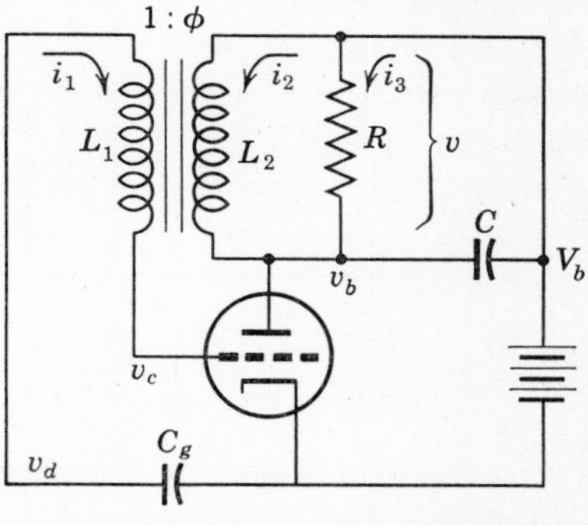

In Chapter 2 it was shown that while the tube is cut off the plate

FIG. 12.26. Analysis of pulse length.

circuit is critically damped, provided $R = \frac{1}{2}\sqrt{L_2/C}$. However, a heavier damping is desirable, and we shall assume that

$$R = \frac{1}{4}\sqrt{L_2/C}. \tag{12.44}$$

With this substitution and the choice $R = \frac{1}{3}r_p$, suitable for typical triodes, eq. 12.43 becomes

$$\mu > 5.5\phi. \tag{12.45}$$

This condition is readily satisfied by conventional triodes in conjunction with transformers having turns ratios near one.

Although an exact analysis is impractical, we may obtain useful information about the operating cycle of the blocking oscillator by means of suitable approximations. Let us first explore the pulse length, that is, conduction interval. On the basis of experimental data and experience with the multivibrator we anticipate that the parasitic capacitances are unimportant and that the governing factors are the transformer, the condenser C_g, the tube, the supply voltage, and possibly the load resistor. Unity coupling between the windings is assumed, because of the tight coupling commonly used in transformers for this purpose.

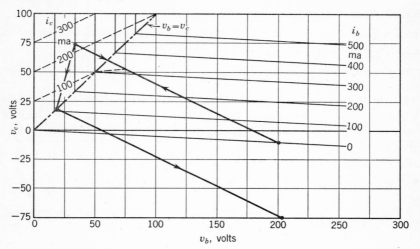

Fig. 12.27. Approximate constant-current curves of 6J5.

Conduction begins at the instant, $t = 0$, when the grid bias voltage v_d falls to the cutoff value V_{co}. The first small increment of plate current induces a positive voltage in the grid winding which increases the conduction, and the plate current increases rapidly and exponentially with time. In a very short interval the grid is driven positive and both plate and grid draw quite large currents. Because of the short time involved there can be no appreciable storage of energy by establishment of flux in the transformer. Therefore, we may write

$$i_1 = \phi i_2. \tag{12.46}$$

The extent to which the grid is driven positive and the magnitude of i_1 and i_2 can only be determined by reference to the characteristic of the vacuum tube used. Figure 12.27 shows the properties of the 6J5 or 6SN7. The characteristics shown are somewhat idealized to emphasize the properties of present interest and to simplify the calculations; they are, however, essentially correct. The exceptional feature of these curves, which are obtainable only by pulse techniques because of the large values of power dissipation involved, is that *the plate current is independent of the grid voltage if the grid is more positive than the plate. It is this fact which permits the tube to conduct a substantially constant current for a finite interval.*

Provided $v_c > v_b$, the characteristics of the vacuum tube may be represented approximately by the equations

$$i_b = g_p v_b \tag{12.47}$$

and

$$i_c = i_1 = g_c v_c - g_b v_b, \tag{12.48}$$

where g_p, g_c, and g_b represent the self-conductances of plate and grid, and the transfer conductance of the grid, respectively. Moreover, we may write

$$v_b = V_b - v, \tag{12.49}$$

$$v_c = v/\phi - v_d, \tag{12.50}$$

and

$$i_b = i_2 + v/R. \tag{12.51}$$

Solving simultaneously, we have at the beginning of the interval of conduction

$$v_b' = \frac{V_b g_c + \phi^2 V_b/R - \phi g_c v_d}{\phi^2/R + \phi^2 g_p + \phi g_b + g_c}. \tag{12.52}$$

As a numerical example consistent with Fig. 12.27, let us substitute $V_b = 200$ and $v_d = 10$ volts, $R = 2000$ ohms, $\phi = 2$, $g_p = 0.006$, $g_c = 0.004$, and $g_b = 0.002$ mho. These values correspond to the load line shown and lead to $v_b' = 32.9$ volts. The corresponding parameters are $v' = 167.1$ volts, $v_c' = 73.6$ volts, $i_1' = 228$, $i_2' = 114$, and $i_b' = 198$ ma.

During the conduction interval the grid has negligible control over the plate current, which tends to remain constant because of the low dynamic plate resistance. However, both the grid current and the voltage decrease rapidly for two separate reasons. First, the large grid current charges C_g, thereby increasing v_d and reducing v_c. Second, because the self-inductances of the transformer are finite, the relationship represented by eq. 12.46 is departed from to a degree given by

$$v = L_2 di_2/dt - M \, di_1/dt. \tag{12.53}$$

If the grid condenser is large, v_d will remain substantially constant. Moreover, because the transformer is assumed to have unity coupling, the relationship between plate and grid voltages represented by the load line of Fig. 12.27 is preserved. The operating point simply travels to the right along the load line until the condition $v_b = v_c$ is reached, at which time the conduction ceases. Because v does not change by a large amount during this interval, we may obtain a good approximation to the conduction interval by the use of simple increments. The currents which correspond to the intersection of $v_b = v_c$ with the load line may be represented by i_b'' and i_c''. With this substitution the approximate value of *the inductance-controlled pulse length is*

$$t = \frac{L_2(i_b'' - i_b') - M(i_c'' - i_c')}{v}. \tag{12.54}$$

In the numerical example cited, conduction ceases when $v_b = v_c = 60$ volts, at which point $i_b'' = 360$, $i_1'' = 120$, and $i_2'' = 290$ ma. Substitution of $v = 150$ as a rough average value and, using $L_2 = 3.2$ and $M = 1.6$ mh in eq. 12.54, we have from the initial and final current values the inductance-controlled pulse duration $t = 4.6$ μs.

When the grid condenser is relatively small it exercises the main control over the pulse length. When this is true, we can obtain a fair approximation to the pulse duration by assuming that the transformer inductances are infinite. The pulse will end when v_d increases to some new value v_d''' which satisfies eq. 12.52 at some point where $v_b''' = v_c'''$. The resulting condition may be shown to be

$$v_d''' = V_b\left(\frac{1}{\phi} - \frac{\phi + 1}{R\phi g_p + Rg_b - Rg_c + \phi}\right). \tag{12.55}$$

Moreover the charge must represent the accumulation of grid current according to the expression

$$v_d''' - v_d = \frac{1}{C_g}\int_0^t i_1\,dt. \tag{12.56}$$

The associated variation of voltages is represented in Fig. 12.27.

Consistent with the same numerical example we have $v_d''' = 72.7$, $v_b''' = 18.18$, and $v = 181.8$ volts, and $i_1 = 36.36$, $i_2 = 18.18$, and $i_b = 109.1$ ma. Assuming that the grid current decreases linearly with time, we may use the average to approximate *the condenser-controlled pulse duration*

$$t = 2C_g\frac{(v_d''' - v_d)}{i_1 + i_1'''}. \tag{12.57}$$

Further assuming that $C_g = 2000$ $\mu\mu$f, a typical value, we have, from eq. 12.57, $t = 0.95$ μs. In practice, both C_g and L_2 influence the pulse duration. However, one or the other parameter usually exerts the main control so that a good approximation to the behavior may be obtained from eqs. 12.54 or 12.57, whichever is appropriate.

The pulse length of a blocking oscillator may, within limits, be controlled by means of a delay line which is substituted for C_g in Fig. 12.25a. The line is open-circuited at both ends except for the high impedance of the grid leak. Provided the line has a suitable impedance and the transformer is capable of creating pulses somewhat longer than the desired value, the pulse length will correspond to the round-trip time of the line. Conduction ceases because the bias voltage v_d approximately doubles at the instant when the wave reflected by the open circuit returns to the input end of the line.

12.21 Rise time and overshoot

The preceding discussion has inferred that the plate potential drops instantly when conduction begins and rises instantly when it ceases. Actually, of course, this is not true because of parasitic capacitance, leakage inductance, and other distributed elements. However, the transitions may be made very rapid because of the low impedance levels and large effective transconductance which exist during the pulse. As a crude approximation we may write for the rise time in Fig. 12.26

$$t_r = \frac{vC}{i_b + i_1/\phi}. \tag{12.58}$$

Returning to the numerical example, where $C = 50 \times 10^{-12}$, $v = 167$, $i_b = 198$, and $i_1 = 228$, we have $t_r = 0.026$ μs, a reasonable value. It is possible to make more accurate calculations of rise time, but the circuit parameters are rarely known well enough to justify the extra effort.

At the end of the conduction interval the energy stored in the transformer inductance is dissipated in the load resistor R. The sudden termination of i_1 and i_b causes a decrease in i_2 and a consequent reversal of i_3 and v. The magnitude of the reverse voltage developed across C and R is readily calculated by transient theory. Moreover, we can immediately set an upper bound on this reverse voltage or *overshoot* by ignoring C and using the continuity of current in an inductance.

Consistent with the 4.6 μs pulse of eq. 12.54 we find that the current transferred to the resistor is $(290 - 120/2)$ ma and the reverse voltage

TABLE 12.1. TRANSFORMERS FOR USE IN BLOCKING OSCILLATORS

Rad. Lab. Number*	W'hse Number†	Winding Turns‡	Load, Ohms	Pulse Length, μs	GE Number§	Winding Turns‡	Pulse Length, μs	Raytheon Number	Winding Turns‡	Pulse Length, μs
132-AW	P1	32-32-32	250	0.3 to 1.5	68 G 505	82-74/82-74	0.5 to 10	UX 7307‖	50-50-50/50-50-50	0.1 to 5
132-BW	P2	32-32-32-10	200	0.3 to 1.5	68 G 627	140-140/140-70	1 to 20	UX 7350‖	50-50-50/50-50-50-50	0.1 to 5
132-DW	P3	20-20-20	300	0.1 to 0.5	68 G 709	150-150/150-150	1 to 20	UX 7852	32-32-32	0.3 to 1.5
134-BW	P4	140-140/140-70	1500	1 to 5	68 G 712	150-150/150-150	1 to 20	UX 7853	32-32-32	0.3 to 1.5
134-CW	P5	140-140-70	1200	1 to 5	68 G 813	37-74/74-111	1 to 20	UX 8091	70-70-140	1 to 5
134-EW	P6	50-50-25	800	0.3 to 1.5	68 G 828	140-140/140-70	1 to 20	UX 8092	40-40-80	0.5 to 2
145-CW	P7	125-125-125	500	1 to 5	68 G 979	140-140/140-70	1 to 20	UX 8205	60-60-80	1 to 5
145-EW	P8	150-150-150	800	1 to 5	80 G 240	150-150/150-150	1 to 20	UX 8413	140-140/140-70	1 to 5
166-AW	P9	90-90-135	800	1 to 5	80 G 459	50-100-70	1 to 20	UX 8496‖	50-50-50/50-50-50	0.1 to 5
176-AW	P10	70-70-140	1000	0.5 to 2	80 G 587	100-100-100	0.5 to 10	Utah No.		
187-AW	P11	40-40-80	400	0.1 to 0.5	80 G 754	125-75-50	1 to 6	OA 18‖,¶	50-50-50/50-50-50	0.1 to 5
224-AW	P12	35-35-35-10	1000		713 0884	20-20-20	0.1 to 2	OA 15**	80-80/80-80	1 to 50

* These twelve designs originated at the M.I.T. Radiation Laboratory. The suffix "2" is sometimes used to indicate that the Hypersil core stock is 0.002 inch rather than 0.003 inch thick.

† Made by Specialty Transformer division of Westinghouse Electric Corporation, Sharon, Pa. Depending upon the impregnation and mounting, the type number is preceded by 1, 4, or 7. Rated at a maximum duty of 0.002, although a larger value should be safe at lower levels.

‡ The number of turns in each separate winding is given. The slant bar indicates windings on the opposite leg of a simple core.

§ Made by the Specialty Transformer division of the General Electric Company, Fort Wayne, Ind. The wide range of pulse durations represents a difference of rating rather than of construction.

‖ These units appear to be identical in essential characteristics. The wide range of pulse duration is achieved by variation of the manner in which the windings are connected.

¶ The Utah OA 18 is the basis of a long series of sealed transformers which differ in internal connection and inductance tolerance. The X139 uses only two windings on one leg; the X143 uses three windings on one leg. The X124 uses all windings in three series-aiding pairs; the X146 differs from it only in that one pair of windings is ignored. The X148 uses all windings in two series-aiding groups. The X140 uses four series-aiding coils and two separate coils; whereas the X138 uses series-aiding groups of two and four coils. A green dot indicates a close tolerance on primary inductance, a yellow dot is intermediate, and a red dot indicates a relatively wide tolerance. The 9280 and 9262 are equivalent to the X124.

** The X154 and X166 transformers are based on the OA 15 design. These and nearly all other Utah designs are currently available from Fisher Engineering, Inc., Maple Grove Road, Huntington, Ind. Certain of the Utah designs are also manufactured by Chicago Transformer Company and United Transformer Company.

could not exceed 460 volts. Consistent with the assumption of eq. 12.57 there would be *no overshoot* because no energy was assumed to have been stored. In practice there is usually an appreciable overshoot, but the magnitude of this effect can be kept within tolerable limits.

The wave forms produced by practical blocking oscillators are seriously degraded by leakage inductance, distributed capacitance, and saturation in the transformer. Moreover, if the core laminations are too thick, the resulting eddy currents excessively reduce the transient inductance of the windings. These effects are so pronounced in the transformers commonly used in television sweep circuits that the wave form is smoothed to the approximate form of a single sinusoidal cycle. In view of these effects, and contrary to our definitions, Maloff and Epstein[203] assert that the blocking oscillator is *not* a relaxation oscillator.

The performance of a blocking oscillator is greatly affected by the construction of the transformer, which ordinarily employs several single-layer windings on one or both legs of a small core of thin magnetic laminations or ribbon. The design of such transformers is a complicated matter, based very largely upon empirical procedures. It is therefore desirable to use a ready-made unit whenever possible. To facilitate experimental work, the properties of some transformers which have been manufactured in quantity are presented in Table 12.1.

12.22 Variations of the blocking oscillator

A number of variations of the blocking oscillator exist. One of these, shown in Fig. 12.28a, employs coupling between the plate and cathode circuits, and uses the tube as a grounded-grid amplifier. In this arrangement the grid is substantially at ground potential and the flow of plate current drives the cathode negative with respect to the grid. Because the cathode impedance is low, it is necessary to use a step-down ratio between plate and cathode. The plate winding ordinarily has two or three times as many turns as the cathode winding. The remarkable feature of this circuit is that the maximum voltage developed across the load R is considerably larger than V_b. This situation exists because the cathode is driven negative with respect to ground by the transformer action. And, as already shown, a quasistable state can exist only if the plate is negative with respect to the grid, which in turn is negative with respect to ground by the amount of the bias. This arrangement is good on the basis of parasitic capacitances, because one end of each winding is effectively at ground potential and because the grid serves as a grounded shield between plate and cathode.   More-over, for reasons that are not well understood, the operating cycle is relatively insensitive to tube and voltage variations.

The grounded-plate form of the blocking oscillator is shown in Fig. 12.28b.   The arrangement shown suffers the disadvantage that the rapidity of transfer is degraded by the relatively large cathode-to-

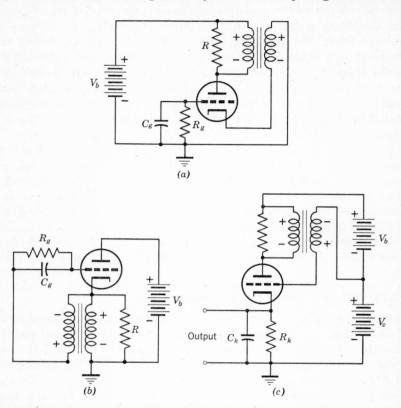

Fig. 12.28.   Variations of the blocking oscillator: (a) grounded grid, (b) grounded plate, and (c) Kobayashi's sweep.

ground capacitance and by direct grid-to-ground capacitances.   How-ever, these effects can be minimized by careful layout and by feeding the heater through appropriate chokes.

The advantage of the grounded-plate connection is that elec-tron coupling is readily achieved by substitution of a pentode with by-passed screen grid and with a suitable load in series with the plate. Because the full transconductance is available, the transition rates may be made relatively fast.   Electron coupling has the usual advantage of isolating the timing functions from the load circuit; here it permits the generation of powerful negative pulses which are quite free from oscillations or overshoot.

Electron coupling may also be obtained by using the screen of a pentode as an equivalent plate, in a grounded cathode circuit.   However, the reduced transconductance which is inherent in this arrangement seriously limits the performance.

A circuit due to Kobayashi,[175] which is related to Puckle's sweep, is shown in Fig. 12.28c.   The circuit differs from the ordinary blocking oscillator in that the grid is returned to a fixed positive voltage, and the relaxation occurs in the cathode circuit.   The operating cycle is readily explained on the basis of the previous work.   The charge placed on C_k by preceding cycles leaks off through R_k until the condenser voltage approaches V_c.   At this point plate current begins to flow, and the regenerative action drives the grid positive.   The large cathode current which results from the combined grid and plate currents rapidly charges C_k toward the supply voltage V_b.

As with the normal blocking oscillator, the conduction interval will end by the action of the transformer itself if no other influence is present.   This is the desired condition in the present case.   The transformer is so proportioned that the conduction interval is no longer than the allowable flyback time.   The cathode condenser is chosen so that the total charge delivered by the cathode will produce a suitable increase of cathode voltage, the desired value depending upon considerations of linearity, etc.   Finally, R_k, which may be replaced by a pentode in the interest of linearity, is chosen to give the desired sweep period consistent with the capacitance of C_k and the voltage excursion already fixed.

Few data are available concerning this circuit, but it appears that the arrangement should be capable of producing a relatively large sweep voltage with exceptionally short flyback time over a wide range of frequencies.   For extremely high frequencies, it should be superior to Puckle's sweep in that even larger values of grid and plate current are realizable.

PROBLEMS

12.1. Derive eqs. 12.3, 12.5, and 12.6.

12.2. A thyratron oscillator similar to that of Section 12.5 has values $V_3 = 150$, $V_4 = 20$, and $V_0 = 500$ volts; $C = 1000$ $\mu\mu f$, $R_1 = 300$, and $R = 10^7$ ohms. Calculate the period, and flyback time, the amplitude, and nonlinearity and displacement error.

12.3. In Fig. 12.6, $C = 10^{-9}$ farads, $R_2 = 2 \times 10^4$, and $R_1 = 2 \times 10^6$ ohms, and $V_b = 200$ volts.   Calculate the wave form and periods, using the curves of

Fig. 12.8 and assuming that the third grid has an effective resistance of 5000 ohms when positive.

12.4. Discuss the design of Puckle's sweep, giving special emphasis to the ways in which the conduction of T_1 may be brought to an end.

12.5. Referring to Section 12.13, determine the period and wave forms produced by a 6SN7 provided $C = 500$ $\mu\mu f$, $R_L = 10^4$ and $R_g = 10^6$ ohms, and $V_b = 300$ volts.

12.6. Repeat Prob. 12.5, assuming the grid leaks are returned to $+300$ volts.

12.7. Taking characteristics of the 6SJ7 from a tube handbook, design a multivibrator like Fig. 12.21 to generate 30 volts output at a frequency of 5 kc.

12.8. Design a multivibrator corresponding to Fig. 12.22 to generate a 20-kc wave with the 6SN7 tube, $V_b = 300$ volts and $R_k = 25,000$ ohms.

12.9. Calculate the frequency and wave forms produced by the multivibrator given as a numerical example in Section 12.19.

12.10. Verify eqs. 12.54 and 12.57.

12.11. Under the assumptions made in Section 12.20 show that the actual plate voltage tends to *decrease* during conduction if the pulse duration is controlled by C_g; to *increase* if it is controlled by the transformer inductance.

12.12. The 6SJ7 pentode is to be used in an electron-coupled blocking oscillator corresponding to Fig. 12.28b. Discuss the parameters which must be specified in order to obtain desirable operation.

13

LOCKING AND
SYNCHRONIZATION

This chapter is concerned with the behavior of an oscillator which is subjected to a signal injected from an external source. The performance depends greatly upon the frequency, amplitude, and shape of the injected wave, and the characteristics of the oscillator itself. In general, however, the output contains a component of the injected frequency. And in many cases the original frequency of oscillation becomes equal or harmonically related to the injected frequency.

The terms *locking* and *synchronization* are used interchangeably to designate the interaction between two oscillators or between an oscillator and a separately supplied signal. The term pulling, although sometimes used in this connection, is reserved here to designate the effect of the load impedance upon the operating frequency, especially in microwave oscillators. An oscillator is said to be locked if the output frequency contains only the input frequency and its harmonics. If the injected signal is inadequate to produce locking, the output contains both the injected and the generated frequency.

Synchronization is important as a nuisance effect in beat-frequency oscillators and similar devices where a relatively small difference frequency is desired. It is usefully employed in frequency-modulation receivers and related devices as a means of amplification and limiting. As long as the input signal is sufficiently large to produce synchronization, the output is substantially constant in magnitude and contains a single frequency equal to that of the input. Finally, a locked oscillator may serve as a detector of frequency-modulated waves, if the average current in some part of the system is made a function of the input frequency.

In linear oscillators the injected signal affects the operating frequency only if the two frequencies are nearly equal. But in ordinary harmonic oscillators there is an appreciable effect if any reasonably

311

simple harmonic relationship exists between the two frequencies. In relaxation oscillators the tendency toward synchronization is so strong that frequency ratios as great as ten to one are commonly employed.

If the injected signal is derived from a second oscillator, there will be a reaction which tends to modify the amplitude and frequency of its oscillation. That is, when two separate oscillators are coupled together, both are affected. This phenomenon was probably first noted by Huygens, who discovered that two similar clocks hung on the same wall tend to synchronize and operate at the same rate. This effect, which is discussed toward the end of this chapter, was originally described in a very clear and thorough paper by E. V. Appleton.[12]

13.1 Locking in a linear oscillator

The lamp bridge oscillator discussed in several previous chapters is chosen to illustrate the analysis of thermistor-controlled linear oscillators. The arrangement shown in Fig. 13.1 has been chosen to simplify the analysis. We assume that the grid and plate impedances of the tube are very high, and that the tuned grid circuit provides the

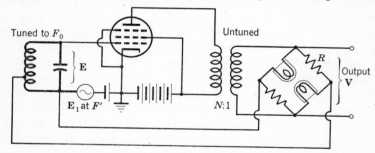

FIG. 13.1. Synchronization in lamp bridge oscillator.

entire selectivity of the system. In the absence of an injected signal, the circuit oscillates at a frequency F_0 determined by the LC combination. The amplitude of oscillation is such that a voltage V_0 exists across the lamp bridge, and a voltage E_0 exists in the grid circuit.

Before proceeding further, it is appropriate to note that the lamp bridge ordinarily is nearly balanced. Therefore, for a voltage V_B only slightly larger than V_0 the bridge will reach balance, and the voltage E returned to the grid will be zero. Accordingly, if the synchronizing signal is sinusoidal with an amplitude $E_1 = E_B$ such that the output voltage $V = V_B$, there will be no output signal of frequency F_0 produced regardless of the injected frequency F'.

Let us now assume that the synchronizing signal has a frequency

$F' = F_0$ and that E_1 is in phase with E, and is arbitrarily varied in amplitude. Under these circumstances the feedback action of the oscillator serves to stabilize the output voltage, as indicated by Fig. 13.2. It is seen that for $E_1 > E_B$ the phase of the feedback voltage is reversed, and the system is degenerative rather than regenerative. The output is, of course, a sine wave of frequency F_0.

The crucial step in the argument arises when we consider a shift in the phase of the injected voltage. The situation is shown by the phasor diagram of Fig. 13.3. It is seen that the returned voltage E is more nearly in phase with total grid voltage than is the injected voltage, and that the oscillation will quickly pull itself into phase with E_1.

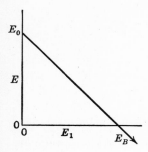

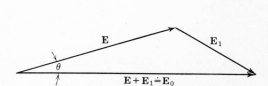

FIG. 13.2. Variation of feedback with synchronizing voltage for $F' = F_0$.

FIG. 13.3.   Phase shift associated with synchronization.

The phase relationship shown in Fig. 13.3 can remain fixed only if the synchronizing frequency F' differs from the natural frequency of the system to such an extent that the loop phase shift is just equal to θ. Under these circumstances the entire system operates at the input frequency F', and there is no output at the natural frequency F_0. So long as the input is large enough to produce synchronization, the output is nearly constant, independent of E_1, and identical to it in frequency. Such operation is referred to as locked oscillation and is useful in numerous applications.

13.2 Quantitative requirements for locking

The conditions which may arise as the amplitude and frequency of the synchronizing voltage are varied are conveniently studied by use of the modified phasor diagram of Fig. 13.4. At any specified frequency F' there is a unique phase angle θ between E and $(E + E_1)$ as determined by the selectivity of the system. Therefore, there is a certain minimum synchronizing voltage E_1', in quadrature with E, required to produce locking. If the synchronizing voltage is below this value the output will contain both F' and F_0, and the total output power is the same as if no synchronizing signal were supplied. If the synchronizing voltage exceeds E_1', as shown by E_1'' in Fig. 13.4, there are two

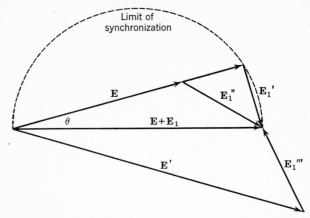

FIG. 13.4.   Calculation of voltage required for synchronization.

possible phase relationships which satisfy the stated requirements. However, the position shown by E_1''' is unstable because it requires an unnecessarily large value of E. If the synchronizing voltage is made larger than the balance value E_B, the phase of the returned voltage E is reversed.

The calculation of the minimum voltage which will produce synchronization is relatively simple because in the marginal case $E + E_1$ must equal E_0 for all values of θ in order to maintain the loop gain at zero.   Therefore, provided $E_1 < E_0$, the governing equation is

$$E_1/E_0 = \sin \theta. \tag{13.1}$$

The phase shift θ is produced by the tuned grid circuit.   Because this circuit has a moderately high Q we may use the approximate expression.[*]

$$\theta = \tan^{-1} \frac{2Q(F' - F_0)}{F_0}. \tag{13.2}$$

When E_1 is below the value required for synchronization, the output contains both frequencies as previously noted.   Provided that the

[*] An expression corresponding to eqs. 13.1 and 13.2 for the region where $\theta = \tan \theta$ is obtained by Aigrain and Williams.[5]

period of the difference frequency between F' and F_0 is short compared to the time constant of the lamp bridge, there is no interaction, and the total power output V (at two frequencies) is exactly normal because the loop gain must be unity for the production of F_0. The boundary of synchronization corresponding to the above equations is plotted in Fig. 13.5.

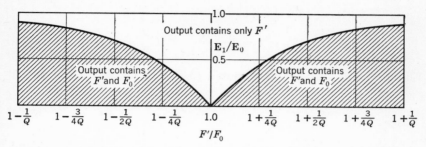

Fig. 13.5.   Voltage required for synchronization at various frequencies.

When E_1 exceeds the minimum value which produces synchronization, the output voltage is somewhat increased.   It is clear that the output is constant at the value $V = V_B$ for all values of F' if $E_1 = E_B$ because the lamp bridge is balanced, and no regeneration occurs.   The behavior at other frequencies may be obtained by use of the amplitude stability factor developed in Section 7.6.   In the notation of Chapter 7 we may write

$$\mathbf{V} = NRg_m(\mathbf{E} + \mathbf{E}_1),\tag{13.3}$$

which upon differentiation yields

$$d\mathbf{V} = NR[g_m\,d\mathbf{E} + (\mathbf{E} + \mathbf{E}_1)dg_m].\tag{13.4}$$

Combining these equations with the basic definition of amplitude stability, and assuming $\mathbf{E}_1$ constant, we have

$$S_A\frac{d\mathbf{V}}{\mathbf{V}} = \frac{dg_m}{g_m} = S_A\frac{g_m d\mathbf{E} + (\mathbf{E} + \mathbf{E}_1)dg_m}{(\mathbf{E} + \mathbf{E}_1)g_m}\tag{13.5}$$

or

$$S_A = 1 - \frac{d\mathbf{E}}{(\mathbf{E} + \mathbf{E}_1)} \cdot \frac{\mathbf{V}}{d\mathbf{V}}.\tag{13.6}$$

Provided the limiter has a linear characteristic in the operating region, as indicated in Fig. 13.2, we may write

$$\mathbf{E} = \frac{k(\mathbf{V}_B - \mathbf{V})}{1 + j\tan\theta},\tag{13.7}$$

where the factor k depends upon the amplitude stability factor, and the denominator term accounts for transmission through the tuned circuit. The parameter k is in turn evaluated by noting that in the absence of a synchronizing signal we may differentiate eq. 13.7 to obtain

$$d\mathbf{E} = -k\,d\mathbf{V}. \tag{13.8}$$

Together with eq. 13.6 this yields

$$S_A - 1 = k\,\frac{\mathbf{V}}{\mathbf{E} + \mathbf{E}_1} = k\,\frac{\mathbf{V}_B}{\mathbf{E}_B}. \tag{13.9}$$

Elimination of k and $\mathbf{E}$ between eqs. 13.7 and 13.9 gives as the output voltage

$$\mathbf{V} = \mathbf{V}_B\,\frac{S_A - 1 + (1 + j\tan\theta)\mathbf{E}_1/\mathbf{E}_B}{S_A + j\tan\theta}, \tag{13.10}$$

which is valid only provided a single output frequency is present. This expression reduces to the identity $\mathbf{V} = \mathbf{V}_B$ if $\mathbf{E}_1 = \mathbf{E}_B$ as it should. A plot of this expression for $S_A = 10$ and $Q = 50$ is shown in Fig. 13.6.*

In the upper curve, corresponding to $|E_1/E_B| = 2$, the output is at a single frequency equal to F', and decreases in magnitude as the natural frequency is approached. For the second case, $|E_1/E_B| = 1$, the output contains only the frequency F' and is constant in magnitude. In the lower curve, where $|E_1/E_B| = \frac{1}{2}$, two frequencies are present over most of the range. When F' is remote from F_0, the output at

---

* In using eq. 13.10 it is necessary to remember that $\mathbf{E}_1$ and $\mathbf{V}$ are not in phase. That is, $\mathbf{E}_1/\mathbf{E}_B$ must be treated as a complex number. Computation is facilitated by use of the substitutions $|E_1/E_B| = c$ and $\mathbf{E}_1/\mathbf{E}_B = a + jb$, which require $c^2 = a^2 + b^2$. With these substitutions, eq. 13.10 becomes

$$\frac{V}{V_B} \equiv Y = \frac{S_A - 1 + a - b\tan\theta + j(b + a\tan\theta)}{S_A + j\tan\theta}.$$

Because the new variable Y is a real number, we may expand and separately equate real and imaginary parts to obtain

$$YS_A = S_A - 1 + a - b\tan\theta \text{ and } Y\tan\theta = b - a\tan\theta.$$

Solving for $\tan\theta$ yields

$$\tan\theta = b/(Y + a) = (a + S_A - 1 - YS_A)/b.$$

Cross multiplication and introduction of c^2 yields

$$c^2 = Y(a + S_A - 1 - YS_A) + a(S_A - 1 - YS_A).$$

It is now possible to calculate a explicitly by substitution of known values of c and Y. Use of $b = \sqrt{c^2 - a^2}$ permits calculation of $\tan\theta$, which, with eq. 13.2, yields the output at F'.

F_0 represents about three-fourths and that at F' represents one-half of the reference (V_B) value. The power represented by F_0 falls off rapidly as F' approaches F_0.

At first sight it might appear that the power output at frequency F_0 would be constant for a given value of E_1 as long as F' lay outside the range of synchronization. Actually, however, there is feedback at the synchronizing frequency as well as at the natural frequency, so that the output at F' increases and that at F_0 diminishes as F' approaches F_0.

Subject to the assumptions made, the foregoing analysis indicates that no hysteresis is present. That is, if at some suitable frequency F', E_1 is increased, the voltage at which F_0 disappears should not differ from the voltage at which F_0 reappears when E_1 is again reduced.

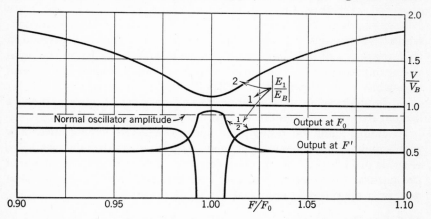

FIG. 13.6.   Variation of output voltage under synchronization ($Q = 50$, $S_A = 10$).

In practice, however, there may be some hysteresis, especially if the time constant of the lamps is not long compared to the period of the difference between F_0 and F'.

Finally, we may readily account for any selectivity which exists between the point at which the synchronizing voltage is injected and the thermistor limiter. Both the attenuation and the phase shift which occur at frequencies away from the natural frequency require an increase in the magnitude of the synchronizing voltage. Equation 13.1 still applies, but eq. 13.2 must be modified to account for the increased phase shift.

13.3 Synchronization in a linear bias-controlled oscillator

As a second example of the synchronization of a linear oscillator let us consider the system of Fig. 7.16. Again, we assume that the time constant of the rectifier system is long compared to the period which corresponds to the difference between the natural and the synchronizing frequency.

A careful comparison of this and the previously studied systems shows that they operate in an identical manner under all conditions which lead to a single output frequency. If the synchronizing signal is relatively large, the transconductance of the tube is depressed to a point which will not support self-oscillation, and the system serves as a simple stabilized amplifier. If the synchronizing signal is small but near the natural frequency there is an addition of voltages as shown in Fig. 13.3.

The only novelty is observed when the injected voltage is inadequate to produce synchronization. If this case, two output frequencies are observed as before, but the amplitude sum is now constant on a voltage rather than a power basis, because the rectifier serves as a peak-reading voltmeter. Therefore, the total power output is depressed in this region; and as the natural frequency departs from the synchronizing frequency, the output at the natural frequency increases somewhat more slowly than in the termistor oscillator. A similar effect is observed in most nonlinear oscillators, which also tend to be limited by peak voltage rather than by power.

It should again be noted that linear oscillators synchronize only with signals of a frequency very near to their natural frequencies. No effect is produced if the injected signal is a multiple or submultiple of the natural frequency unless the level is raised to such a point that nonlinear operation is produced.

13.4 Synchronization in an ordinary harmonic oscillator

Unlike linear oscillators, ordinary harmonic oscillators are synchronized by signals which are related in any simple manner to the natural frequency. Before studying these more complex cases, however, let us examine the behavior when the frequencies are nearly equal. The system to be studied is the ordinary tuned plate oscillator. Analytically, the most important difference between this oscillator and the ones previously studied is that the time constant of the limiter is very short compared to the period of the highest difference frequency of interest. Physically, this means that limiting takes place cycle by cycle rather than over a period of many cycles. In such oscillators, the behavior will follow rapid variations in the frequency or amplitude of the synchronizing signal, whereas linear oscillators respond much more slowly and are subject to transient effects, which may prove quite undesirable.

Within the range of synchronization, the behavior of a nonlinear oscillator is very similar to that of a linear oscillator; all the voltage waves are nearly sinusoidal, and the plate current, although flowing in pulses, has its timing or phase set by the sum of the returned and the injected voltage.   Under typical operating conditions the output voltage **V** is substantially unchanged by the addition of the synchronizing voltage.   The alternating grid voltage and the grid bias increase about equally, and the average and effective plate current are little affected.   The situation is illustrated in Fig. 13.7, which shows typical operating wave forms.

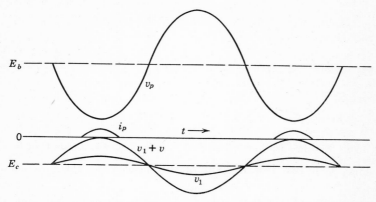

FIG. 13.7.   Synchronization at fundamental frequency in a class C oscillator.

Inspection of Fig. 13.7 shows that the synchronizing voltage is effective only during the short interval of conduction.   Therefore, any other signal which coincides with the indicated sine wave over the period of interest would give the same result.   The double frequency input wave of Fig. 13.8 is seen to approximate this condition, and is found to produce a strong locking tendency.   The input frequency is the second harmonic of the oscillator frequency; or, alternatively, the oscillator operates at a *subharmonic* of the input.   As might be anticipated from the wave forms, the tendency to synchronize decreases as the frequency ratio is increased, but ratios as high as ten to one may be used under special conditions.

There is also a tendency to lock when the input is at a submultiple of the oscillator frequency or is related to it by a simple ratio such as 3:2.   However, the lock is never strong, and the conditions are too complicated and specialized to warrant treatment here.   The interested reader is referred to the work of van der Pol,[322] Tucker,[315, 316] and Schaffner.[269]   David[70, 71] has shown that the synchronization of microwave oscillators is governed by the same principles which apply at lower frequencies.

In linear oscillators the natural frequency of oscillation is not perturbed by the synchronizing signal. The amplitude of the self-oscillation merely decreases smoothly toward zero as synchronization is approached. In nonlinear oscillators the behavior is considerably more complex. As synchronization is approached, the self-generated

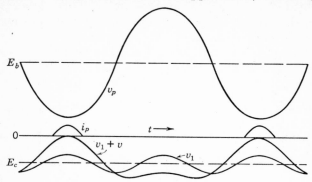

FIG. 13.8. Synchronization at a subharmonic frequency in a class C oscillator.

frequency is drawn toward that of the injected signal and becomes modulated. The difference frequency, which exists as a physical beat, is described in a markedly nonuniform manner. The following analysis is limited to an injected signal which is small in comparison to the self-generated signal at the corresponding point in the system.

13.5 The differential equation of synchronization

The first step in the analysis, which follows that of Huntoon and Weiss,[151] is to assume that the synchronizing emf in the grid circuit is replaced by an incremental impedance $\mathbf{z} = r + jx$. The output voltage and frequency are then affected by this small impedance according to the derivatives

$$\frac{\partial V}{\partial r} = A_r, \quad \frac{\partial F}{\partial r} = F_r, \quad \frac{-\partial V}{\partial x} = A_x, \quad \frac{-\partial F}{\partial x} = F_x \qquad (13.11)$$

where the derivatives are evaluated for

$$\mathbf{z} = r + jx = 0. \qquad (13.12)$$

The output voltage and frequency corresponding to any small $\mathbf{z}$ are then given to the first order by

$$A = A_0 + rA_r - xA_x \qquad (13.13)$$

and

$$F = F_0 + rF_r - xF_x, \qquad (13.14)$$

where A_0 and F_0 are the values observed for $\mathbf{z} = 0$.

The compensation theorem is used to obtain expressions in terms of voltage instead of impedance. The desired equation is

$$\mathbf{E}_1 = \mathbf{I}_0 \mathbf{z} e^{-j\phi} \quad \text{or} \quad \mathbf{z} = (\mathbf{E}_1/\mathbf{I}_0)e^{j\phi}, \qquad (13.15)$$

where $\mathbf{I}_0$ is the current which flows through $\mathbf{z}$ when $\mathbf{z} = 0$, and ϕ (later identified) is a function of time. The compensation theorem, although normally limited to linear systems, is valid here because the system is subject to equivalent linearization.

The derivative coefficients are now combined in complex form to obtain compliance coefficients

$$\mathbf{C}_A = A_r + jA_x = \sqrt{A_r{}^2 + A_x{}^2}\, e^{j\alpha} = C_A e^{j\alpha} \qquad (13.16)$$

and

$$\mathbf{C}_F = F_r + jF_x = \sqrt{F_r{}^2 + F_x{}^2}\, e^{j\beta} = C_F e^{j\beta} \qquad (13.17)$$

where

$$\tan \alpha = A_x/A_r \quad \text{and} \quad \tan \beta = F_x/F_r. \qquad (13.18)$$

Multiplying eq. 13.15 by eqs. 13.16 and 13.17, and taking the real parts, we have

$$(Real)(\mathbf{z}\mathbf{C}_A) = rA_r + xA_x = A - A_0 = C_A(E_1/I_0) \cos (\phi + \alpha), \qquad (13.19)$$

and

$$(Real)(\mathbf{z}\mathbf{C}_F) = rF_r + xF_x = F - F_0 = C_F(E_1/I_0) \cos (\phi + \beta). \qquad (13.20)$$

The variation of ϕ is now defined by the relationship

$$\frac{1}{2\pi} \frac{d\phi}{dt} = F' - F = (F' - F_0) - (F - F_0). \qquad (13.21)$$

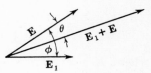

FIG. 13.9. Condition of partial synchronization.

This expression is given physical significance in the phasor diagram of Fig. 13.9. Consistent with eq. 13.15, ϕ may be taken as the instantaneous phase angle between the injected signal and the voltage of self-oscillation. This phase angle ϕ will tend toward a constant under conditions of synchronization but will vary periodically in the absence of synchronization.

The changes of variable

$$f = F' - F_0, \tag{13.22}$$

$$\gamma = \phi + \beta, \tag{13.23}$$

$$k = C_F/I_0, \tag{13.24}$$

and

$$a = f/kE_1, \tag{13.25}$$

inserted in eqs. 13.20 and 13.21 lead to the important differential equations

$$\frac{1}{2\pi} \frac{d\phi}{dt} = f - kE_1 \cos \gamma \tag{13.26}$$

and

$$\frac{d\gamma}{a - \cos \gamma} = 2\pi kE_1 \, dt. \tag{13.27}$$

The solution of eq. 13.27 is a simple damped function provided

$$a < 1 \tag{13.28a}$$

but is periodic and relatively complicated if

$$a > 1. \tag{13.28b}$$

13.6 Solution of the differential equation

The aperiodic solution $a < 1$, corresponding to eq. 13.28a, is undertaken first. By using formula 300 of Peirce's book,[235] subject to $a < 1$, eq. 13.27 may be integrated to yield

$$\frac{1}{\sqrt{1 - a^2}} \ln \left[\frac{\sqrt{(1 + a)/(1 - a)} + \tan (\gamma/2)}{\sqrt{(1 + a)/(1 - a)} - \tan (\gamma/2)} \right] = t_0 + 2\pi kE_1 t \tag{13.29}$$

or

$$\frac{\sqrt{(1 + a)/(1 - a)} - \tan (\gamma/2)}{\sqrt{(1 + a)/(1 - a)} + \tan (\gamma/2)} = Ke^{-2\pi kE_1\sqrt{1 - a^2}\,t}, \tag{13.30}$$

where $K = e^{-\sqrt{1 - a^2}\,t_0}$ is the constant of integration. The steady state of synchronization corresponds to

$$a = \cos \gamma, \tag{13.31}$$

as may be seen directly from eq. 13.26 or which can be obtained from eq. 13.30 by setting $t = \infty$.

A transient, which might arise from a sudden change in the amp-

litude or frequency of the synchronizing signal, disappears at a rate
corresponding to a time constant of

$$T = \frac{1}{2\pi k E_1 \sqrt{1 - a^2}} = \frac{1}{2\pi f \sqrt{1/a^2 - 1}}. \tag{13.32}$$

It should be noted that γ and ϕ themselves are not governed by eq.
13.32, which applies to the entire function given by eq. 13.30.   However, the decay of ϕ is monotonic rather than oscillatory, and occurs at
a rate which is nearly equal to that of eq. 13.32 unless the parameter a
approaches one.

This decay rate is important because it is a measure of the rapidity
with which a locked oscillator can follow a frequency-modulated wave.
Evidently, the period t_m of a highest modulating frequency should be
large compared to eq. 13.32 if serious distortion is to be avoided.

Synchronization is lost if the input signal is inadequate.   When a
is slightly larger than 1 corresponding to eq. 13.28b, the behavior of γ
and ϕ becomes complicated and interesting.   Over a large portion
of the cycle the cos γ term in eq. 13.27 is negative and nearly equal to a,
so that $d\gamma$ is small.   The portion of the cycle in which the cosine term
is positive is described in a relatively short time because of the relatively large derivative term.   Integration of eq. 13.27 subject to the
restriction $a > 1$ leads to

$$\frac{2}{\sqrt{a^2 - 1}} \tan^{-1}\left[\sqrt{\frac{a - 1}{a + 1}} \tan \frac{\gamma}{2}\right] = t_0 + 2\pi k E_1 t \tag{13.33}$$

or

$$\tan \frac{\gamma}{2} = \sqrt{\frac{a + 1}{a - 1}} \tan\left[\frac{1}{2} \sqrt{a^2 - 1} \, (t_0 + 2\pi k E_1 t)\right]. \tag{13.34}$$

Under these circumstances γ and hence ϕ is a continuously varying
function of time.   Moreover, at uniform intervals of time, the quantity

(a)   (b)

Fig. 13.10.   Frequency perturbation in the region of synchronization of a nonlinear oscillator.

in brackets will reach values of 0, $\pi/2$, π, $3\pi/2$, etc.   The tangent of
these angles is successively 0, ∞, 0, $-\infty$, etc.   Accordingly, γ also

reaches 0, $\pi/2$, π, $3\pi/2$, etc., at uniform time intervals. At intermediate values of time the relationship is more complicated; therefore, the beat produced is ordinarily quite nonsinusoidal. The wave forms of beat notes corresponding to eq. 13.34 are plotted in Fig. 13.10 for a value of a slightly greater than one and for $\beta = 0$ and $\pi/2$.

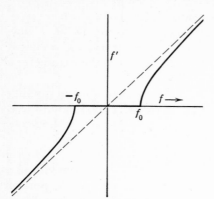

FIG. 13.11.   Wave form of beat note:
(a) for $\beta = 0$ and (b) for $\beta = \pi/2$.

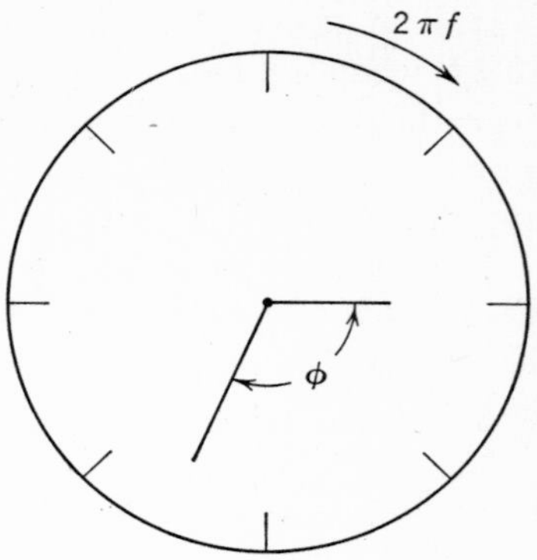

FIG. 13.12.   Mechanical model of
synchronization.

The average beat frequency is readily obtained. Because one cycle of γ corresponds to an interval of π in the quantity in brackets, in eq. 13.34, we may write for the actual beat frequency

$$f' = kE_1 \sqrt{a^2 - 1} = f \sqrt{1 - 1/a^2}, \tag{13.35}$$

which approaches f for large values of a. For smaller values of a, however, the beat frequency rapidly drops to zero as shown in Fig. 13.11. This behavior is in marked contrast to that of linear oscillators in which no such frequency perturbation occurs.

13.7 A mechanical model

Adler,[2] in an important paper, presents a very elegant mechanical model to illustrate the synchronizing action described by eq. 13.26. A cylinder containing a viscous fluid is imagined to rotate about a horizontal axis as shown in Fig. 13.12. A pendulum or vane, supported at the center of rotation, is acted upon by the rotating fluid and by the restoring force of gravity. The angular velocity of the drum with respect to the stationary observer may be taken as $2\pi f$ radians per second. Thus, the pendulum experiences a clockwise torque due to the fluid proportional to $f - \dfrac{1}{2\pi}\dfrac{d\phi}{dt}$ and a clockwise or counterclockwise force due to gravity proportional to cos ϕ, as shown. The effects of inertia are assumed to be negligible; therefore, subject to $\beta = 0$, the differential equation for this system is the same as eq. 13.26.

If the cylinder is rotated uniformly at a slow speed, the pendulum assumes a fixed small angle, as indicated. If the velocity is suddenly increased, a transient will occur, during which the pendulum moves without oscillation to a new equilibrium position. If the velocity is increased above a critical value, corresponding to $a = 1$ in the previous work, the pendulum is carried above the horizontal position, equilibrium is destroyed, and the pendulum begins to rotate. However, the velocity is relatively slow as the pendulum is raised by the fluid, and is much greater as the pendulum falls under the combined force of the fluid and of gravity.

If the angular velocity is further increased, the viscous force becomes large compared to that of gravity, and the pendulum is carried along at an almost uniform rate. However, the pendulum never quite reaches the velocity of the drum.

13.8 Application as a limiting amplifier

A locked oscillator may be used as a limiting amplifier in a receiver for frequency-modulated signals. In this application a relatively large and constant output at the frequency of a small input signal is desired. A rapid response is necessary because the input frequency changes according to the modulation of the transmitter. Moreover, it is desirable that the output be substantially unaffected by other signals or noise having frequencies near that of the desired signal. A locked oscillator has all these properties to a rather remarkable degree.

With this objective in mind, let us examine the behavior of a locked oscillator. We must use a nonlinear oscillator having cycle-by-cycle limiting to obtain the required rapidity of response, which must be sufficient to follow the highest frequency present in the modulation. The situation is comparable to that of establishing the cutoff of a single-section RC filter in terms of its time constant. Using this analogy, we observe the point of 3 db loss and 45° phase shift for

$$ R = \frac{1}{2\pi f_1 C} \quad \text{or} \quad \frac{1}{f_1} = 2\pi RC = 2\pi t_1, \qquad (13.36a) $$

where f_1 is taken as the highest modulating frequency. On this basis with eq. 13.32, we may write

$$ 2\pi t_1 = \frac{1}{f_1} \geq \frac{1}{f \sqrt{1/a^2 - 1}}. \qquad (13.36b) $$

As before, f represents the difference between the injected and the natural frequency. Let the oscillator be tuned to the nominal carrier frequency, and let f_m represent the *maximum* instantaneous excursion of the frequency modulation. We require, consistent with eq. 13.36b,

$$\frac{1}{a^2} - 1 \ge (f_1/f_m)^2 \quad \text{or} \quad a^2 \le \frac{1}{1 + (f_1/f_m)^2}. \tag{13.37}$$

Because f_1 (the speech bandwidth) is always small compared to f_m (the maximum modulation excursion) in practical systems, the restriction is substantially equivalent to the restriction $a < 1$. Physically, this means that the response will be adequately rapid if the oscillator holds in step over the entire frequency range. And in practice it is desirable to provide a reasonable margin such as two to one, in this range, in the interest of certainty of synchronization. That is, it is desirable to restrict ourselves to the condition $a < \frac{1}{2}$.

The design therefore reduces to the problem of obtaining the largest possible output voltage consistent with synchronization across the band by a prescribed small signal. The situation is conveniently discussed in terms of the tuned plate oscillator. Evidently, a large voltage amplification and a small rate of change of phase with frequency are desired. A high-μ tube with a large load impedance R and a small plate capacitance C is indicated.

Let us assume a pentode with a total effective load impedance equal to R and an effective transconductance of g_m. We may then write

$$V = g_m R E. \tag{13.38}$$

In the oscillator in question, the compliance coefficients are most conveniently obtained directly. The situation corresponds to synchronization in a linear oscillator, and eq. 13.1 is applicable, with the additional condition that θ is small. Equations 13.1 and 13.2 therefore correspond to

$$E_1/E = 2Qf_m/aF_0, \tag{13.39}$$

where f_m represents the maximum instantaneous frequency deviation, and a represents, as before, the margin above minimum synchronization. Elimination of E and Q in terms of the plate capacitance yields

$$V/E_1 = ag_m/4\pi C f_m. \tag{13.40}$$

It should be noted particularly that the load resistance and carrier frequency do not appear in eq. 13.40, and that the ordinary video-amplifier figure of merit g_m/C applies.

Therefore, the effective voltage amplification which may be obtained is independent of the operating frequency, proportional to the transconductance, and inversely proportional to the effective capacitance and the band of synchronization. For this reason locked oscillators are often worked on a subharmonic basis in order to reduce the synchronizing band required. Moreover, it should be noticed that the operating frequency is not a matter of complete indifference; for, if it is made too low, the oscillations may fail to be harmonic, in which case the basic assumptions would be violated.

As a numerical example let us choose a 6SJ7 pentode operated in moderate class C and receiving the commercial FM band of ± 75 kc. Reasonable values of the parameters are $g_m = 500$ micromhos, $a = \frac{1}{2}$, and $C = 15$ $\mu\mu$f. Then we have, by eq. 13.40, $V/E_1 = 17.7$.

The resulting equivalent amplification is quite small, being comparable to that obtained in the same tube as a linear amplifier. Moreover, a large input signal would be required, so the particular example is clearly impractical. However, the 6AH6 pentode used under similar circumstances would yield an amplification of about 400 because of its higher transconductance and lower plate capacitance. Beers[28] has obtained an effective gain of 30 from an oscillator locked at one-fifth the driving frequency and used as an amplifier and limiter in a frequency-modulation receiver.

13.9 Increase in the synchronizing sensitivity

The factor which limits the bandwidth over which synchronization may be maintained is the phase shift in the tuned circuit or circuits. Evidently, any modification which would reduce the rate of change of phase shift would correspondingly broaden the band of synchronization. Carnahan and Kalmus[53] have used for this purpose a circuit which, except for the crystal, is identical to the broad-band grounded-grid crystal-controlled oscillator of Chapter 9. Moreover, the design considerations are substantially identical. In the present case, however, the coupling to the auxiliary tuned circuit should not exceed the critical value; otherwise the circuit will be capable of operating at either of two separate frequencies, and synchronization with small signals will be lost.

The phase characteristic of coupled circuits is not readily expressed in simple equations. However, it is easy to show that the bandwidth over which the phase remains less than some small fixed quantity, such as half a degree, is increased by at least a factor of ten by the addition of the coupled load. On this basis the 6SJ7 and the 6AH6 are capable of effective gain values of 177 and 4000, respectively, for the present FM band.   If the output voltage were restricted to 10 volts in each case, the required input would be 55 and 2.5 millivolts, respectively.

These are attractive values of amplification, but they can be obtained only by careful design and construction.   In particular, the coupled circuits must be accurately tuned to the same frequency, the plate tuning must be accomplished by a variable inductance to maintain the minimum possible value of capacitance, and the coefficient of coupling must be accurately controlled.   These practical difficulties restrict the use of this scheme to rather special applications.

13.10 The locked oscillator as a detector of frequency modulation

The use of a locked oscillator as a detector of frequency modulation depends upon the fact that the average current at some point in the system may be made a function of the injected frequency.   It appears that this application was first suggested by Woodyard,[349] although the arrangement which he used had been described earlier by Appleton.[12] The circuit tested by Woodyard is shown in Fig. 13.13a.

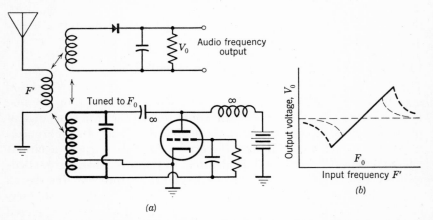

FIG. 13.13.   Detection of frequency modulation: (a) circuit and (b) response.

Figure 13.13b shows that the response observed in the independent coupled circuit is remarkably similar to that of a conventional discriminator, as described in Chapter 17.   The central portion of the characteristic is quite linear, and the slope is independent of the magnitude of the input signal.   However, the length of the linear region, which corresponds to the range of synchronization, is approximately proportional to the input voltage.

The linearity of the characteristic depends upon the phase relationships which exist between the several circuits. If, at the midfrequency, the voltage induced in the load circuit by the signal is in quadrature with that produced by the oscillator, it is clear that the total amplitude will change more or less linearly as the phase of the synchronizing voltage varies through a moderate angle in the center of the locking range. Such a phase relationship may be obtained in the circuit of Fig. 13.13a if the coupling paths are appropriately adjusted. However, the arrangement is inherently insensitive because the maximum output voltage is no larger than the input voltage.

A more useful approach to the detector problem is obtained by returning to the analysis of Section 13.5. It is seen that the output amplitude will vary linearly with frequency if $\alpha = \beta$ in eqs. 13.19 and 13.20; this requires that

$$A_x/A_r = F_x/F_r. \tag{13.41}$$

Moreover, large values of the amplitude coefficients are desirable in the interest of sensitivity. That is, the amplitude should be made as sensitive as possible to impedance changes at the driving point.

In a practical detector the average plate current rather than the amplitude of oscillation is of principal concern, because it offers a convenient means for delivering the signal output without resorting to an additional rectifier. A figure of merit for a locked oscillator can therefore be established on this basis. First we assume that the injected signal is small compared to the voltage of self-oscillation so that we may rewrite eq. 13.1 in the form

$$E_1/E \geq \theta. \tag{13.42}$$

Moreover, the maximum possible increment in plate current within the range of synchronization is

$$\delta I = \frac{dI}{d\theta}\,\theta. \tag{13.43}$$

Combining these expressions yields

$$\delta I \leq \frac{E_1\,dI}{E\,d\theta}. \tag{13.44}$$

Thus, for a given injected voltage E_1, the sensitivity increases with a decrease of the returned voltage E and with an increase of the derivative $dI/d\theta$. That is, to obtain high sensitivity, the tube should have a large transconductance, and the Nyquist diagram for the circuit should come as close as possible to coinciding with the positive real axis.

That this is a legitimate and valid criterion becomes more apparent if we recall that E_1 is constant as the frequency, and hence θ, is varied. Finally, if the tube operates in class C, the average and the fundamental frequency components of the plate current are proportional.

13.11 A pentagrid detector for frequency modulation

The use of a locked oscillator as a detector of frequency-modulated waves has been reduced to practice by Bradley.[37] His arrangement is shown in Fig. 13.14. The oscillating circuit consists of the cathode and first grid operating in an electron-coupled arrangement with respect to the other electrodes as an effective grounded plate. The input signal, applied to the third grid, controls the division of electrons between the second grid and the plate, as in other pentagrid applications. The plate current, as influenced by both the first and the third

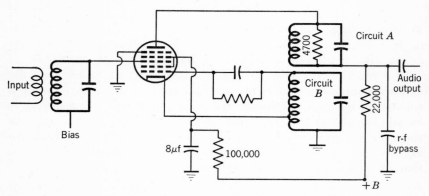

Fig. 13.14.   A practical frequency-modulation detector, using the FM–1000 as a locked oscillator.

grids, is passed through a second tuned circuit and the audio load circuit. This second resonant circuit is tuned to approximately the operating frequency and is heavily damped so that its phase angle changes relatively slowly with frequency. By this arrangement the synchronizing voltage is amplified before being injected into the oscillatory circuit, and a stabilizing action due to feedback results.

The tube operates in class C, preferably at such an amplitude that current flows only in relatively short pulses. Depending upon the phase of the injected signal with respect to the oscillation, the magnitude but not the phase of the plate current pulses is affected. This dependence is illustrated in Fig. 13.15, in which the normal situation is represented by (b). That is, if the input signal is at the mean frequency, the pulse of plate current flows at the instant of zero input, and its magnitude is the same as if no input were present.

The tuning and coupling of the circuits are such that the voltage induced in the oscillator circuit B by circuit A is in quadrature with that due to the self-oscillation. Therefore, the phase relationships and hence the oscillating frequency depend upon the amplitude of the plate current pulses. The amplitude of oscillation is practically constant because of the specified quadrature relationship. The equilibrium is most conveniently expressed by assuming a particular amplitude of the plate current pulses and a corresponding average plate current. A particular phase condition, and hence frequency, in the self-oscillating system corresponds to this plate current and will

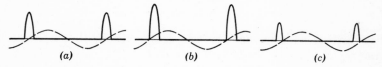

(a)   (b)   (c)

FIG. 13.15.   Variation of the amplitude of plate current pulses due to phase shift between signal and self-oscillation.

exist only if the incoming signal has the same frequency and a sufficient amplitude to produce the assumed current. The proportionality between the average plate current and the operating frequency is fundamental and is the basis of the excellent linearity which can be obtained. A variation of the amplitude of the input signal merely modifies the phase relationship with the self-oscillation but cannot appreciably change the effective or average plate current. In several respects the operation of this detector is similar to the more complicated negative feedback system devised by J. G. Chaffee.[55]

The above circuit employing the FM-1000 tube at an intermediate frequency of about 10 Mc was tested and found to lock across the full standard 75-kc deviation with an input signal of about one-half volt rms. The output for this deviation is 20 volts peak to peak, and the distortion is negligible. Moreover, amplitude modulation is suppressed by some 50 db. That is, the performance is in every respect equal or superior to that of conventional discriminator detectors.

13.12 Interaction of two similar oscillators

In the foregoing analysis it has been assumed that the oscillator under study has no effect upon the source of the synchronizing voltage. This situation is approximated in practice if the driving oscillator is very powerful and is loosely coupled to the locked oscillator or if a unilateral amplifier provides the coupling. The locked oscillator in a radio receiver is an excellent example of loose coupling. However, in some cases two similar oscillators in proximity operate at nearly the same frequency. The coupling present, whether it is by accident or design, will set a lower limit to the frequency difference which may exist between them.

To investigate this situation let us suppose that two tuned plate oscillators are coupled in such a way that the total grid voltage of oscillator 1 is represented by $\mathbf{E}_1'' + \mathbf{E}'$, and the total grid voltage of oscillator 2 is represented by $\mathbf{E}_1' + \mathbf{E}''$, where E represents a self-generated voltage and E_1 a coupling voltage. Subject to the assumed condition of reciprocity we have

$$E''/E_1'' = E'/E_1'. \tag{13.45}$$

Let us further assume that the two are locked so that a single frequency is produced. Because each oscillator is drawn *toward* this common frequency, it follows that the operating frequency must necessarily lie between the natural frequencies of the two separate oscillators. Synchronization can be maintained only over such a range that neither oscillator experiences a phase shift in excess of 90°. Assuming that the two oscillators are equally powerful and the coupling is small so that $\theta = \sin \theta$, we may use eq. 13.1 to establish the limit of synchronization. It is seen that synchronization will be lost when *each* oscillator differs from the output frequency by an amount equal to its own synchronizing limit.

It is interesting to note that the total synchronizing range is increased if the amplitude of the second oscillator is either raised or lowered from the condition of equality. If, for example, the voltage level of one oscillator is doubled, the extent to which it can be drawn into synchronization is cut in half, but the extent to which it can influence the other oscillator is doubled. In general, the total range over which synchronization can be produced subject to a given coupling between specified oscillators is proportional to $E'/E'' + E''/E'$, as confirmed experimentally by Appleton.[12]

The effects which occur outside the range of synchronization are similar to those already described, but are more complicated because neither frequency is generated in a uniform manner. It is significant, however, that the frequencies differ by a smaller amount than they would in the absence of coupling, and that this effect is opposite to the well-known effect of coupling upon the natural frequencies of passive linear circuits.

13.13 Synchronization of relaxation oscillators

Relaxation oscillators are readily synchronized by signals of all sorts. The injected wave form may be sinusoidal, or in the form of pulses, and the injected frequency may be equal or unequal to that produced, so long as some reasonably simple frequency ratio exists. Synchronization in a ratio such as 2:1 may be maintained over a considerable

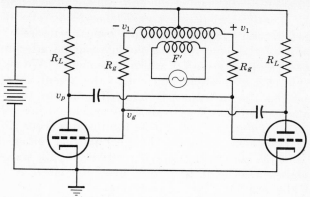

FIG. 13.16. Symmetrical multivibrator arranged for synchronization at an odd subharmonic.

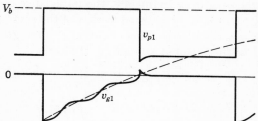

FIG. 13.17. Wave forms in either tube of Fig. 13.16. Corresponding waves displaced one half cycle are observed in the other tube.

range of the input frequency, in the order of ± 25 per cent. In this respect the performance considerably exceeds that of the conventional locked oscillator. However, consistent with synchronization at a given operating frequency, the permissible variation of the tube characteristics is not appreciably different from that of a conventional oscillator.

The multivibrator is selected to illustrate the synchronization of relaxation oscillators because it demonstrates all the important principles, and because it is the most widely used in this application; a typical arrangement is shown in Fig. 13.16. A symmetrical triode multivibrator is used, and the grid leaks are returned to B^+ through the symmetrical windings of a transformer which injects the synchronizing voltage. Wave forms corresponding to operation on a fifth subharmonic are shown in Fig. 13.17, in which it is assumed that the cutoff bias is substantially zero. The use of a *balanced* synchronizing voltage for *odd* frequency ratios is desirable because it leads to an appropriate slope of the grid voltage at *both* transitions of the circuit. For the same reason, an *unbalanced* or parallel synchronizing voltage is favored when *even* frequency ratios are desired.

The action of the synchronizing voltage can be interpreted from either of two viewpoints, both of which have merit. We may employ the principle of superposition and obtain the actual voltage at the grid by adding the (attenuated) injected wave to that normally present; alternatively, we may regard the synchronizing voltage as a variable return voltage, which affects the instantaneous slope of the grid circuit relaxation. Although the synchronizing voltage developed at the grid of the conducting tube is relatively small, because of the low impedance associated with zero bias, the effect is important because of the large effective amplification.

The superposition method is easiest to use for numerical work. Because the synchronizing voltage usually has a frequency several times that of the operating frequency, the impedance of the grid condensers of Fig. 13.16 is low compared to that of the plate load resistors. Therefore, the synchronizing voltage delivered to the grid of the *cutoff* tube is related to the injected voltage by the ratio

$$v_g' = v_1 R_e/(R_e + R_g), \tag{13.46}$$

where

$$R_e = R_L r_p/(R_L + r_p), \tag{13.47}$$

and r_p is the dynamic plate resistance of the *conducting* tube operating at zero bias. The voltage delivered to the conducting grid is approximately

$$v_{g1} \doteq v_1 r_g/R_g. \tag{13.48}$$

where r_g is the dynamic resistance of the grid at zero bias. As a result of this voltage and the amplifying action of the tube the direct synchronizing voltage v_g' on the cutoff grid will be supplemented by a voltage

$$v_g'' \doteq v_1 g_m r_g R_e/R_g, \tag{13.49}$$

where g_m is the transconductance of the conducting tube.

With the balanced synchronizing arrangement of Fig. 13.16, the direct and amplified voltages represented by eqs. 13.46 and 13.49 add in phase, reducing the requirement on the applied voltage v_1. However, when division by an even frequency ratio is desired, the synchronizing voltage should be applied in like phase to the two grid leaks. In this case the direct and amplified voltages are out of phase, and a larger synchronizing voltage is required. More serious is the fact that in typical situations $R_g \gg R_e$ and $g_m r_g$ is of the order of one so that v_g' and v_g'', the direct and amplified voltages, are comparable. When such a partial balance exists, a relatively large change of effective synchronizing voltage may result from a moderate change of tube parameters. In cathode-coupled multivibrators, on the other hand, the conducting tube operates at negative bias, and the amplified voltage is large compared to the direct synchronizing voltage. Thus, their behavior with respect to synchronization is more stable than that of ordinary multivibrators.

13.14 Optimum synchronizing voltage

There is an optimum amplitude for the synchronizing voltage; a small voltage produces synchronization only over a narrow range of frequency or circuit parameters, and a large voltage leads to operation at an entirely different frequency. This effect is illustrated in Fig. 13.18, which shows locking at the third rather than the fifth subharmonic.

The magnitude of the optimum synchronizing voltage is explored in terms of a variation of the effective cutoff voltage, which affects the natural period of the multivibrator. As in other oscillators, such a variation leads to a shift of phase between the

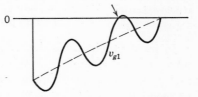

FIG. 13.18. Excessive synchronizing voltage.

injected and generated waves. Loss of synchronization occurs when the phase shift amounts to 90° with respect to the synchronizing frequency, as shown in Fig. 13.19. The critical voltage at which the transition occurs is now regarded as a variable, whereas in previous figures it has been regarded as constant and substantially zero.

It is seen that premature triggering cannot occur unless the slope of the grid voltage wave is negative at certain points. The condition in which the slope becomes zero once per cycle is shown in Fig. 13.19 and is regarded as a practical optimum, although a slightly larger range of synchronization may be secured by increasing both the injected voltage and the natural period of the multivibrator. In terms of superposition, this corresponds rather closely to the condition that the maximum slope of the total synchronizing voltage, v_g, shall equal the slope of the natural grid relaxation in the cutoff region.

If the amplitude of the plate voltage excursion, or the time constant of the grid circuit, or the period of the injected wave is assumed to vary instead of the critical bias, a similar situation exists. In all cases, the synchronizing voltage should be equal to or slightly larger than that which leads to zero slope near the cutoff point. The behavior in the region of cutoff is the same in all cases, and is correctly represented by Fig. 13.19.

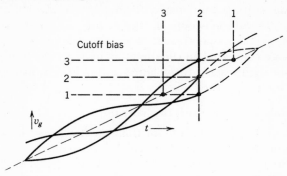

FIG. 13.19. Enlargement showing effect of variation of cutoff bias on phase of synchronization. Maximum, normal, and minimum values of cutoff bias and of natural period are indicated.

In most applications the frequency of the synchronizing voltage is quite constant, and the multivibrator is used to obtain harmonic and/or subharmonic frequencies. The firmest possible lock is desired to avoid the possibility of operation at an incorrect frequency due to loss of synchronization, and to minimize the timing errors associated with changes of phase within the range of synchronization. These objectives are best met by making the natural frequency of the multivibrator as stable as possible and by using the largest practical synchronizing voltage. The use of positive grid leak return, as discussed in Chapter 12, is desirable because it improves the inherent frequency stability and also permits the use of a larger synchronizing voltage. In at least some cases, it appears that even better results would be obtained with the symmetrical cathode-coupled multivibrator.

13.15 Synchronization with nonsinusoidal waves

In harmonic oscillators the synchronizing voltage is usually sinusoidal and a small simple multiple of the operating frequency. In relaxation oscillators, on the other hand, the synchronizing voltage is often

markedly nonsinusoidal.   An important practical example is the series
or chain of multivibrators, commonly used in frequency standards as
frequency dividers.   The primary oscillator ordinarily operates at a
frequency of 100 kc, and successive multivibrators operate at frequencies such as 25, 5, and 1 kc.   The first multivibrator is synchronized by a sinusoidal wave derived from the primary oscillator,
but the other multivibrators are synchronized by waves derived from
preceding multivibrators.   Fortunately, nonsinusoidal waves are
favorable for synchronization, and a good phase lock is associated with
a large slope of the voltage wave.   The situation is illustrated in
Fig. 13.20, which indicates that a square wave is favorable, but that

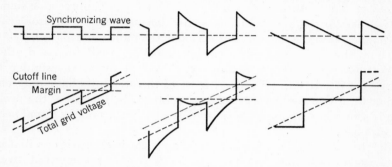

FIG. 13.20.   Synchronization of multivibrator by nonsinusoidal wave forms.

a sloped-off square wave is preferable because it permits greater margin against premature triggering, and that a *negative* saw-tooth wave of
suitable amplitude is ideal.   The sloped-off square wave produces a
slightly smaller margin against variation of the cutoff bias than does
the triangle and requires an increase of the free-running period.   Best
results are obtained when the time constant of the relaxation is
about one-third the period of the square wave, as indicated.   As
previously noted, synchronization is produced at the grid of the cutoff
tube, but the actual synchronizing voltage wave form may be greatly
affected by loop transmission.

The arrangement of Fig. 13.16 is unsuitable for the injection of
nonsinusoidal waves because the high resistance of the grid leaks in
conjunction with stray capacitances to ground degrades the slope
obtainable.   Small capacitances, of the order of 10 $\mu\mu$f, coupling the
synchronizing voltage directly to the multivibrator grids are frequently
used but are somewhat objectionable because they increase the total
effective capacitance to ground in the synchronized multivibrator.
Both the speed of transition and the harmonic content of the output

suffer.   Moreover, the synchronized multivibrator often reacts upon the source in such a way as to complicate the operation.   This effect is most easily suppressed by using a vacuum tube as a unilateral coupling element to separate successive multivibrators.   However, by additional design effort, it is usually possible to achieve the desired isolation without use of a vacuum tube.   Excellent practical data on this subject are given by Gordon.[116]

The symmetrical pentode multivibrator may be synchronized by means of signals applied to the suppressor grids.   Because the suppressor of the cutoff tube has no effect, the amplified signal from the active tube must be used.   Therefore, negative pulses, or preferably a *positive* saw-tooth wave, should be provided.   No appreciable signal is returned to the synchronizing source because the suppressor grids are not active in the regenerative action of the multivibrator cycle.

As previously stated, sweep circuits, blocking oscillators, and other relaxation oscillators are readily synchronized by means similar to those just described.   However, most of these circuits have only one rather than two comparable relaxation intervals, therefore, the problem is somewhat simplified because only one synchronizing signal need be supplied.

Before leaving the subject of synchronization in relaxation oscillators we should note that the preceding discussion is somewhat oversimplified.   As shown in Chapter 12, the transition does not occur instantly when the grid voltage reaches the cutoff bias.   There is a degenerative interval during which plate current flows but the loop gain is less than unity, and a succeeding regenerative interval during which the loop gain is greater than unity and the transition is in process.   If the synchronizing frequency is high, or if the synchronizing voltage is a single short pulse, the grid may be driven past cutoff into the degenerative or even the regenerative region and again withdrawn without causing a complete transition.   This action is shown in an enlarged view of the cutoff region of Fig. 13.21.   This and other properties of the multivibrator are discussed in a series of three papers by Shenk.[281]

The effects of imperfect synchronization are particularly likely to be observed when a blocking oscillator is used as a high-ratio frequency divider.   In such applications a firm phase lock is desired although the exact frequency ratio is unimportant.   Unless the transition interval of the relaxation oscillator is short compared to the period of the synchronizing wave, the results are likely to be very unsatisfactory.   Furthermore, it is highly desirable that the relaxation oscillator have no natural frequencies comparable to the synchronizing

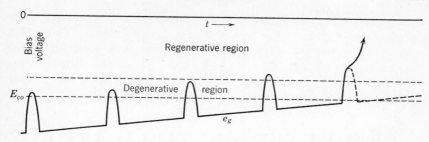

FIG. 13.21.   Faulty synchronization by short pulses.

frequency; otherwise the synchronizing frequency will be greatly amplified as the transition is approached. This behavior seriously interferes with the desired synchronization.

PROBLEMS

13.1. In an absolutely linear system the principle of superposition may be used to prove that the addition of a signal has no effect on existing voltages and currents. Reconcile this with the fact that the lamp bridge oscillator is readily synchronized.

13.2. Show that the situation corresponding to E_1''' in Fig. 13.4 is unstable.

13.3. Calculate curves for F_0 and F' corresponding to Fig. 13.6 for $Q = 100$, $S_A = 100$, and $E_1/E_B = 0.1$.

13.4. Indicate how the curves of Prob. 13.3 would be affected if the amplitude were limited on a total-peak-voltage rather than power basis.

13.5. Show by a sketch like Fig. 13.8 how a class C oscillator can lock at two-thirds of the input frequency.

13.6. In connection with eq. 13.15, show why the compensation theorem may be used.

13.7. Identify Adler's mechanical model with the behavior shown in Figs. 13.10 and 13.11.

13.8. Verify eq. 13.37 and justify the conclusion that a locked oscillator does not distort a FM signal, provided synchronization is never lost.

13.9. Verify eq. 13.40 and interpret it in terms of practical locked oscillators for the amplification of FM signals.

13.10. Following the discussion of Section 13.10, design a locked oscillator which will be a sensitive detector of FM signals.

13.11. By wave form sketches show why balanced synchronization favors *odd* frequency ratios and unbalanced synchronization *even* ratios in multivibrators.

13.12. Show that Fig. 13.19 represents the optimum synchronizing condition with respect to changes of amplitude and natural period as well as to change of the cutoff bias.

13.13. Sketch a circuit arrangement by which waves like those of Fig. 13.20 may actually be produced without seriously affecting the operation of the multivibrator.

14

FREQUENCY MULTIPLICATION AND DIVISION

14.1 Applications

In a variety of circumstances which arise in practice it is desirable to produce a given frequency indirectly rather than directly. It is then appropriate to use frequency multiplication or division, together with modulation for addition and subtraction of frequency if need be. These various techniques are often lumped together and called frequency synthesis or frequency composition.

There are at least four situations when frequency composition methods are appropriate: (1) when the available power is in the form of an alternating rather than a direct current; (2) when the desired signal must have an exact frequency relationship to an available signal; (3) when resonators having suitable characteristics are not available at the desired frequency, but are available at some lower or higher frequency; and (4) when a large number of distinct frequencies are to be produced from a small number of stable resonators. The subcycle ringers employed in the telephone plant to provide 20-cycle ringing current from the 60-cycle power line are an example of (1). The harmonic generators used in long-distance telephone systems to produce an exactly related group of carrier frequencies are an example of (2). The frequency dividers used to operate a low-frequency electric clock motor from a high-frequency quartz crystal oscillator in standard-frequency systems are an example of (3). The "crystal saver" units[133] used in certain military radio systems are an example of (4).

Considerable emphasis is placed upon devices which do not employ vacuum tubes. Such devices are very desirable in practice because they are compact, rugged, reliable, and require no power supply other than the signal.

14.2 Fundamental principles

It is well known that the response of a linear system contains only those frequencies which are present in the driving force. Therefore, all systems of frequency composition must be based upon *nonlinearity* in one or more of the elements. Ordinarily, it is desirable to employ only one nonlinear element in a given unit in order to simplify the functioning and analysis. In theory, the nonlinear device may exist as a resistance, capacitance, or inductance, and may appear as a self or as a mutual element. All these possibilities have been reduced to practice on a more or less general scale.

Nonlinear resistances are widely used in the form of rectifiers such as vacuum or germanium diodes, varistors such as copper oxide or thyrite, and vacuum tubes. Of these, vacuum tubes are the most convenient because the presence of the grid offers great flexibility and because, as active rather than passive impedances, they are capable of amplification. Nonlinear inductances, both self and mutual, have long been used as amplifiers, modulators, and frequency multipliers and dividers. The use of these nonlinear devices has recently been greatly expanded because of improvements in magnetic materials[141, 294] and a better understanding of design considerations. Nonlinear capacitances suitable for circuit application have only recently become available, largely through the work of von Hippel[334] and Roberts,[265] and they have as yet found little use. It appears, however, that dielectrics such as barium titanate and barium strontium titanate[323] have properties which will make them useful as nonlinear capacitances over a very wide range of frequencies.

The use of modulation by means of a nonlinear impedance to obtain sums and differences of frequencies is adequately covered in many places[87, 307] and will not be treated here. The essential fact is that if voltages at two frequencies F and f are applied to a nonlinear element, an output is available at any frequency f_0 which satisfies the equation

$$f_0 = nF + mf, \tag{14.1}$$

where m and n are positive or negative integers. It is worth mentioning in this connection that positive and negative frequencies are not physically distinguishable.

Before proceeding, we should note that multiplication of frequency is division of time. That is, the period of the original wave is subdivided into n equal periods where n is the order of multiplication. Clearly, this will not be possible if the periods of successive half cycles of the original wave differ by an amount comparable with the period of the desired wave.   It is therefore highly important to avoid jitter and to control the harmonic content of any wave whose frequency is to be multiplied.   Frequency division, on the other hand, involves multiplication of time.   Imperfections in the input wave therefore tend to vanish rather than be magnified when this process is employed.

Depending upon whether or not a balanced frequency multiplier is used, energy is delivered to the tuned output circuit only once or twice per input cycle.   A high effective Q in the resonant circuit is therefore desirable, especially if the order of multiplication is large; otherwise, the output voltage wave form will be amplitude modulated at the input period.   Extreme values of Q are required if the order of multiplication is large and if only a single tuned circuit is used.

The question of time delay or phase lock arises in all methods of frequency composition.   The requirements vary greatly with the particular application; but in all cases it is desirable that the input and output waves have a phase relationship which is stable and independent of element values, because a *changing phase* constitutes a *frequency error*.

14.3 Methods of frequency multiplication

Frequency multiplication is a special case of modulation, as may be seen by setting m or $f = 0$ in eq. 14.1.   Therefore, in principle, we may obtain any desired frequency multiplication by applying a sinusoidal voltage to a nonlinear impedance.   In practice, the situation is much less simple, because the output so achieved is often too small or too contaminated with other frequencies to be useful.   A great variety of arrangements have been employed to alleviate these difficulties. Useful arrangements may be catalogued roughly, according to the source of nonlinearity, as follows: (1) passive structures using nonlinear elements operating according to eq. 14.1; (2) active unilateral structures (vacuum tubes without feedback); (3) active stable structures (vacuum tubes with limited feedback); and (4) unstable structures (free running systems).   All depend upon the use of tuned circuits to select the desired output frequency.

An additional basis for classifying frequency multipliers depends upon whether a single frequency or a group of harmonically related frequencies is desired at the output.   A single frequency at reasonably high power and efficiency is desired in multipliers for radio transmitters.   On the other hand, uniformity of output at a large number of harmonics is the principal requirement on multipliers for frequency measurement.

14.4 A diode frequency multiplier

Perhaps the simplest frequency multiplier is the full-wave rectifier circuit of Fig. 14.1a. The primary circuit is tuned to series resonance at the driving frequency f, and the secondary circuit is tuned to anti-resonance at the desired harmonic nf. Figure 14.1b shows the various wave forms which exist in this system for $n = 2$ under the assumption that the transformer and rectifiers are ideal, that the primary has the

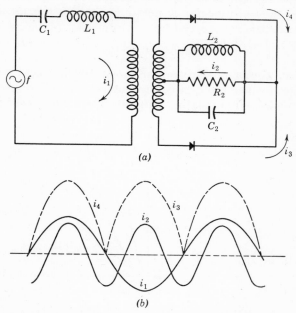

FIG. 14.1. Rectifier frequency multiplier: (a) circuit and (b) wave forms.

same number of turns as the total secondary, and that both the primary and the secondary constitute high-Q systems. Under these assumptions the system approaches 100 per cent efficiency, and we may evaluate the input resistance by use of the principle of conservation of energy. The second-harmonic content of a rectified sine wave is readily determined by use of Fourier analysis. According to the *Federal Handbook*,[92] page 287, we have

$$i_2 = 8i_1/3\pi. \qquad (14.2a)$$

Therefore, the effective input impedance R_1 is given by

$$R_1 = 0.72R_2. \qquad (14.2b)$$

The assumptions made in the foregoing analysis are approximated reasonably well in practice, and efficiencies in excess of 50 per cent may be realized at most frequencies.

It should be noted that the system of Fig. 14.1 is not limited to frequency doubling. In theory, all even harmonics are present in the current wave, and may be obtained by suitable tuning of the secondary circuit. In practice, the magnitude of the current falls off rapidly with the order of harmonic, and the parasitic losses become excessive. For $n = 4$, the effective input resistance, under the assumption of 100 per cent efficiency is given by

$$R_1 = 0.0288R_2. \tag{14.3}$$

In this case, however, the assumption of 100 per cent efficiency is unjustifiable because the desired current is so small compared to the associated undesired circulating currents that serious losses cannot be avoided.

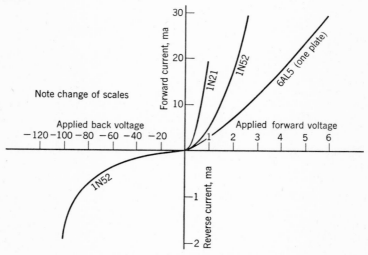

FIG. 14.2.   Properties of various diodes.

The performance of this circuit depends greatly upon the characteristics of the rectifier or diode employed. The back or leakage resistance must be large and the forward resistance low compared to the load resistance R_2 if efficient operation is to be secured. Vacuum diodes, such as the 6AL5, are suitable for operation up to frequencies of the order of 500 Mc, and give good performance with load resistors of the order of 5000 ohms. Germanium diodes, such as the 1N52, require no heater power, but are restricted to somewhat lower frequencies and efficiencies.   They also operate best with loads of the order of 5000 ohms.   Silicon diodes are useful at frequencies as high as 25,000 Mc, but are limited to one or two volts and are characterized by poor efficiency.   The average characteristics of typical diodes are shown in Fig. 14.2.   The reverse conductivity of electronic diodes is negligible. The reverse conductivity of the 1N21 is far from negligible but cannot be shown on the scales chosen.

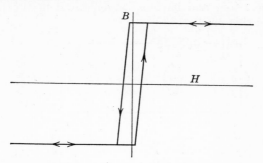

FIG. 14.3.   Approximation to hysteresis curve of a saturable core.

Provided the rectifiers are linear, that is, have different fixed resistances in the forward and back directions, the output is *proportional* to the input.   This condition is never exactly fullfiled in practice, but is closely approximated by vacuum diodes operated with large signals and relatively high load impedances.   This proportionality between output and input is important in many applications, notably as a part of the stable regenerative frequency dividers described later in this chapter.

14.5 Frequency multiplication by magnetic saturation

It is well known that nonlinearity due to magnetic saturation in iron-core coils results in the production of harmonics; and this effect has been intentionally employed by many workers.   However, developments in magnetic materials have greatly increased the efficiency and frequency range of such devices.   The characteristic features of materials, such as Permalloy, Mumetal, Orthonol, and Deltamax, are that the initial permeability is large, the hysteresis loop is narrow,[10] and the saturation is very sharp, as indicated in Fig. 14.3.   Because the self-inductance of a coil depends upon the slope of the *B-H* curve of its core, it follows that a coil having a core of these materials will have an inductance which changes sharply and by a large ratio as the current is varied.   This property has been employed by Peterson[238] in a very efficient circuit to generate a group of harmonics for a carrier-frequency telephone system. The basic circuit is shown in Fig. 14.4a.

The input circuit is series tuned to the driving frequency, f, which is 4 kc in the system cited. It presents a high impedance to all harmonics; therefore the current through this mesh is substantially sinusoidal. Harmonics which might be present in the source do not affect the operation, and harmonics generated in the nonlinear coil are not lost in this mesh.

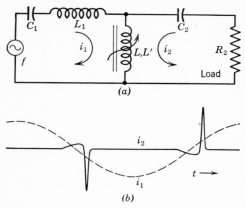

(a)

(b)

Fig. 14.4.   Harmonic generator using saturable reactor: (a) circuit and (b) wave forms.

During part of the cycle the primary current is low, L is free from saturation, and its inductance is relatively high. In this period C_2 acquires a considerable charge which is suddenly dissipated through R_2 and L when the region of saturation is reached. The resulting highly peaked current wave through R_2 is rich in odd harmonics. If, therefore, R_2 is replaced by a group of filters, with their inputs in parallel, each tuned to a different harmonic, these separate loads will each receive one of the odd harmonics of the input frequency. Quartz crystal filters are employed to obtain the required low loss and high selectivity. By correct proportioning of R, C_2, and the saturated inductance L', the pulses may be made quite short compared to the total period, and the power available in the first twenty or so harmonics is substantially uniform. An overall efficiency as high as 75 per cent was observed when several dozens of harmonics were taken from a driving frequency of 4 kc. When only one or two harmonics are desired the efficiency is considerably degraded because the sharply peaked current wave cannot be used directly, and additional losses must be incurred in the reactive elements.   Efficiencies of the order of 20 per cent may be anticipated under these conditions.

In practice, the losses in the input and output filters increase with the order, n, of the harmonic required, and the losses in the nonlinear coil increase with both f and n, so that the method becomes unattractive for orders of n above about 50 or for output frequencies in excess of about 5 Mc.

It is desirable to proportion R_2 and C_2 with respect to L' so as to obtain critical damping, thus bringing the discharge to an end in the shortest possible time.   The primary inductance L_1 must be large compared to the unsaturated inductance L in order to insure that the primary current will be substantially sinusoidal.   The *power level* at which the desired operation will occur is roughly proportional to the mass of the saturable core and the frequency, whereas the values of L and L' and hence the impedance level of the various circuits may be adjusted by the number of turns used in the winding.

If the driving current is truly sinusoidal, the successive positive and negative pulses of current are accurately uniform in magnitude and spacing, as is necessary if high-order harmonics are to be selected.   In this respect the saturable reactor is superior to electronic devices for harmonic production.   The operation of this circuit has been analyzed in detail by Peterson;[238] and additional information on the subject is given by Tucker.[314]

14.6 Magnetic multiplier for a single frequency

As stated in the preceding section, the saturable reactor is particularly favorable for the simultaneous generation of a group of odd harmonics. However, it can be used with reasonable success for the generation of a single harmonic.   Peculiarly enough, the analysis of the operation for a single frequency is considerably more complicated than that for a group of frequencies.   The difficulty arises from the fact that the output circuit must be tuned to the desired frequency, and that this tuned circuit is subjected to both a periodic (nonsinusoidal) driving voltage and a periodic variation of its inductance.   A very lucid explanation of those effects has been given by Guillemin and Rumsey.[125]

Guillemin used a saturable reactance in the form of a transformer with unity turns ratio, but equivalent results would have been obtained by adding in series with C_2 an inductance L_2, to resonate it at the desired frequency.   The addition of this inductance serves to restrict the current through R_2 to a single frequency, n times the input frequency f.   Therefore, no large spike of current, such as that of Fig. 14.4b, can flow at any point in the circuit.

For purposes of analysis it is convenient first to assume that the secondary circuit is open and that the maximum inductance, L, of the nonlinear coil is small compared to L_1. If the maximum value of the primary current is considerably larger than I_0, the current at which the self-inductance of the nonlinear coil drops from L to L', the voltage across the nonlinear coil must take the form of Fig. 14.5a. The Fourier analysis of such a voltage wave shows that it contains only odd harmonics of f. However, the coefficient of any particular harmonic is rather sensitive to the fraction ϵ of the total time which the coil is unsaturated. This, in turn, is seen to depend upon the primary current.

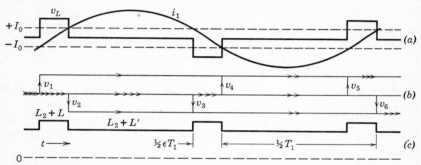

Fig. 14.5. Analysis of magnetic frequency multiplier: (a) idealized open-circuit voltage across coil, (b) synthesis of coil voltage by addition of step functions, and (c) variation of total secondary inductance.

In principle, the Fourier series approach gives a complete solution to the operation of this device. In practice, however, we wish to obtain a considerable power output at the harmonic frequency nf, and this is possible only if the secondary current, i_2, has a considerable amplitude. Unfortunately, the assumptions underlying the analysis are now invalid because the secondary current interacts with the primary current to modify the shape and duration of the pulses of emf. An alternative approach is therefore desirable.

14.7 Repeated transients

The operation of the single-frequency magnetic multiplier may also be analyzed from the viewpoint of a succession of transient disturbances. The secondary is then considered to be a series resonant circuit subjected to a succession of alternating steps of emf and to corresponding steps of total self-inductance as shown in Fig. 14.5b and 14.5c. It is clear that the natural frequency of the secondary is periodically shifted by this change of inductance, but that the overall period must correspond to that of the driving voltage. This viewpoint is adequate to explain all the observed facts, including the production of even harmonics, and permits reasonably satisfactory calculations of performance.

On the basis of such calculations, supplemented by extensive experimental work, Guillemin states that optimum efficiency and wave form are observed when the parameters are adjusted to meet the approximate formula

$$i_2 \doteq 1.5i_1/n. \tag{14.4}$$

Under these conditions the current through the nonlinear coil must have at least two maxima and minima per cycle (and may have as many as four zeros per cycle). An experimental $5:1$ magnetic frequency multiplier tested by Guillemin had an efficiency of 30 per cent.

Magnetic frequency multipliers tend to generate only *odd* harmonics because the $B\text{-}H$ curve is symmetric; however, even harmonics may be generated by supplying a suitable magnetic bias. This method is quite practical when a relatively high multiplication is desired, but requires an inconveniently large bias if $n = 2$. If, for example, the sixth harmonic is desired the bias should be chosen so that five and then seven half cycles of output are produced between excitations.

Although highly reliable and capable of good efficiency, frequency multipliers of the magnetic type do not yield an output which is proportional to the input. Ordinarily, the output is zero until some critical input is exceeded, then jumps to a considerable value, and remains relatively constant as the input is further increased. This behavior is undesirable in some situations but is quite satisfactory in others.

Frequency multipliers based upon nonlinear dielectrics have not been developed to a point such that design information and performance may be reported. However, it appears that excellent performance to frequencies up to about 10^8 can be anticipated. A material having a very sharp-cornered curve of D vs. E, analogous to the saturation curve of Fig. 14.3, is required. There is reason to believe that every material having this desired dielectric behavior is both crystalline and piezoelectric. Therefore, the mechanical resonance of the nonlinear element may be used to select the desired frequency.

14.8 Frequency multiplication by means of vacuum tubes

The use of vacuum tubes as frequency multipliers is well known. Ordinarily, the vacuum tube is operated in class C with relatively large values of bias and driving voltage.   Under these conditions the plate current flows in short pulses, and it is possible for the tuned plate circuit to describe several complete cycles during each cycle of the driving voltage.   The arrangement and typical wave forms are shown in Fig. 14.6.   It is immediately apparent that a specified vacuum tube as a multiplier cannot give as large values of efficiency and power

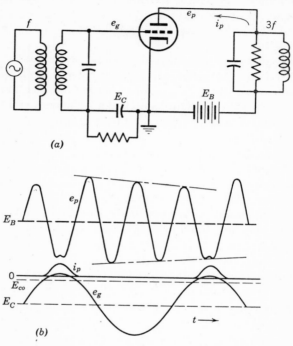

(a)

(b)

Fig. 14.6.   Class C frequency tripler: (a) circuit and (b) wave forms for $Q = 27$.

output as it does as an amplifier because of the unfavorable angle of conduction.   Under the conditions shown, the plate draws current for more than half of the output cycle in spite of the large values of both direct and alternating grid voltage indicated.

Sarbacher[267] has shown that the efficiency of class C amplifiers and frequency multipliers is considerably improved by injection of harmonic voltages in the grid and plate circuits.   In the grid circuit, the harmonic should be phased so as to sharpen the positive peak, shortening the period of conduction.   In the plate circuit the harmonic should be oppositely phased so as to broaden the negative peak, thus permitting a long period of conduction without loss of efficiency due to a high voltage drop in the tube. The simplest method of injecting a harmonic in the grid circuit is by feedback from the plate.

In triodes, which are commonly used for frequency multipliers, a considerable amount of feedback normally exists through the grid-plate capacitance. However, at the output frequency the grid circuit is nearly a pure capacitance so that the feedback is negative, that is, tends to broaden rather than sharpen the grid voltage peaks. The feedback phase can be reversed by the addition of a small inductance in series with the grid tuning condenser. Self-oscillation will occur if too large a value is used; but a considerable increase in efficiency and output may be secured before instability occurs.

It should be pointed out that the circuit of Fig. 14.6 is capable of self-oscillation, as a tuned grid, tuned plate circuit, even without the addition of an inductance. However, difficulty of this kind is rarely observed because circuit parameters which are consistent with efficient amplification are unfavorable to oscillation. This is one of several aspects of the operation of frequency multipliers which has been investigated by Page[233] and Brown.[42] Very useful curves showing the relative magnitude of the first ten harmonic currents as a function of the conduction angle are presented by Furst.[106]

Output frequencies up to about 1000 Mc may be obtained by means of more or less conventional triodes and pentodes operating as class C frequency multipliers. Still higher frequencies up to at least 25,000 Mc may be obtained by means of two-gap klystrons operating on essentially the same principles. The multiplication factor obtainable with a single tube is, however, limited to a small number, usually two or three, because of the drastic loss of efficiency which is associated with larger factors. The klystron is considerably more favorable in this respect, a frequency ratio of ten being quite practical.

Balanced multipliers are often used, especially when the requirements are severe. The two tubes are driven in push-pull so that two current pulses are obtained per cycle. If an *even* harmonic is desired, the plates are connected in *parallel;* if *odd,* in *push-pull.* Provided perfect symmetry exists, odd harmonics are absent in the output of the parallel arrangement and even harmonics are absent in the other. In practice, the balance is never perfect, but the problem of filtering the output is considerably simplified.

It is known that in a frequency multiplier the load impedance and working Q should be higher than in a corresponding class C amplifier. The analysis of Section 11.7 may be extended to show that, if the current pulses are sufficiently short, maximum output is obtained when $Q = \sqrt{nQ_0\pi/2}$, where Q_0 is the intrinsic selectivity and n is the multiplication factor. However, the condition of short pulses is rarely even approximated, and empirical design is usually necessary. The problem is a complicated one: but experience indicates the wisdom of using two or more coupled circuits having the highest practical value of Q. The use of such highly selective filters suppresses a large number of undesired frequencies, which are likely to cause trouble in practical systems.

Frequency multiplication is sometimes obtained by means of a blocking oscillator synchronized with the input signal. This method has the advantage that both even and odd harmonics are generated at a reasonable power level because of the large peak power produced. The multivibrator is commonly used for the same purpose; however, the amplitude of high-order harmonics is very sensitive to the symmetry of the output wave, and the general power level is much smaller than in the blocking oscillator. All such arrangements suffer the drawback that an output is produced in the absence of a driving signal, and erratic results are produced when the input is inadequate to ensure complete synchronization.

14.9 Principles of frequency division

The principles which govern frequency division are quite similar to those already discussed in connection with multiplication. As previously pointed out, both procedures depend upon nonlinearity and can be carried out in a variety of ways. Although frequency division is probably the easier process because it does not involve interpolation in time, it is probably less familiar to most readers. One important difference should be noted. *Harmonic frequencies are generated in nonlinear impedances when driven sinusoidally, whether resonant circuits are present or absent, and may be selected in a variety of ways, whereas subharmoic frequencies are generated in nonlinear impedances when driven sinusoidally only if suitable resonant circuits are present; the resonant circuit must therefore be regarded as part of the source rather than as a selection device.* Moreover, harmonics are generated in passive systems, whether the nonlinearity is in resistance, inductance, or capacitance, whereas subharmonics are *not* generated in passive systems where the only nonlinearity is in resistance. Because suitable nonlinear inductances and capacitances have been available only recently, the preceding statement was formerly equivalent to saying that subharmonics could not be generated in passive circuits. However, present materials are sufficiently promising that a lively development in passive frequency dividers is anticipated.

One additional remark, in the nature of a caution, is appropriate.

In passive nonlinear resistive devices the frequencies produced are certain to be simply related to the driving frequency. In systems involving nonlinear reactance, on the other hand, it is possible to produce all manner of frequencies even though the system is passive. These new frequencies need not be integrally related to the supply frequency but are consistent with the modulation eq. 14.1 (where f_0 is the driving force) and only arise at resonant frequencies of the system. The reader who wishes to pursue this interesting subject is referred to the work of Hartley,[130] Hussey,[152] van der Ziel,[323] and North.[225]

It should be noted that frequency division is by no means uncommon in everyday experience. Perhaps the most universal example of the phenomenon is "pumping" a swing. It is well known that, given an initial start, we can increase the amplitude of our oscillation by lowering the center of gravity at the point of greatest displacement and raising it at the point of greatest velocity. In practice, the change of position is necessarily accomplished at a finite rate; and it is sufficient to supply energy only during one-half the cycle, but the principle is still the same.

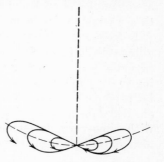

FIG. 14.7. Motion in pumping a swing.

That energy is delivered to the system is readily demonstrated, because the individual works against centrifugal force as he raises his body near the center of the motion; whereas he lowers himself at a time of low velocity when the force is much less. In the absence of friction this energy can only go to increase the amplitude of oscillation. The situation is illustrated by Fig. 14.7, which shows a somewhat idealized path of the center of gravity. The path is very similar to the familiar Lissajous figure for a 2:1 frequency ratio, as it should be since two full cycles of "pumping" are performed per cycle of the main oscillation.

Frequency dividing systems may be roughly catalogued according to the operating principle as follows: (1) passive structures using nonlinear reactive elements; (2) active stable structures using any form of nonlinear element; (3) unstable (free-running) structures; and (4) devices based upon counting.

14.10 Variation of reactive elements

Two distinct but closely related classes of elements may be used to produce the energy transfer which is basic to passive frequency dividers. The first class contains elements which are nonlinear but time invariant. These are identified by the fact that the reactance is expressible as a single-valued function of the current or voltage only. Nonlinear inductors and capacitors are examples of such elements. The second class contains elements which are linear but time variant. They are identified by the fact that the reactance is expressible as a single-valued function of time and is independent of current or voltage. Air condensers and air-core variometers, driven by an external motor, are examples of such elements. Excellent discussions of nonlinear and time variable systems are given by Bennett[30] and Kingston.[171]

In frequency division systems the variable reactance must be a suitable periodic function of time, but it makes no difference whether this periodicity is achieved by electrical or by mechanical means. Accordingly, the choice of type of element will depend upon the frequency to be produced and whether the available power is in mechanical or electrical form. For simplicity of exposition the discussion will begin with time-variable elements, although practical frequency dividers always use nonlinear elements.

14.11 Oscillations in a circuit containing a time-variable inductance

Let us examine the behavior of a linear series-resonant circuit in which the inductance varies periodically about an average value as a function of time, according to the equation

$$L(t) = \frac{L}{(1 + b \sin 2\omega t)} \tag{14.5}$$

where 2ω represents the angular velocity of the driving force. The circuit diagram is shown in Fig. 14.8a. From Chapter 2 we write immediately for the free oscillation, the differential equation for the electric charge q,

$$L \, d^2q/dt^2 + R \, dq/dt + qD(1 + b \sin 2\omega t) = 0, \tag{14.6}$$

where the term involving $R \sin 2\omega t$ is neglected in comparison to the others. Substitutions similar to those used in Chapter 4 are helpful in simplifying this equation. We write

$$\omega_0{}^2 = D/L, \tag{14.7}$$

$$k = R/L, \tag{14.8}$$

and

$$b\omega_0{}^2 = -2a. \tag{14.9}$$

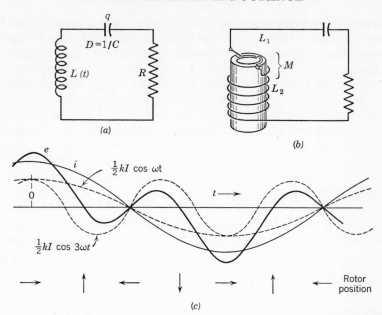

Fɪɢ. 14.8. Circuit with time-variable inductance: (a) circuit, (b) mechanical
arrangement, and (c) generation of voltage.

With these substitutions the differential equation simplifies* to

$$d^2q/dt^2 + kdq/dt + q(\omega_0{}^2 - 2a \sin 2\omega t) = 0. \qquad (14.10)$$

In spite of its apparent simplicity this differential equation does not
possess a general closed solution expressible by a finite number of
terms.   However, experience indicates the existence of steady oscillations of nearly sinusoidal form.   Accordingly a series solution is
attempted in the form

$$q = A_1 \sin \omega t + A_3 \sin 3\omega t + A_5 \sin 5\omega t + \cdots$$
$$+ B_1 \cos \omega t + B_3 \cos 3\omega t + B_5 \cos 5\omega t + \cdots. \qquad (14.11)$$

If we obtain the first and second derivatives of this quantity and
substitute them in eq. 14.10 we may test the validity of the solution by
separately equating to zero the coefficients of the sine and cosine terms
at the various frequencies.   It should be noted that the product of
sines which thus arises in the last term of eq. 14.10 accounts for sum

---

* This equation is closely related to the Mathieu and Hill equations.   A discussion of these equations pertinent to this book is given by van der Pol and
Strutt.[321]   The present treatment is the electrical paraphase of a vibration problem treated on page 84 of Rayleigh's book.[251]

and difference frequencies, and it is this fact which necessitates the series expansion. When the appropriate substitutions and trigonometric reductions are made, we are led to the following series of equations:

$$(\omega_0^2 - \omega^2)A_1 - k\omega B_1 - aB_1 + aB_3 = 0, \qquad (14.12)$$

$$(\omega_0^2 - \omega^2)B_1 + k\omega A_1 - aA_1 - aA_3 = 0, \qquad (14.13)$$

$$(\omega_0^2 - 9\omega^2)A_3 - 3k\omega B_3 - aB_1 + aB_5 = 0, \qquad (14.14)$$

$$(\omega_0^2 - 9\omega^2)B_3 + 3k\omega A_3 + aA_1 - aA_5 = 0, \qquad (14.15)$$

$$(\omega_0^2 - 25\omega^2)A_5 - 5k\omega B_5 - aB_3 + aB_7 = 0, \qquad (14.16)$$

$$(\omega_0^2 - 25\omega^2)B_5 + 5k\omega A_5 + aA_3 - aA_7 = 0. \qquad (14.17)$$

This formidable array of equations is readily reduced by use of the known facts that the oscillation is nearly sinusoidal, that is, $A_1 \gg A_3 \gg A_5$ and $B_1 \gg B_3 \gg B_5$. Neglecting A_3 and B_3 in eqs. 14.12 and 14.13, and taking the product, leads to the equality:

$$(\omega_0^2 - \omega^2)^2 = a^2 - k^2\omega^2. \qquad (14.18)$$

Since the left side of this equation is inherently positive, we may write

$$a \geq k\omega, \qquad (14.19)$$

which establishes the fractional inductance variation required to produce sustained oscillation. Moreover, if A_3 and B_3 are sufficiently small, we may write to a good approximation

$$\omega \doteq \omega_0 \qquad (14.20)$$

and

$$a \doteq k\omega. \qquad (14.21)$$

In terms of the original variables, the drive requirement is

$$b = R/\omega_0 L = 1/Q, \qquad (14.22)$$

where Q has its normal significance of selectivity. Subject to this condition, an oscillation of frequency ω will be sustained constant at any arbitrary initial amplitude by the inductance variation at 2ω. A larger value of b will produce expanding oscillations which will presently overload the system and reduce b or Q to the value required by eq. 14.22.

It will be noted that the system just described is more accurately a magnetic, shaft-driven generator than a frequency divider, because the input is supplied by a uniformly rotating shaft. However, the generated frequency is exactly half the frequency of reactance variation. More important to our present purpose, the same output is observed if the reactance variation is produced by means of a nonlinear inductance under the influence of a driving current instead of mechanically.

The behavior of this system of Fig. 14.8b may be interpreted from the generator viewpoint. Provided a current flows, an emf is induced in both the stationary and the moving coils by the relative motion. For convenience, we shall consider only the emf induced in the moving coil, because reciprocity proves that an equal voltage is induced in the fixed coil. The situation at various points of the cycle are shown in Fig. 14.8c where, for convenience, the rotor is represented by an arrow perpendicular to its coil, and is referred to a fixed coil with vertical axis. It is seen that, although the rotor describes 720 mechanical degrees per cycle of the output current, the voltage generated aids the current flow most of the time. The equations which represent the generator viewpoint are readily manipulated to yield eq. 14.22.

14.12 A passive magnetic frequency divider

A particularly simple and elegant arrangement for producing frequency division by means of magnetic saturation in a passive system has been described by McCreary[196] and is shown in Fig. 14.9. Laminations of a thickness and magnetic material appropriate to the frequency of

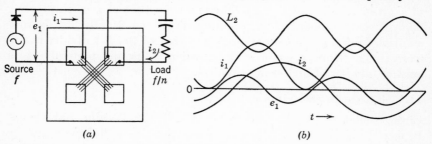

FIG. 14.9. Magnetic frequency divider: (a) laminations and winding and (b) wave forms for 2:1 ratio.

interest are punched in the form shown and are wound with separate, mutually perpendicular coils. This arrangement eliminates virtually all direct mutual inductance between the input and output circuits; accordingly, the behavior[26] depends almost entirely upon saturation, which occurs only in the central portion of the core.

The direct current bias, which is secured by the rectifier of Fig. 14.9, is appropriate to the generation of even submultiples of frequency as shown by the wave forms. The curves indicate a small degree of saturation consistent with the mathematical relationships previously developed. As with the magnetic multiplier, however, efficiency is greatly increased by high degrees of saturation. It is seen that, because of saturation in the common portion of the core, the self-inductance of the secondary describes one full cycle about its average value per cycle of the input wave. Consistent with the previous section, therefore, an output frequency equal to half the input frequency will be observed, provided the secondary is suitably tuned and is not excessively loaded.

Odd submultiples may be obtained with the same apparatus by omitting the bias in the primary circuit and by suitably retuning the secondary. In this case the common portion of the core is saturated *twice* per cycle of the input frequency so that the secondary inductance varies at twice its former rate. Evidently, therefore, a 3:1 frequency division corresponds to a 6:1 division with respect to self-inductance. A 4:1 frequency division has also been obtained with this circuit by suitable tuning of the secondary and application of a primary bias. Both the 4:1 and 3:1 devices require auxiliary starting devices, whereas the 2:1 unit is completely self-starting.

The 2:1 divider at 60 cycles input is capable of efficiencies of the order of 70 per cent, and the output is relatively insensitive to input voltage or output current. Moreover, the power-handling capacity of a given core is not greatly different from that of a corresponding 30-cycle transformer. The performance of the 3:1 divider is substantially inferior in every respect, and that of the 4:1 divider is still worse. Therefore, a chain of 2:1 dividers is usually preferable to a smaller number of high-order dividers.

14.13 The subcycle ringer

Closely related to McCreary's divider is the Loraine Sub-Cycle* Ringer[193] widely used in telephone plants to provide the low-frequency current to ring subscribers' telephones. In its 2:1 form it differs from Fig. 14.9a principally in that the saturable core is made from conventional "E" laminations, with the input winding on the center leg. The output windings are balanced so that none of the input frequency is induced in the secondary, and vice versa. Like McCreary's 2:1 (30-cycle) unit, it employs a rectifier to bias the core and is completely self-starting.

The 3:1 (20-cycle) Sub-Cycle is illustrated in Fig. 14.10 and ex-

---

* The term Sub-Cycle is a trademark of the Loraine Products Corporation.

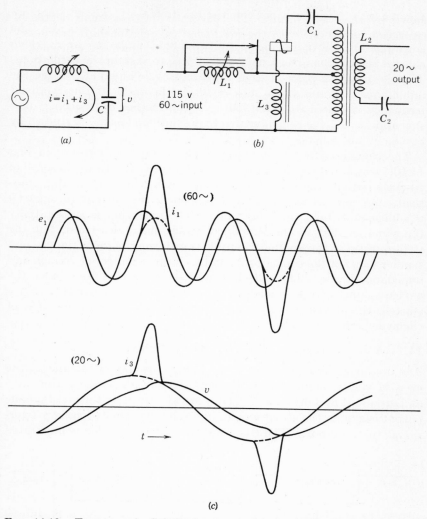

FIG. 14.10. Twenty-cycle Sub-Cycle ringer: (a) simplified circuit, (b) actual circuit, and (c) wave forms.

plained in terms of the simplified schematic diagram. The condenser C is chosen to resonate the *unsaturated* inductance of the nonlinear coil at approximately one-third of the supply frequency. The operation is initiated by short-circuiting the saturable coil for an instant when the applied voltage is relatively large. The charge which is thus transferred to the condenser initiates oscillations at the fractional frequency, and these are maintained by the mechanism indicated in

Fig. 14.10c.   Near each peak of the low-frequency current, the core saturates by the combined action of the two currents present.   The corresponding low inductance permits the flow of a large current which charges the condenser in a polarity suitable to sustain the oscillations. That is, near the peak of each third half cycle of input voltage the inductance saturates and a pulse of current favorable to the fractional frequency is drawn from the source.   This method of frequency division appears to have been invented by Fallou[91] and has been studied by Spitzer[293] and others.

The commercial 3:1 Sub-Cycle employs the circuit shown in Fig. 14.10b, which features an automatic starting relay.   In the absence of 20-cycle output, the relay contacts close and deliver a starting transient.   As soon as an output is established, the current through C_1 is sufficient to hold the relay open.   The operation is substantially the same as that of the simplified arrangement described, but the step-up ratio of the nonlinear output transformer permits the use of a smaller value of the capacitor C_1 and facilitates control of voltage and impedance levels.   The output condenser C_2 serves to protect the device against excessive loads by limiting the output current.   Once started, this device is very stable and operates with good values of efficiency and regulation.

14.14 A stable regenerative frequency divider

The frequency divider due to R. L. Miller[210] is a good example of the class of stable, nonpassive frequency dividers, devised by Horton[143] and discussed by Fortescue.[98]   They are identified by the fact that the output is zero in the absence of an input, and is usually nearly proportional to the input.   The basic principle of this device is illustrated

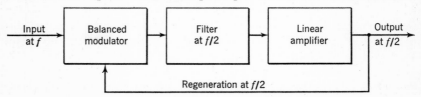

FIG. 14.11.   Miller's 2:1 frequency divider.

in Fig. 14.11.   The key feature is the balanced modulator, which delivers a voltage to the selective filter *only if voltages are simultaneously applied to its two "inputs."*   In the absence of the input signal f, therefore, there is no loop transmission, and the system is absolutely stable.   When an input is supplied, the modulator will convert any assumed frequency f_1 into a frequency $f - f_1$, and deliver it through the filter to the amplifier.   However, the loop is closed so the assumed frequency must be equal to the output frequency, which can only happen if $f_1 = f/2$.

The operation is *not* dependent upon the phase shifts of the amplifier, filter or modulator, since a suitable shift of the phase of the input voltage will compensate for any shift phase assumed to exist in these units; moreover, the system is self-starting.   For a small fixed value of input at f the conversion loss of the modulator is a constant. Therefore, if the gain of the amplifier including the filter is greater than this constant loss, the level of fractional frequency will increase

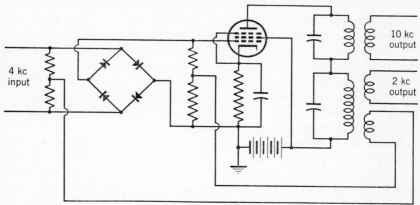

FIG. 14.12.   Circuit diagram of regenerative frequency divider.

exponentially with time until overload occurs.   If, as is ordinarily done, the overload is made to occur in the modulator, the output wave form is good, and the amplifier operates well within its linear range. Although the modulator is saturated with respect to the regenerated signal at $f/2$ it may still be linear in its conversion from the input at f to its output at $f/2$.   Over a considerable range, therefore, the output and input are closely proportional in amplitude.   Finally, the phase shift between input and output is practically independent of the level and is quite insensitive to the condition of the tube and modulator; moreover, it is possible to obtain additional simply related frequencies, which are produced in the modulator, by addition of suitable tuned circuits.

A practical circuit for obtaining 2 and 10 kc from a 4-kc source is shown in Fig. 14.12.   The 10-kc output is due to the third-order modulation process, discussed in the next paragraph.   Using a low-power tube in the unit, Miller obtained power outputs well in excess of one milliwatt at both frequencies, and very good linearity between the input and the 2-kc output.   The input frequency could be varied over nearly an octave without loss of the dividing property, and at the limits the output disappeared rather than occurring at the wrong frequency.

Several important variants of this circuit were described by Miller. In one the modulator is designed to work in a more complicated manner according to the relationship

$$f_0 = f - mf_1, \tag{14.23}$$

where f_0 is the output frequency, f_1 is the frequency returned to the modulator, and f is the input frequency.   This equation is seen to satisfy the loop conditions of Fig. 14.11 if $f_0 = f_1 = f/3$ and $m = 2$. Therefore, the original arrangement is not limited to division by two. However, it is not self-starting for ratios above two, because the output of a modulator representable by eq. 14.23 varies as the square of the voltage at f_1.   Therefore, the loop gain approaches zero as the output approaches zero.   Operation is obtained by providing a relatively generous gain margin in the operating condition and by giving the circuit a starting transient.

In the other variant of this general system, Miller inserted a frequency multiplier with associated filter between the amplifier and the modulator to obtain division by ratios in excess of two.   Provided the multiplier has, at small amplitudes, an output proportional to the input, the resulting system is self-starting.   For example, a self-starting three-to-one frequency divider results from the combination of a rectifier-type frequency doubler with suitable filters and a linear modulator.   At least in principle, we should be able to extend this method to higher orders of division.   This matter is of some theoretical interest, because, to the author's knowledge, this is the only way of obtaining a completely stable self-starting frequency divider having a ratio larger than two.   It is very desirable that a frequency divider be self-starting; otherwise a starting transient must be supplied after each interruption of operation, and no output is observed if the input falls below some critical value.   Following the general method used by Miller, Stansel[295] has devised stable frequency dividers in which the modulation process is performed by vacuum tubes and in which the input frequency may be as high as 50 Mc.   Lyons[194] proposes to extend the method to microwaves, at frequencies as high as 24,000 Mc.

14.15 A stable class C frequency divider

The configuration of a practical stable frequency divider which requires no separate modulator is shown in Fig. 14.13.   Its operation

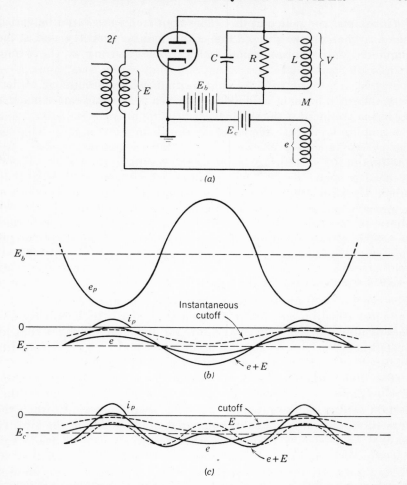

FIG. 14.13.   Stable class C system: (*a*) schematic, (*b*) amplifier wave form, and
(*c*) wave forms as 2:1 divider.

resembles that of Sterky's[296] divider, but the circuit requires only one
rather than two tubes, and the division ratio may be greater than two.
The tuned circuit should have a moderate value of Q (for example, 20),
and an impedance consistent with efficient class C operation of the
tube.   The grid is biased substantially beyond cutoff, and the transformer coupling is reduced to the point that oscillation would occur
only if the bias were reduced to the point of class A operation.   Under
these conditions the circuit is absolutely stable in the sense that it
cannot produce an output in the absence of an input.

If an input is supplied at the frequency f and if the output circuit is tuned to the same frequency, the system acts as a stable regenerative amplifier. Wave forms typical of such operation are shown in Fig. 14.13b. Because plate current flows during only a small portion of the cycle, it is clear that the same output could be obtained with a very different form of grid voltage wave. In particular, the same output is produced if the frequency of the input wave is doubled, and the amplitude slightly increased as shown in Fig. 14.13c. That is, the system operates efficiently as a 2:1 frequency divider. The addition of a grid leak and condenser is desirable as in other class C systems so that the bias will increase with increase of input. In principle, the method is capable of extension to any frequency ratio; in practice ratios in excess of about 3:1 are difficult to control. An alternate form of stable vacuum tube frequency divider has been devised by Groszkowski.[120]   However, it suffers the basic disadvantage that the power output is less than the power input.

14.16 Free-running frequency dividers

The synchronized multivibrator, discussed in Chapter 13, is probably the most widely used form of frequency divider. Its simplicity and ease of adjustment largely compensate for its faults, which are that an output is present in the absence of an input, and that the output frequency may not be correct even when the input is normal.

The design of multivibrators for frequency division has been extensively studied by Andrew,[9] Shenk,[281] and others, but it appears that certain aspects of the problem are still obscure, especially when the transition interval is not short compared to the period of the injected wave. At moderate frequencies the transition may be made sufficiently sharp and the following design procedure is appropriate. (1) Design the multivibrator to run free as stably as possible at the desired fraction of the synchronizing frequency. This will ordinarily involve the use of large plate load resistances and positive return of the grid leaks. (2) Adjust the amplitude of the synchronizing voltage so that its maximum slope is equal to the slope of the unmodified grid voltage in the region of cutoff. This is desirable because it leads to maximum tolerance of the actual cutoff voltage without loss of synchronization at the desired frequency; whereas, a larger value of synchronizing voltage could cause the transition to occur too early. As shown in Chapter 13, the wave form of the synchronizing voltage is important. A square wave is slightly superior to a sinusoid, a "sloping off" square wave is substantially better, and a saw tooth is ideal.

Frequency division by means of a stabilized relaxation oscillator has been obtained by Builder.[48]   Using a type 885 gas tube in conjunction with a stable tuned circuit, he is able to produce a free-running oscillator which has excellent intrinsic frequency stability, but is subject to synchronization over a considerable range of input voltage and a moderate range of input frequency.

Norrman[224] has shown that frequency division by ratios as great as 10:1 may be reliably obtained by means of synchronized LC oscillators.   He recommends the use of large excitation ratios and large L/C ratios, which lead to highly distorted wave forms and relatively poor inherent frequency stability.   Under these conditions the synchronizing voltage is quite effective in controlling the operating frequency.

Schmidt[271] has obtained results comparable to those of Norrman by means of phase-shift oscillators.   Frequency ratios up to 7:1 are found to be entirely practical.   For many experimental purposes the phase-shift arrangement is preferable because resistances and condensers are easier to obtain and adjust than are coils.

14.17 Frequency division by counting

The frequency dividers described in the previous sections are all based on the premise that the input wave is essentially periodic and reasonably stable in frequency.   Some waves of practical interest do not meet those conditions.   It is still possible to obtain an analogous operation by means of various schemes, depending upon the counting of cycles of impulses.   A circuit which is basic to this art is the well-known Eccles-Jordan[81] trigger or "flip-flop" circuit, which differs from the multivibrator only in that the coupling condensers are shunted by resistors and the grid leaks are returned to relatively large negative biases.   The conditions are such that the circuit is in stable equilibrium with either tube conducting, in which case the other tube is permanently cut off by the action of the coupling and grid leak resistors.

If a series of suitable negative pulses is injected into the grid circuit through the synchronizing condenser it will be found that the cutoff versus conducting state is reversed once for each pulse.   That is, *two* pulses must be injected to cause the circuit to return to its original condition and thus complete *one* cycle.   Therefore, this circuit constitutes an absolutely stable, frequency halver.   The fact that a pulse injected symmetrically will cause the circuit to "flip" depends upon the fact that the two coupling condensers assume quite different charges during the interval between pulses.   As the triggering pulse decreases to zero, the two grids therefore return toward zero bias at different rates. The tube which was formerly nonconducting easily wins the race and thereby holds the other tube in a nonconducting condition until the next triggering pulse appears.

By using a chain of n of these circuits, as is commonly done in radiation-measuring equipment, it is possible to obtain an output transition as a consequence of 2^n input pulses, whether these are distributed uniformly or nonuniformly in time.

Moreover, by reasonably simple modifications of this circuit, it is possible to provide units which divide by ten or other factors, not necessarily powers of two. Davis[72] describes free-running multivibrators based on these methods which are capable of dividing frequencies by fractional ratios. The art of frequency division by counting has become quite extensive, but is somewhat beyond the scope of this book. A good treatment of the subject is to be found in Chapters 16 and 17 of *Waveforms*[57] and in papers by Sharpless[279] and Regener.[255, 256]

PROBLEMS

14.1. Why is the tuned circuit necessary in the primary of practical rectifier-type frequency doublers? Explain.

14.2. Verify eqs. 14.2a and 14.3.

14.3. Design a frequency doubler to yield a 2-Mc output, using the 6AL5 diode, a 5000-ohm load, and coil having a Q of 100. Justify the element values chosen and calculate the overall efficiency. (Assume the diode has a fixed forward resistance of 200 ohms.)

14.4. Explain the detailed operation of the frequency multiplier of Fig. 14.4.

14.5. Show why the output of a magnetic frequency multiplier is zero until the input is increased to some critical level.

14.6. Sketch an arrangement for obtaining frequency tripling with nonlinear condensers.

14.7. Explain the observed fact that one or both "coasting" cycles of Fig. 14.6 may be of larger amplitude than the cycle of conduction.

14.8. Derive eq. 14.22 by treating Fig. 14.8b as an induction alternator, assuming an initial excitation.

14.9. Sketch an arrangement for obtaining 2:1 frequency division with nonlinear condensers.

14.10. Discuss the design and operation of a stable class C triode frequency halver.

14.11. Design a practical "flip-flop" frequency halver, using the 6SN7 triode with a common cathode resistor to avoid the need for a negative bias supply. Show how to inject either positive or negative triggering pulses, and justify the element values chosen.

15

TUBE AND THERMAL NOISE

It is well known that the small voltages and currents generated by the thermal agitation of electrons within solid conductors and the corresponding random emission of electrons within vacuum tubes set a lower limit on the magnitude of electrical signals which may be amplified and detected. These undesired voltages and currents consist of small pulses which occur at completely irregular times; and may therefore be thought of as comprising all possible steady-state frequencies. They are commonly referred to as noise because they produce a smooth continuous sound if amplified and presented in acoustical form by means of a loudspeaker. They are sometimes referred to as "snow" or "grass" in connection with television or radar systems where the signal is presented in visual form by means of an oscilloscope tube. Good general discussions of noise are given by Llewellyn[191] and Moullin.[218]

It is not so commonly realized that noise voltages also affect the operation of oscillators. It is true that in most oscillator applications the effects of noise are quite small; but in some cases, for example in microwave oscillators used in superheterodyne receivers, the noise sidebands seriously restrict the choice of the intermediate frequency. And in systems employing pulse time modulation the overall signal to noise ratio is affected by the influence of tube noise on the time of build-up of oscillation.

15.1 Review of thermal noise

The thermal agitation of the molecules of a gas, the so-called Brownian movement, is well known, and is fundamental to an understanding of the behavior of gases. The individual molecules move in all directions and with various velocities, experiencing collisions with each other and with the walls of the container. An increase in the temperature of the gas increases the average velocity of the molecules, which leads to an increase in the pressure exerted on the surrounding walls. A similar situation exists within solid electrical conductors; but in this case the moving particles are free electrons, and most of the collisions are with the fixed portions of the molecules of the substance rather than with other electrons.

Because a moving charge constitutes an electric current, and produces voltage in a system of finite resistance, it is clear that the thermal agitation of electrons in a conductor must produce a random electric voltage across its terminals. The truth of this statement has been amply confirmed by both theory and experiment. One means of calculating the magnitude of the effect, originated by Nyquist,[227] assumes that an ideal microphone, perhaps of the condenser type, is located in a gas at $T°$ absolute temperature. The microphone impedance is matched by means of an ideal transformer to a resistor R. We know that the Brownian movement of the gas will generate small voltages in the microphone, and that the resulting currents will heat the resistor. Evidently, thermal equilibrium is possible only if the resistor R returns an equal amount of energy to the gas through the microphone as a loudspeaker, so that both the resistor and the gas remain at temperature $T°$. By this means it is possible to calculate the voltage or power generated in a resistor at a given temperature. This voltage is referred to as Johnson[157] noise after its discoverer.

It is immediately clear that the power must be independent of both the material and magnitude of the resistor R, because the power delivered by the microphone is constant as long as the load presents an impedance match, which may always be accomplished by a suitable choice of the transformer. It would also be anticipated that the power interchange would be greater if the microphone were capable of transmitting a wide band of frequencies than if it were limited to a narrow band. The derivation, which is tedious, is omitted here and the result is stated as follows: The power P delivered by a resistor at an absolute temperature $T°$ to an equal resistor (at any temperature) is given by

$$P = KTB \text{ watts,} \qquad (15.1)$$

where $K = 1.37 \times 10^{-23}$ joules per degree is Boltzmann's constant, and B is the bandwidth of the coupling system, in cycles per second, as indicated in Fig. 15.1. The second resistor will return a power corresponding to its own temperature, which is usually nearly the same as that of the first. (Some carbon resistors have noise properties in excess of that given by eq. 15.1, but this effect is of little interest in the present situation.)

It is often desirable to express the magnitude of this effect in terms of voltage instead of power. This is readily done because, in a linear

FIG. 15.1. Transfer of power due to thermal noise.

system such as this, the maximum power available is equal to $V^2/4R$. Therefore, the equivalent open-circuit voltage is given by

$$V^2/4R = KTB \text{ volts}^2. \tag{15.2}$$

This result is itself often convenient, but is principally important because it leads to an equation applicable in situations where a sharp cutoff does not exist. The expression then becomes

$$V^2 = 4KT \int_0^\infty R \, df \text{ volts}^2, \tag{15.3}$$

where R, a function of frequency, is the equivalent series resistance of the network at temperature $T°$.

Alternatively, we may regard a physical resistor as a noise-free resistance in shunt with a constant-current noise generator. Consistent with the foregoing expressions, the effective current from this source may be written in terms of the conductance G

$$I^2 = 4GKTB \text{ amperes}^2 \tag{15.4}$$

or

$$I^2 = 4KT \int_0^\infty G \, df \text{ amperes}^2. \tag{15.5}$$

Equation 15.5 is the more general; eq. 15.4 applies only when the edges of the frequency band are well defined.

Because most apparatus operates at a temperature close to 300°K we may substitute this value to obtain simple results useful in normal situations. We have, corresponding to eqs. 15.1, 15.3, and 15.5, respectively,

$$P = 4.1 \times 10^{-21} \text{ watts per cycle}, \tag{15.6}$$

at 300°K

$$V^2 = 16.4 \times 10^{-21} \int_0^\infty R \, df \text{ volts}^2, \tag{15.7}$$

$$I^2 = 16.4 \times 10^{-21} \int_0^\infty G \, df \text{ amperes}^2. \tag{15.8}$$

Stated in another way, the power available from a pure resistor at 300°K is 204 db below one watt per cycle of bandwidth.

15.2 Noise in conventional vacuum tubes

As in passive resistors, noise is produced in vacuum tubes because electricity is not capable of unlimited division. In vacuum tubes, however, noise is produced because the current flow produced by a stream of electrons is necessarily discontinuous rather than because of thermal agitation. Tube noise is frequently referred to as shot noise, especially if space charge is absent. It is also referred to as Schottky[272] noise after its discoverer. The noise figure of a triode is quite high if the applied voltages are such that all the electrons emitted from the cathode reach the plate. Ordinarily, however, the potentials are such that most of the electrons emitted return to the cathode, and a dense cloud or space change of electrons forms near by. The effect of this space change is to cushion the motion of the individual electrons, thus greatly reducing the noise produced. In tetrodes and pentodes the noise voltage is somewhat larger than in triodes because the space charge is less effective in smoothing the random manner in which electrons divide between the plate and the screen grid.

It is convenient and customary to express the noise produced by a vacuum tube in terms of that due to thermal agitation in an equivalent resistor in the grid circuit. The resistance in the grid circuit is increased from zero to such a value that the power indicated at the output of the amplifier just doubles. When this condition prevails, the tube and resistor contribute equal amounts of noise, and the value of the grid resistor is the noise rating of the tube under the particular operating conditions chosen. The noise voltages due to the tube and the resistor add on an rms or power basis—a situation which results from the fact that both are random in character so that there is no possibility of systematic addition of the peak values.

Fortunately, the equivalent noise resistance of typical vacuum tubes is represented to an accuracy adequate for most purposes by very simple formulas. Harris[128] has shown that for triodes operating with complete cathode emission the equivalent noise resistance R_{eq} is given by

$$R_{eq} \doteq 2.5/g_m, \tag{15.9}$$

where g_m is the nominal transconductance in mhos.

For pentodes we must include an additional noise term due to screen grid current. The corresponding equation is

$$R_{eq} \doteq \frac{I_p}{g_m I_k} \left[2.5 + \frac{20 I_{g2}}{g_m} \right], \tag{15.10}$$

where g_m is the grid-to-plate transconductance in mhos; and I_p, I_k, and I_{g2} are, respectively, plate, cathode, and screen current in amperes. It is assumed that the cathode current is the sum of the screen and plate currents. These equations show the desirability of a large value of transconductance and a small value of screen current where noise is of importance. In commercial tubes operated at relatively low frequencies the equivalent noise resistance ranges from about 200 to 5000 ohms.

This method of rating the noise output of vacuum tubes may seem somewhat arbitrary, but it is actually quite convenient. Its particular merit is that it points directly to the requirements on input trans-formers. In a typical amplifier application a very small signal is available from a source having a fixed resistance at approximately room temperature. Nothing can be done to improve the signal with respect to the noise produced by this resistance, but a voltage step-up in the input transformer will serve to make both signal and thermal noise large compared to tube noise. Evidently, this objective is met if the source presents through the transformer a resistance large compared to the equivalent noise resistance of the tube. Adequate resistances are readily obtained at low frequencies where moderate bandwidths are required, but are rarely obtainable in high-frequency, broad-band amplifiers. Moreover, Thompson et al.[312] show that the input loading due to transit-time effects and lead losses at high frequencies contributes noise in addition to that corresponding to R_{eq}.

15.3 Noise from the viewpoint of time distribution

The foregoing sections have pointed out that ordinary forms of noise may be regarded as possessing an infinite number of frequencies having no systematic phase relationship and possessing uniform infinitesimal amplitude. The results found above are useful in many situations, but need to be supplemented by information as to the actual time variation of voltage and current. A very comprehensive statistical treatment of noise effects has been given by Rice,[260] and the most important of these results have been collected in a form more readily useful to engineers by Pierce.[240]

A typical example of a noise voltage is given in Fig. 15.2. The variation is entirely random in character, there being no definite period, amplitude, shape, or slope. Therefore, all statements concerning the behavior must be made in terms of statistics. Such statements, however, can be very exact and meaningful. If, for example, the noise voltage has an rms value V, then the probability that the voltage at a given instant lies between v and $v + dv$ is given by

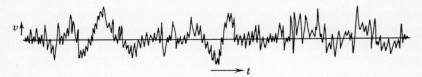

Fig. 15.2. Typical specimen of random noise.

$$\text{PR} = \frac{dv}{V\sqrt{2\pi}}\, e^{-v^2/2V^2}. \tag{15.11}$$

This is the so-called normal-distribution equation, symmetrical about a maximum at $v = 0$. The probability that at a given instant the absolute voltage is less than v_0 is expressed by the integral

$$\text{PR}_1 = 2 \int_0^{v_0} \frac{dv}{V\sqrt{2\pi}}\, e^{-v^2/2V^2}. \tag{15.12}$$

These functions are plotted in Fig. 15.3.

When a noise signal is passed through a low-pass filter, its frequency spectrum is changed in accordance with the properties of the filter.

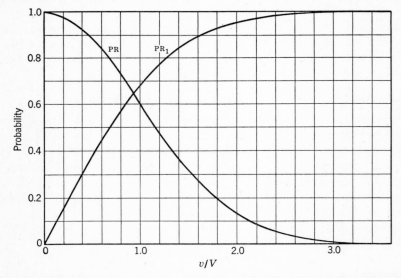

Fig. 15.3. Probability distributions: PR is the probability that the instantaneous voltage lies between v and $v + dv$ or that the envelope of filtered thermal noise exceeds v. PR$_1$ is the probability that the instantaneous signal is less than v.

It is ordinarily assumed that the filter has an extremely sharp cutoff characteristic. (Such a cutoff characteristic is necessarily associated with an extremely large phase shift in the cutoff region, but this has no effect upon noise spectrum calculations because the phase is assumed to be random.)   In consideration of wave shapes and probability functions the phase characteristic enters, in that it sets a limit to the rate at which the filtered wave may change with respect to time. This is illustrated in Fig. 15.4, which shows the wave form of typical filtered noise.   The principal change from Fig. 15.2 is a general round-

FIG. 15.4.   Random noise passed through a low-pass filter.

ing-off of all peaks without any significant change in the slower varia-tions.   At first glance this rounding-off of peaks would seem to reduce the probability of large instantaneous voltages.   However, it reduces the rms voltage in the same ratio, so that eqs. 15.11 and 15.12 and the curves of Fig. 15.3 may still be used for this case.

When noise is passed through a relatively narrow band-pass filter the character is markedly changed, as indicated in Fig. 15.5.   The

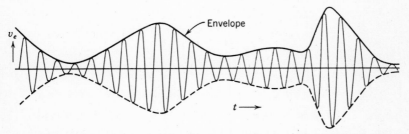

FIG. 15.5.   Random noise passed through a band-pass filter.

individual cycles are now similar in period and shape, but differ in amplitude in a random manner.   This behavior is most conveniently expressed in terms of the envelope which passes through the suc-cessive maxima of the wave itself.   The probability that a given maximum is less than some specified fraction of the rms value is of the same form as eq. 15.11 and is represented by PR in Fig. 15.3. This function is of interest because it is later used to calculate the magnitude of jitter in the starting time of pulsed oscillators.

15.4 Noise sidebands during sustained oscillation

It is ordinarily assumed that a conventional vacuum-tube oscillator generates a truly periodic wave representable as a fundamental frequency and a series of harmonics. This representation, although adequate in most situations, is not completely correct. A better interpretation is obtained by a study of the lamp bridge oscillator reproduced in Fig. 15.6. It is assumed that the output transformer is

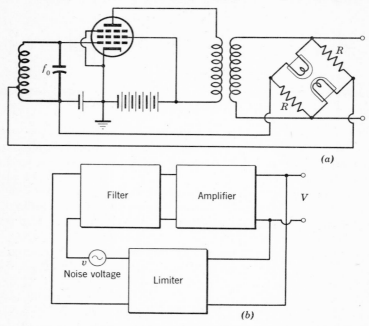

FIG. 15.6. Lamp bridge oscillator: (a) schematic and (b) block diagram

untuned and has a bandwidth large compared to that of the input circuit, which in turn is supposed to have an impedance large compared to the equivalent noise resistance of the vacuum tube. The latter condition ensures that any noise present in the output will come from thermal agitation in the lamp bridge rather than from the vacuum tube.

If the gain of the amplifier is very high (probably requiring additional tubes) a condition will be reached in which the lamp bridge is exactly balanced. The entire input to the amplifier will be provided by the thermal noise of the balanced lamp bridge, which will be somewhat increased by the elevated temperature of the tungsten filaments. Under this balanced condition, represented by μ_c, the output will consist of filtered thermal noise and will have a spectrum governed by the selectivity of the filter (grid circuit), as shown in curve a of Fig. 15.7.   As shown in Fig. 15.5, a spectrum such as this corresponds to a voltage wave which resembles a sinusoid of frequency f_0, but has successive cycles which differ somewhat in amplitude and in period. Moreover, the differences are of a random nature, but on the average are proportional to the bandwidth transmitted through the filter.

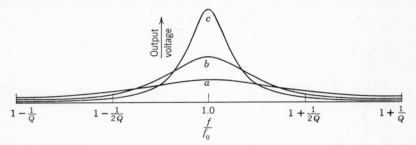

FIG. 15.7.   Variation of output spectrum with change of amplifier gain.   Legend (a) $\mu_0 = \mu_c, \beta = 0$; (b) $\mu_0 = 0.707\mu_c, \beta = 0.707/\mu_c$; and (c) $\mu_0 = 0.50\mu_c, \beta = 1.5/\mu_c$.

The width of the noise spectrum decreases rapidly as the inherent gain of the amplifier is reduced, and regeneration occurs through the resulting unbalance of the lamp bridge.   In Chapter 5 it was shown that feedback modifies the gain of an amplifier by the factor $(1 - \mu\beta)$. In the present case β is the loss in the lamp bridge and is independent of frequency, whereas μ is the gain of the amplifier-filter combination.

The parameters μ and β may be defined by reference to Fig. 15.6b. If the lamp bridge were removed and a voltage v in series with a resistor R were applied to the input of the filter, then a voltage $V = \mu v$ would be developed across another resistor equal to R connected across the output of the amplifier.   Alternatively, if the amplifier were turned off and a voltage V applied at its output terminals, a voltage βV would appear across the input terminals of the filter.

In the active system of Fig. 15.6b, both V and v contain many frequencies, and it is necessary to proceed with caution.   However, we know that the output power is substantially equal to the value P_0 which balances the bridge.   Therefore, we may write

$$P_0 = \frac{1}{R} \int_0^\infty V^2 \, df. \tag{15.13}$$

As long as $\mu\beta$ is less than one, it is certain that we may treat the system as a stable feedback amplifier with thermal noise having a uniform spectral distribution as its only input. The gain μ of this amplifier may be written

$$\frac{V}{v} = \mu_1 = \frac{\mu}{1 - \mu\beta} = \frac{\mu_0}{\mu_0/\mu - \mu_0\beta}, \qquad (15.14)$$

where the inherent selectivity of the filter relates the gain to the reference value μ_0 at the midband frequency f_0 by the equation

$$\mu = \frac{\mu_0}{1 + 2jQ(f - f_0)/f_0}. \qquad (15.15)$$

Elimination of μ leads to an equation in noise voltages

$$V = \frac{\mu_0 v}{1 - \mu_0\beta + 2jQ(f - f_0)/f_0}. \qquad (15.16)$$

Inspection of this equation shows that the output noise power will fall to half its maximum value at two frequencies separated by the noise bandwidth

$$B = (1 - \mu_0\beta)f_0/Q. \qquad (15.17)$$

Substitution of these equations into eq. 15.13 and use of the absolute value to obtain power yield the equation

$$P_0 = \frac{\mu_0{}^2 v^2}{RQ^2} \int_0^\infty \frac{f_0{}^2 \, df}{B^2 + 4(f - f_0)^2}. \qquad (15.18)$$

Replacing $f - f_0$ by δf, changing limits, and rearranging, we have with the help of eq. 15.2

$$P_0 = 5.48 \times 10^{-23} T \frac{\mu_0{}^2 f_0{}^2}{BQ^2} \int_0^\infty \frac{(B/2) \, df}{B^2/4 + (\delta f)^2}. \qquad (15.19)$$

Integrating by formula 480 of B. O. Peirce's book[235], we obtain

$$P_0 = 5.48 \times 10^{-23} T \frac{\mu_0{}^2 f_0{}^2}{BQ^2} \cdot \frac{\pi}{2} = 8.61 \times 10^{-23} T \frac{\mu_0{}^2 f_0{}^2}{BQ^2}. \qquad (15.20)$$

Ordinarily the bandwidth is the parameter of principal interest; it is given explicitly by

$$B = 8.61 \frac{\mu_0{}^2 f_0{}^2 T}{Q^2 P_0} \times 10^{-23} \text{ cycles}, \qquad (15.21)$$

where μ_0 is the amplification at the nominal operating frequency f_0, P_0 is the total power output, and T is the effective absolute temperature of the lamp bridge.

In reviewing the derivation it should be noted that the basic assumption that $\mu\beta$ is smaller than one was never violated.   In fact, eq. 15.19 is satisfied only if $(1 - \mu_0\beta)$ is a positive but very small quantity. Thus we are led to the rather remarkable conclusion that the lamp bridge oscillator is merely an amplifier which automatically raises its gain to such a value that thermal noise is amplified sufficiently to operate the limiter.   Moreover, this conclusion is readily extended to all linear oscillators; and the same general concept is applicable to ordinary nonlinear oscillators.   In some cases, particularly at the higher frequencies, the tube rather than a circuit element contributes the principal source of noise, but the same general situation prevails.

In particular, the output is not a pure sinusoid accompanied by noise sidebands, because both the period and the amplitude are subject to random variations.   It may, however, be thought of as a sinusoid subjected to noise modulation of both its amplitude and frequency.   It is seen that the purity of the wave increases with increase of output and selectivity, and with decrease of frequency and inherent noise.   Thus, under imaginable circumstances, we might need to generate oscillations at an undesirably high level and then attenuate them in order to achieve a satisfactorily narrow spectrum.

However, we must accept these results with some reservations, because of the action of the limiter.   As a following numerical example will show, the noise bandwidth of typical oscillators is very narrow. Therefore, the amplitude tends to change very slowly, and the limiter is able to remove practically all the amplitude modulation of the type shown in Fig. 15.5.   That is, our assumption that the thermistors have constant resistance must be somehow amended.   It appears, however, that phase or frequency modulation cannot be removed in this way, so that a considerable noise bandwidth remains.   The output spectrum depends upon the speed of the limiter in relation to the bandwidth indicated by eq. 15.21, and is therefore rather complicated. The output wave corresponds to that obtained by passing smooth noise through a filter having the characteristics represented by eq. 15.21 in tandem with a linear automatic-output-control amplifier having an appropriate response speed.

The noise bandwidth corresponding to eq. 15.21 increases as μ_0 is decreased and $\mu_0\beta$ is simultaneously increased, as shown in Fig. 15.7. In this connection it is instructive to note that if μ_0 is increased above the critical value the bridge is unbalanced with reversed phase, negative feedback results, and the noise spectrum becomes even wider to correspond to the increased effective pass band of the amplifier.

It is interesting to calculate the noise bandwidth of a typical lamp bridge oscillator, for which the following parameters are representative: $T = 500°K$, $\mu_0 = 100$, $f_0 = 10^6$ cycles, $Q = 100$, $P_0 = 10^{-2}$ watts. The corresponding noise bandwidth is very narrow

$$B = 8.61 \times 10^{-23} \times 500 \times 10^4 \times 10^{12} \times 10^{-4} \times 10^2$$
$$= 4.3 \times 10^{-6} \text{ cycles.} \quad (15.22)$$

The noise spectrum is considerably affected if both input and output transformers are tuned. Assuming that the two circuits have equal selectivity, we find that for any particular deviation from the midband frequency the attenuation in decibels or nepers is doubled from that of a single circuit. Therefore, the bandwidth defined by eq. 15.21 must be interpreted as between 6 db (one quarter maximum power) points rather than the original 3 db. As in other situations involving tuned circuits in tandem, the selectivity near the center of the band is not greatly affected, but the "skirt selectivity," that is, attenuation at relatively remote frequencies, is greatly increased. This is ordinarily desirable.

We may also derive eq. 15.21 by considering an oscillator as a dissipative tuned circuit in parallel with a negative noise-free conductance, identified with the vacuum tube. Therefore $\mu_0 \equiv 1$. The advantage of this development (omitted for brevity), is that it applies to any oscillator representable as a linear feedback system driving a single antiresonant circuit.

The calculation of noise bandwidth in nonlinear oscillators is very difficult. Evidently, however, the contribution due to linear elements is independent of the driving system. Because tube noise is proportional to transconductance (eq. 15.9), and because the *time average* of transconductance must be just sufficient to maintain oscillation, it is concluded that the contribution of tube noise is also constant as operation is shifted from class A into class C. That is, eq. 15.21 is applicable to all sorts of single-resonator oscillators.

15.5 Significance of noise bandwidth

At the present time the greatest practical importance of noise sidebands is in connection with the local oscillators used in microwave radar receivers. Let us first calculate the bandwidth of a reflex oscillator, using eq. 15.21, which should apply because the structure represents a single antiresonant circuit driven by the negative resistance of an electron stream. Typical values are: $\mu_0 = 1$, $f_0 = 10^{10}$ cycles, $P_0 = 10^{-2}$ watts, $Q = 400$, $T = 15 \times 10^6 \,°K$. The exceptional value of T is introduced to take account of the fact that the noise power of such tubes, as given on page 675 of the article by Pierce and Shepherd,[241] is about 50,000 times higher than that contributed by thermal noise in the resonator. The corresponding noise bandwidth is 81 cycles. This value is consistent with the familiar observation that an audible beat tone is not ordinarily obtainable from such oscillators, and is believed to be substantially correct in spite of the fact that the rapid inherent limiting action of such oscillators removes practically all the amplitude modulation implicit in the development. A substantially narrower spectrum may be produced by the negative-feedback frequency stabilization schemes described in Chapter 17, because both slow and rapid frequency deviations are corrected thereby.

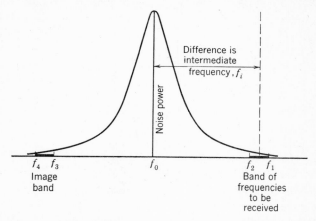

FIG. 15.8.   Effect of noise sidebands in a superheterodyne receiver.

The reduction of the limiting sensitivity of a superheterodyne receiver due to noise in the local (beat) oscillator is studied with reference to Fig. 15.8, in which f_0 represents the nominal frequency of the local oscillator and f_1 and f_2 represent the limits of the band of signals to be received. The main part of the receiver gain is provided by a very selective *intermediate frequency amplifier* which transmits the required band of signals and has its response centered at f_i. Unless suitable precautions are taken, *image* signals lying in the frequency band between f_3 and f_4 will also be received; and even if a filter is used to reject external signals in this band, it will not remove corresponding noise signals produced by the local oscillator.

To obtain the true noise power delivered to the amplifier by the action of the local oscillator, we should sum the products of the amplitudes of all signals whose difference frequencies lie within the pass band of the amplifier, and should take into account the properties of the modulator. However, we are interested in the relative rather than the absolute noise power, and the large concentration of power near f_0 makes it possible to obtain a good approximation to this value by summing noise components between f_1 and f_2 and doubling the result to take account of the image response.

The doubled noise power in the frequency band $f_2 - f_1$ is obtained by combining eqs. 15.19 and 15.20 in the form

$$P_s = \frac{2P_0}{\pi} \int_{f_2 - f_0}^{f_1 - f_0} \frac{(B/2)\, df}{(B/2)^2 + \delta f^2}. \tag{15.23}$$

Integration yields

$$P_s = \frac{2P_0}{\pi} \left[\tan^{-1} \frac{f_1 - f_0}{B/2} - \tan^{-1} \frac{f_2 - f_0}{B/2} \right]. \tag{15.24}$$

The substitutions

$$f_1 - f_0 = f_a \quad \text{and} \quad f_2 - f_0 = f_b \tag{15.25}$$

and the fact that these quantities are large compared to B permit use of the relations

$$\tan(\pi/2 - \phi) = \cot \phi = 1/\tan \phi \doteq 1/\phi \tag{15.26}$$

to obtain

$$P_s \doteq \frac{P_0 B}{\pi} \left[\frac{1}{f_b} - \frac{1}{f_a} \right]. \tag{15.27}$$

In a typical radar application f_b and f_a are respectively, 25 and 35 Mc, and the power delivered to the converter, represented by P_0, is 10^{-3} watts. Corresponding to a bandwidth of 81 cycles, the total side band noise power is 2.9×10^{-10} watts. This value is known to be about one hundred times too high; the discrepancy is attributed to the fact that the limiting action of reflex oscillators is so rapid that the amplitude disturbances implicit in eq. 15.27 are not actually present.

15.6 Influence of noise upon the initiation of oscillation

When a system having negative resistance is given an initial transient, the resulting oscillations increase in amplitude exponentially with time until nonlinearity sets in to limit the amplitude. In the absence of an initial transient such a system might remain at rest indefinitely. In practical oscillators, a relatively large transient usually accompanies the switching operation which renders the system active, and oscillations build up rapidly to their final value. In some cases, however, this starting transient is absent or negligible, and oscillations build up from the small random transients which constitute tube or thermal noise.

From the nature of noise it is clear that many separate impulses will join in starting the oscillation, and that the time which elapses from the instant when the system is rendered active until the oscillation reaches a prescribed relatively large amplitude will be somewhat random. This randomness is referred to as *jitter*, and is important in systems which employ pulse-time modulation for the communication of information because it may seriously degrade the overall signal-to-noise ratio. The oscillation envelopes which would be observed if such an oscillator were repeatedly turned off and on are shown in Fig. 15.9 It is noted that jitter associated with the decay, *which can be no greater than the period of a high-frequency cycle*, is usually much less than the jitter associated with build-up. This fact has been used to advantage in some commercial systems.

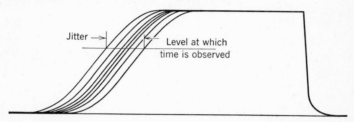

Fig. 15.9. Jitter in the oscillation envelope of a pulsed oscillator.

We may obtain a measure of this uncertainty of pulse time by a relatively simple analysis. No claim is made for the rigor of the process, but the result agrees with that calculated by Dr. C. R. Shannon and reported by Pierce and Shepherd.[241] We start with the assumption that the resonator itself has a relatively high Q and that the system when rendered active is linear for oscillations ranging in amplitude from zero to a value large compared to the noise level. Under these circumstances the initial oscillations will expand according to the simple equation

$$A = A_0 e^{\alpha t}, \tag{15.28}$$

where A_0 is the amplitude in voltage or current at the time $t = 0$ when the system is turned on and α is the increment rate in nepers per second.

We are to imagine that the turn-on process is repeated many times, and to determine the average deviation of the group of results. Before the system is turned on, the voltage across the resonator behaves as filtered thermal noise as pictured in Fig. 15.5. The magnitude of the envelope at the instant of turn-on may, therefore, be substituted for A_0 in eq. 15.28.

By referring to curve PR of Fig. 15.3, we see that in 75 per cent of the trials A_0 will lie above $0.77V$ and in only 25 per cent of the trials will it lie above $1.65V$. Thus, half the total cases fall within a ratio of $1.65/0.77 = 2.14$ of starting voltage. This ratio corresponds to a difference of 0.76 neper, which means that the *probable error* from the average is $0.76/2 = 0.38$ neper. In terms of the time t_0 required to build up to a prescribed amplitude, the probable error is

$$\delta t_0 = 0.38/\alpha \text{ seconds.} \tag{15.29}$$

Specifically, in a large number of repetitions, half will occur within δt_0 of the average value. It should be noted that α is the build-up rate in nepers per second which applies when the signal is at the level of noise. Changes in α as overload is approached do not affect the timing error.

Evidently, jitter can be suppressed completely only if the starting pulse is such as to produce a transient larger than noise or if a suitable pilot signal is supplied. Jitter may be minimized by increasing α to the practical limit, preferably by achieving a high effective transconductance.

15.7 Noise in microwave oscillators

It has already been stated that velocity-modulation tubes are considerably more noisy than conventional tubes operating under space charge conditions. The factors which affect the noise produced in two-gap or reflex klystrons are even more complicated and numerous than those pertaining to triodes or pentodes. However, it is again possible to obtain simple expressions which are adequate for most applications.

In a typical velocity-modulated oscillator the cathode operates under a condition of complete space charge, and the total current flowing in the region between the cathode and first grid is considerably smoothed by space charge. However, this smoothing action does not extend to the gap, where the space charge is quite small. Although the situations are not exactly equivalent, it is found that the equation for noise in a temperature-limited diode is also reasonably accurate for klystrons. That is,

$$P = 2eI_0RB \text{ watts,} \tag{15.30}$$

where P is the power delivered to the resistor R, which shunts the electronic gap or grids, e is the electron charge, I_0 is the beam current, and B is the bandwidth in cycles per second. In case the electron transit time is an appreciable fraction of a cycle at the operating frequency, this result must be multiplied by a factor γ, where

$$\gamma = \frac{\sin (\psi/2)}{(\psi/2)} \tag{15.31}$$

and ψ is the transit angle. In oscillators of the reflex type electrons traverse the gap twice Although additional possibilities of space charge smoothing exist, it appears that little smoothing actually occurs; and a satisfactory approximation for the noise power is obtained by doubling eq. 15.30. Experimental data on noise in klystrons are given by Pierce and Shepherd.[241]

The mechanisms which produce noise in magnetrons are not yet adequately understood. However, it is known that magnetrons are quite noisy, and that noise production is intimately associated with the reactions which produce oscillation. A low-power experimental magnetron had a noise power of about 10^{-3} watts over a bandwidth of 3 Mc. This is an exceptionally high figure corresponding to an equivalent temperature of 4×10^{11} °K. It appears that interactions equivalent to electron collisions contribute to the high degree of disorder represented by such figures.

PROBLEMS

15.1. A 10,000-ohm resistor at 300°K is shunted by 100 $\mu\mu$f; calculate the effective noise voltage by use of eq. 15.3.

15.2. Show that the result of Prob. 15.1 is unchanged if any loss-free inductance is added in shunt.

15.3. Calculate the noise power available from a 1000-ohm resistor at 300°K over a 4000-cycle bandwidth.

15.4. Referring to a tube handbook and eqs. 15.9 and 15.10, calculate the equivalent noise resistance for the 6J4 and 6J5 triodes and 6SJ7 and 6AC7 pentodes under typical operating conditions.

15.5. How would the signal of Fig. 15.2 be affected by transmission through a high-pass filter? Sketch and explain your result.

15.6. Derive eq. 15.21 by assuming that a resistor at temperature T is shunted by a loss-free coil and condenser and by a noise-free negative conductance (vacuum tube) sufficient to sustain oscillation.

15.7. Discuss the interpretation of noise bandwidth in connection with limiting speeds in practical oscillators. Is it legitimate to think of noise superimposed upon a pure sinusoid; and, if so, why?

15.8. Verify the development of eq. 15.29.

15.9. Discuss jitter in an oscillator in which the starting transient is just equal to the average noise level.

15.10. An oscillator is "primed" with a small constant sinusoidal voltage at its natural frequency. It is then pulsed by a voltage of random phase with respect to the "priming" voltage. Discuss the variation of starting jitter as the "priming" voltage is varied above and below the noise level.

16

MODULATION OF OSCILLATORS

It is well known that information cannot be transmitted by a continuous current or by a steady sinusoidal wave. Only by varying the magnitude or polarity of a general wave or the magnitude, frequency, or phase of a sinusoidal wave is it possible to communicate. All such variations are referred to as modulation. The amplitude-modulated waves used in ordinary broadcasting are now usually obta'ned from a modulated amplifier in conjunction with an unmodulated crystal oscillator; but directly modulated oscillators still find many applications. The present treatment is restricted to modulation produced in the oscillator itself.

16.1 General principles of modulation

Before preceeding with a discussion of specific methods of modulation it is well to consider the general principles involved and the basic limitations which exist. It is convenient to refer the discussion to the arrangement of Fig. 16.1 in which L, C, and G represent a passive resonator including any useful load, and N represents the driving system. In the condition of sustained oscillation, power is dissipated in the conductance G, depending upon the amplitude according to the relation

$$P = GV^2, \tag{16.1}$$

where V is the rms voltage. This power is necessarily supplied by the driving system N. In addition, if N has negligible susceptance, there is a fixed amount of energy in the amount

$$W = CV^2 \tag{16.2}$$

exchanged between the coil and the condenser.

In order to change the amplitude of oscillation it is necessary to change the stored energy as well as the rate at which it is supplied. If the supply is removed, the amplitude falls off in the familiar exponential manner as the stored energy is expended in the conductance. Therefore, sudden changes in amplitude require large amounts of positive or negative power.   In practice, this means that oscillators which are to be modulated rapidly must employ low-Q circuits and high transconductance tubes.

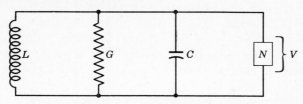

FIG. 16.1.   Generalized oscillator.

If the frequency rather than the amplitude of the oscillation is to be changed, we must concern ourselves with susceptances rather than with conductances.   Let us suppose that the frequency is to be caused to change or deviate somewhat from its original value f_0 to ξf_0.   This deviation will occur if the driving system provides a suitable susceptance B' in addition to the negative conductance G' required to maintain the oscillation.   The total susceptance required of the driving system may now be determined by equating the total current to zero.   Designating the total admittance of N as

$$Y' = G' + jB', \tag{16.3}$$

we have

$$VY' = V(G' + jB') = -V(G + j\xi\omega_0 C + 1/j\xi\omega_0 L), \tag{16.4}$$

where

$$\omega_0 = 1/\sqrt{LC} \quad \text{and} \quad Q = \omega_0 C/G. \tag{16.5}$$

Separating real and imaginary terms yields

$$G' = -G \tag{16.6}$$

and

$$B' = -\xi GQ + GQ/\xi. \tag{16.7}$$

Because $\xi \doteq 1$ this becomes

$$B' \doteq 2GQ(1 - \xi). \tag{16.8}$$

This expression is of considerable interest because it relates the power to the reactive volt-amperes which must be supplied in frequency modulation.   From eqs. 16.6 and 16.8, it is clear that the two will be equal and the phase angle in N will be 45° when

$$\xi - 1 = 1/2Q. \tag{16.9}$$

The question as to how rapidly the frequency may be changed is most conveniently examined by imagining that the susceptance of N is suddenly changed by the addition of a positive (or negative) uncharged condenser at an instant when the voltage is zero. Such a change does not produce a transient, and all following cycles have a longer (or shorter) period in terms of the frequency deviation. We therefore conclude that very rapid changes in frequency are possible. However, under the particular conditions assumed, eq. 16.2 shows that until the driving system adds the required stored energy, the amplitude will decrease by the same factor $(1 - \xi)$ by which the frequency is decreased.

An adequate discussion of the various ideas involved in frequency modulation is beyond the scope of the present treatment. Arguimbau[15] gives a very compact and enlightening discussion of the subject, which is even more fully covered by Hund.[149]

Phase modulation is closely related to frequency modulation, and is readily added to a constant-frequency signal by variable phase-shift networks. Free-running oscillators do not directly yield phase modulation. However, a phase-modulated signal is readily produced by means of a locked oscillator in which the natural frequency is varied and the synchronizing signal has a constant frequency. The subject is somewhat beyond our present purpose and is not discussed further.

16.2 Keying

The simplest possible form of wireless communication involves an oscillator which is successively energized and de-energized by means of a switch or key. The presence or absence of an output signal, in conjunction with an appropriate code, permits the communication of information. Such *keying* represents the simplest possible form of modulation, and is applicable to all kinds of oscillators.

We may imagine that oscillation is established the instant that power is applied to the circuit, and that the oscillations die out instantly when the key is opened. In practice, however, the situation is considerably more complicated. Oscillations do *not* build up instantly when the key is closed nor do they cease instantly when the key is opened. Moreover, the frequency and amplitude of oscillation may change during operation in the "key down" interval; and the behavior does not repeat itself exactly upon successive closures of the key, as shown in the previous chapter. These various effects set a limit to the amount of information which can be transmitted in a given interval of time.

A tuned-plate oscillator with a key in the B^+ lead serves to illustrate the basic ideas.   If the key remains open for any appreciable interval, the various voltages and currents in the system decay to negligible values and the system comes to rest.   When the key is closed, the tube (which has no negative bias) draws a considerable current.   This current will initially flow through the tank condenser, but later trans-

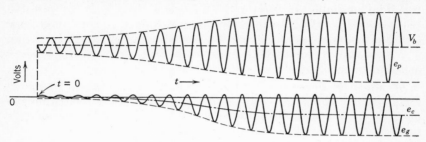

FIG. 16.2.   Wave forms during build up of oscillation.

fers to the plate coil and associated load resistor.   The polarity of the coupled windings is such that the grid tends to be driven positive by the increasing current in the plate coil, and regeneration occurs. Accordingly, oscillation at the natural frequency of the tank circuit is excited, but the initial amplitude is small.   The general behavior is correctly shown in Fig. 16.2; however, exact calculation of this interval is quite difficult because of the effects of nonlinearity.   Grid loading is more important during this interval than it is during the steady state, and the variation of bias complicates the situation.

16.3 Coherent and incoherent oscillations

The operation just described and illustrated is *coherent.*   That is, the phase of the generated wave has a fixed relationship to the instant at which the power is applied.   Under these circumstances the wave forms of Fig. 16.2 will be exactly reproduced each time the key is closed; and it would be possible to obtain a stationary figure on an oscilloscope if the keying were periodic and the sweep were triggered from the keying mechanism.   Coherent operation is important in a number of applications, usually those involving rapidly repeated off-on periods.   In particular, certain radar systems discriminate between fixed and moving targets by means of coherent pulses.

The opposite behavior, known as *incoherent* operation, may be produced in the same circuit by a change of the point of keying.   Let the key, in series with a small resistance, now be connected across the tuned circuit, so that oscillation occurs when the key is open rather than closed.   Again, the alternating voltage will die out and the grid bias will disappear if the system is inoperative for a substantial period. However, the tube will be subject to the full plate voltage, and a considerable current will flow.   When the key is opened there will be no sharp transient because the current to the tube will already be flowing through the negligible resistance of the plate coil.   Oscillations will therefore build up from the tiny random variations of plate current associated with noise, and the phase will have no systematic relationship to the instant at which the key was opened.

We may now predict whether a given keying operation will produce coherent or incoherent waves: *Oscillations will be coherent if and only if the transient produced in the resonator by the action of the key in energizing the system is large compared to the simultaneously present noise level.*   When the two are comparable there will be considerable randomness in the starting phase, but a definite concentration around an average phase will exist.

In microwave oscillators it is extremely difficult to produce coherent oscillations because inherent noise levels are relatively high and because practical keying devices produce very small transient effects in these systems on account of the filtering effect of parasitic inductances and capacitances.   One method of producing coherent pulses at microwave frequencies is to "prime" the oscillator with a sustained sinusoidal frequency at or very near the desired frequency.   If the externally supplied signal is substantially larger than the noise level of the oscillator, the phase of the pulses will be accurately fixed with respect to the supplied signal, not to the keying impulses.   If the signal level is reduced, the starting time is more and more affected by the random character of the noise, and the degree of jitter increases. Moreover, in magnetrons and perhaps in klystrons, the noise level appears to change during the starting interval.   Therefore the behavior is quite complicated.   Readers who wish to pursue this matter further are referred to the work of David.[70, 71]

In triode oscillators at ordinary frequencies, on the other hand, it is difficult to produce incoherent oscillations, because noise levels are quite low and transient effects relatively high.   In the example cited earlier, coherent operation might still result from the small change of current in the coil.   This would occur because unavoidable resistance in the coil would cause some current to flow through the key and associated resistance.   This particular difficulty could be substantially reduced by transferring the key to the grid coil, but an appreciable transient might still be produced by the action of grid current or contact or thermal emfs.

16.4 Keying wave forms

We have seen that it is very difficult to produce an oscillation envelope which rises instantly from zero to full amplitude when the key is closed, or falls instantly to zero when the key is opened. Fortunately, such a performance is rarely desirable because the sharp steps in the envelope correspond to a wide spectrum of sideband frequencies. These sidebands occupy an unnecessary bandwidth, at the risk of interfering with other services in adjacent channels. The required bandwidth decreases with a decrease of the sharpness; so the question arises as to how much the envelope may be rounded off before the intelligibility of the signal is seriously degraded.

The question evidently is an aspect of the general problem of information theory, as developed by Shannon[278] and others. It is, there-

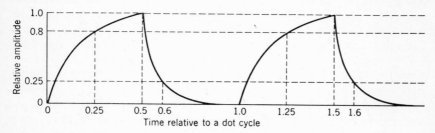

FIG. 16.3. Envelope wave form corresponding to barely readable keying.

fore, impossible to make a rigorous statement except in terms of signaling speed, noise, and bandwidth. However, listening tests reported by this author[83] indicate that in a keyed signal received through a typical communication receiver, the intelligibility has just begun to be seriously degraded when the pulse shape is distorted to the extent indicated in Fig. 16.3. It is particularly important that the signal decay rapidly at the end of each character because the logarithmic character of the sensitivity of the ear makes the signal appear to hang on until the amplitude is quite small. It is interesting that the signal is more pleasing to the ear when some rounding is present than when the corners are square, because transient effects produce the sensation of a click at the beginning and end of each character.

In this connection it may be helpful to note that, according to accepted standards for wireless telegraphy, the interval between characters is equal to the duration of one dot, the duration of a dash is equal to the space between letters, which is three times the duration of a dot, and the space between words is five times the duration of a dot. The standard (International) code is such that when average English sentences are being transmitted at the rate of one word per minute the dot corresponds to 1½ seconds, and a "dot cycle" consisting of a dot and a space occupies 3 seconds. Because the essential features of Fig. 16.3 can be produced by inclusion of only fundamental, second, and third harmonic terms, it follows that *a channel width of approximately one cycle per second must be allotted to each word per minute transmitted.*

Several additional practical difficulties are sometimes observed when oscillators are keyed. The frequency may change with the rise and fall of oscillation during each cycle, the average frequency may drift depending upon the fraction of the time which the key is closed, and the amplitude may change in an undesirable manner for the same reasons. Frequency stability is achieved by the same methods which are applicable to continuous oscillators. That is, the circuit configuration, element values, and components must be chosen to meet the requirements dictated by the particular application. The use of a quartz crystal is often the simplest solution to the problem of obtaining

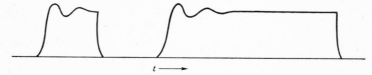

Fig. 16.4.   Envelope wave forms showing clicks due to filter transients.

satisfactory frequency stability. Even when a high-Q crystal is used, it is possible to obtain keying speeds in excess of 150 words per minute (50 dot cycles per second) if the operating frequency is above one megacycle; this speed is adequate for most applications.

The rate of decay of the signal is most readily controlled through the Q of the passive system. However, a compromise may be necessary to satisfy frequency-stability requirements. The rate of build-up is then adjusted through the transconductance of the tube and the amount of feedback provided.

Amplitude disturbances of the general form indicated in Fig. 16.4 are referred to as key clicks or thumps. As shown by Lee[187] they are usually caused by simple transients in the LC circuits of power supply or decoupling filters. Additional filtering and damping at appropriate points in the circuit will suppress the trouble, but in high-power systems these changes may be relatively expensive.

At low signaling speeds and low power levels it is practical to employ a manually operated key such as that used in ordinary telegraphy. At higher power levels it is desirable to employ a keying relay controlled by a manual key or other device. At high signaling speeds, that is, in excess of about 30 words per minute, it is necessary to employ some form of automatic keyer. The keying signal may be applied to the oscillator in a great variety of ways; however, it is ordinarily desirable to key in a grid rather than a plate circuit in order to reduce the voltage and current which the key must handle.

16.5 Pulse modulation

Magnetrons and other microwave oscillators are often operated on a pulsed basis, which is characterized by the fact that the interval of operation is very short compared to the interval between pulses. In this way it is possible to obtain peak powers of the order of a megawatt from relatively small tubes. The method is widely used in radar, loran, ionosphere investigation, and pulse communication. In principle, it is equivalent to the keying process already discussed. In practice, it differs because of the relatively long interval between pulses, because of the various requirements on pulse shape, and because of the keying properties of the oscillators themselves.

Magnetrons are ordinarily modulated by applying a large negative pulse to the cathode by means of a suitable pulse transformer. The anode is grounded to the remainder of the system through the output circuit and is not readily pulsed. The pulse transformer is similar to those discussed in connection with the blocking oscillator in Chapter 12 but is much larger and better insulated, because it must transmit the full level of power supplied to the oscillator, often in excess of one million watts.

High-power triodes and klystrons are often pulsed in the same way as magnetrons. However, they may also be modulated by means of a signal applied to the control grid. The principal advantage of grid keying is the great reduction in the power required of the modulation source; a disadvantage is that secondary emission and related effects in high-power triodes sometimes cause the grid to lose control of the plate current. Under these conditions an excessive plate current flows and the system is inoperative. Methods for generating the high-power pulses used in radar and similar systems are discussed by Seddon[274] and by Glasoe and Lebacqz[113] and will not be described here.

16.6 The start-stop oscillator

In certain applications (for example, radar range calibrators) it is necessary to generate pulses which are coherent with the control signal and of uniform amplitude. Such generators are referred to as start-stop oscillators. The basic difficulty is one of energy storage; just as much energy must be stored in the resonator during the off period as during the operating period if the first cycle is to be of full amplitude.   This difficulty is overcome in the circuit due to Chance[56] by passing a constant current through the tuned circuit, as shown in Fig. 16.5a.

During the off period, T_1 operates at substantially zero bias, and a considerable current flows through L. Oscillation cannot occur because the tuned circuit is shunted by the low dynamic impedance of

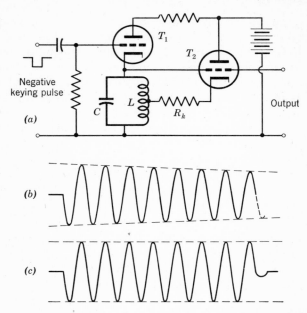

FIG. 16.5.   Start-stop oscillator: (a) circuit, (b) output with T_2 inactive, and (c) output with T_2 active and R_k correctly adjusted.

T_1 as a cathode follower.   When T_1 is cut off by a negative keying pulse the current through L tends to be suddenly stopped, and a transient oscillation is excited in the tuned circuit.   The oscillation would decay exponentially as shown in Fig. 16.5b were it not for the action of tube T_2, which operates in class A and acts as a negative resistance to supply the energy lost in the positive resistance of L. When the cathode resistor R_k is properly adjusted, the amplitude of oscillation is quite constant over a large number of cycles.   Accurate adjustment of R_k is necessary, however, because no limiting process is provided.   Oscillation is terminated very quickly at the end of the keying pulse by the heavy damping provided by the cathode of T_1 when its conduction is restored.   Evidently, the principal LC circuit should have the highest possible values of Q and frequency stability in the interest of a uniform output at a constant frequency.

The basic circuit of Fig. 16.5 is capable of a number of useful modifications. By use of a pentode for T_2 it is possible to add a load in the plate circuit and thus obtain an additional output signal in phase opposition or quadrature with the original output. Moreover, by an extention of the method, it is possible to use a quartz crystal instead of an LC resonator. However, the large intrinsic capacitance ratio of quartz resonators makes it difficult to start and stop the oscillation rapidly or in precisely constant phase. The difficulty of starting may be understood by noting that a large direct voltage is required to produce in the quartz a mechanical deformation equal to that produced by a small alternating voltage at the resonant frequency. Similarly, the oscillations of a vibrating crystal are not stopped by connecting its electrodes to either an open or a short circuit. A conductance equal to the susceptance of the crystal shunt capacitance produces relatively high damping, but it is not always practical to produce this value. Details of a crystal controlled start-stop oscillator are given by Chance.[56]

The performance of the circuit of Fig. 16.5 at high frequencies is unsatisfactory because the transient voltage produced decreases linearly as L is decreased. To alleviate this difficulty Easton[80] has used a condenser discharged through a thyratron to induce a large transient in L by means of mutual inductance. With this arrangement at 20 Mc he has obtained coherent, constant amplitude, pulses as large as 80 volts peak.

16.7 Amplitude modulation

The first system of radio communication which was capable of transmitting speech and music employed amplitude modulation. That is, the magnitude but not the frequency of the wave being transmitted was controlled or *modulated* in accordance with the audible signal. Most forms of the vacuum-tube oscillator are readily amplitude-modulated because the output is approximately proportional to some reference voltage. In such oscillators, the output becomes modulated if the reference voltage is varied about its mean value according to some signal having a relatively low frequency.

In practice, it is desirable that the change in amplitude is directly proportional to the modulation voltage, and that the operating frequency is unaffected by the addition of modulation. Linearity adequate for most applications may be obtained by careful design and adjustment. If necessary, it may be further improved to any required degree by the addition of negative feedback, using a highly linear rectifier to demodulate a portion of the output to be combined in opposition with the original modulating signal, as explained by Bode[34] on page 493 of his book.

Frequency stability may be obtained by the use of a stable high-Q resonator, and by avoiding the use of components which are affected by voltage or temperature. However, the selectivity which may be used is limited by the rapidity with which the amplitude must vary when high modulating frequencies are involved. And the internal capacitances of practical tubes always vary somewhat with both voltage and temperature. Therefore, in practice, it is very difficult to secure adequate frequency stability with respect to either long-term drift or variation over the modulation cycle. It is for this reason that most amplitude-modulated transmitters use a continuous low-level oscillator, usually crystal-controlled, followed by a modulated amplifier.

For applications where a moderate amount of frequency instability may be tolerated the modulated oscillator is very convenient and effective. The several varieties of conventional harmonic oscillators are about equally desirable, the properties of the tube and the various impedance levels being far more important than the circuit configuration in determining the efficiency and linearity of operation.

The fact that the amplitude of a particular oscillator varies linearly with some slowly varied applied voltage does *not* guarantee that it will be satisfactory for speech modulation. If the circuit Q is high, the decrement rate may be so small that the amplitude is unable to follow the more rapid variations in the signal, and only the lower speech frequencies will be present in the output. This requirement is most conveniently expressed by the statement that the tuned circuit in its operating condition must pass a band of frequencies somewhat in excess of twice the highest modulating frequency in order to account for both upper and lower sidebands.

It will be recalled from the analysis of Chapter 8 that the amplitude of a typical class C oscillator is directly proportional to the applied plate voltage. Therefore, it is merely necessary to add the modulating voltage to the plate supply voltage, usually by means of a transformer in series with the B supply. On purely physical grounds, it is clear that oscillation will be completely suppressed during part of each cycle if the peak modulating voltage is larger than the steady voltage E_b. Moreover, difficulties with nonlinearity and frequency modulation are markedly reduced if the peak modulating voltage is held substantially smaller than E_b.

The principal drawback of this arrangement is the large amount of power required from the modulation source. It is readily shown that the instantaneous peak power drawn from the modulator is more than twice the average power in the modulated signal delivered to the useful load. In high-power applications this requires the use of large and expensive tubes and transformers.

Modulation by means of a variable grid bias is not satisfactory in normal class C oscillators because of the bias developed across the grid leak. Application of a voltage in series with the grid leak affects the average grid current somewhat but has relatively little effect on the amplitude of oscillation. However, the resistance stabilized oscillator, in which no grid leak is used and limiting occurs by the large conductance associated with the grid being driven positive, can be grid-modulated with reasonable linearity by a small driving power.

In tetrodes or pentodes, the screen grid offers a convenient means for amplitude modulating a normal class C oscillator. The screen grid voltage rather than the plate voltage determines the cutoff voltage of the grid, and hence the amplitude of oscillation. The plate efficiency in the absence of modulation cannot exceed 50 per cent with this arrangement, and it is difficult to obtain a high degree of linearity. However, the modulating power required is only about one-tenth of that required for plate modulation, and the circuit is simple and readily adjusted. Tubes in which the current and voltage of the plate are large compared to those of the screen grid, typically beam tetrodes, are most desirable in this circuit.

Pentodes may also be modulated by a signal connected in series with a negative bias source in the lead to the suppressor grid. Such a signal affects the effective transconductance of the tube and hence the conduction angle of operation rather than the cutoff bias. The resulting amplitude modulation is not very linear, and is accompanied by a rather large power dissipation at the screen grid of the tube; the method is therefore of limited usefulness.

Where a very high degree of linearity in the modulation of an oscillator is required, the linear oscillator with automatic output control is preferred. The stabilizing factor should be fairly large in the interest of linearity, and the time constant of the bias control system should be short so that high frequencies in the modulation will be accurately followed. The Q of the resonator must not be too high in relation to the oscillation and modulation frequencies; otherwise the level of oscillation is unable to fall rapidly enough. If the Q is low enough to allow the required decay rate, the level of oscillation can be made to rise rapidly enough, provided the tube is still linear, when the bias control acts to call for double the normal transconductance. Finally, there should be a good margin of envelope stability to avoid transients in the modulation envelope. The frequency stability is likely to be good because of the linear operation of the tube.

Velocity-modulation oscillators may be amplitude-modulated by means of a grid which controls the current in the electron beam. Under favorable conditions the modulation is fairly linear, and the associated frequency modulation small. Such oscillators may be keyed or pulsed by this method, by switching off and on the accelerating voltage, or by stepping the accelerating or reflector voltage between oscillating and nonoscillating values. Velocity-modulation oscillators tend to have a relatively long build-up time; therefore, they may be unsatisfactory for the generation of short pulses.

Magnetrons are difficult to modulate. Variation of the magnetic field is difficult and produces undesirable effects, and variation of the applied voltage produces instability and frequency modulation. However, magnetrons have rapid rise time and operate well at high voltages; therefore, they are well adapted to the generation of high-power pulses. Amplitude modulation of good depth and linearity has been produced by Donal and Bush[77] by means of a variable electronic conductance, which, in conjunction with a fixed absorbing load and suitable networks, controls the power delivered by a magnetron to the useful load. However, the process is rather inefficient; only 60 per cent of the available power is delivered to the useful load at the peak of the modulation cycle. The variable electronic conductance is produced in a separate tube which employs controlled electron beams.

16.8 Frequency modulation

Amplitude-modulated oscillators are little used because it is easy to add amplitude modulation to a continuous wave of constant frequency and very hard to remove frequency modulation if once introduced. For the same essential reasons frequency-modulated oscillators are rather widely used. It is relatively hard to add frequency modulation to a continuous wave, and it is easy to remove any amplitude modulation which may accidently accompany the desired frequency modulation. Whether the development of the Phasitron[3] and the Serrasoid[73] methods of frequency-modulating a continuous wave will greatly modify the situation remains to be seen.

The simplest imaginable means of modulating the frequency of an oscillator is to vary mechanically the capacitance (or inductance) of the tuned circuit. This is done in a variety of ways for a number of useful applications. In certain signal generators an ordinary variable condenser is driven by a motor. Moreover, O'Brien[229] has shown that speech communication is possible by coupling a condenser microphone to the tuned circuit of a lumped-circuit oscillator, or by using a diaphragm in the cavity resonator of a microwave oscillator as a microphone. Frequency deviations of the order of ±100 kc are readily produced in this way if suitable precautions are taken.

Relatively little use has been made of nonlinear reactances for the frequency modulation of oscillators. However, it is known that the inductance of an iron-core coil can be substantially altered by introduction of a signal current. Less well known, but perhaps more useful, is the fact that a substantial change in the capacitance of commercial high-K (group C) ceramic condensers is produced by application of a direct potential of a few hundred volts. It appears that these

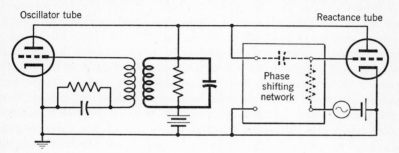

FIG. 16.6. Use of reactance tube to frequency modulate an oscillator.

materials may be used to produce frequency modulation in a variety of situations where more complicated arrangements are now commonly employed.

The circuit of Fig. 16.6 illustrates a simple electronic means of modulating the frequency of an oscillator. The reactance tube, usually a pentode in which the plate and grid voltages are in quadrature, acts as a variable reactance which changes the frequency of oscillation. In its simplest form the phase-shifting network consists of a resistance and a capacitance having a relatively high reactance, as shown by the dotted lines of Fig. 16.6. The effective reactance of the tuned circuit is changed by varying the transconductance of the reactance tube, usually by varying its grid bias. The reader is referred to a fundamental paper by Travis[313] for a discussion of the reactance tube and other methods of frequency modulation. Additional design information is given by Chireix,[60] Hund,[150] and by Young and Beck.[352]

It is convenient and informative to think of the oscillator tube as furnishing the in-phase or real volt-amperes to the load resistor while the reactance tube provides the quadrature or reactive volt-amperes required for the deviation of the actual frequency from the natural frequency of the tank circuit. When the proper relationship between real and quadrature volt-amperes is maintained, the amplitude is quite constant as the frequency is varied. Evidently, the rating of the oscillator tube depends only upon the power output, whereas the rating of the reactance tube depends upon the reactances of the tank circuit and is proportional to the power output and the frequency deviation. Thus, the reactance tube must be larger than the oscillator tube if the power output is small and the required frequency deviation is large. Moreover, because both tubes operate at the oscillation frequency and voltage, they must have comparable characteristics with respect to high-frequency performance and voltage breakdown.

Ordinarily, the oscillator tube operates in class C with relatively high efficiency. The reactance tube, on the other hand, usually operates in class A in order to obtain the desired degree of linearity. This is possible because the capacitance which couples the signal to the grid has an impedance which is very large compared to the grid resistor. If the reactance tube is a pentode with a remote cutoff or a suitable pentagrid type, the transconductance may be made to vary in a nearly linear manner with respect to the bias applied to a high-impedance grid. Although the reactance tube is in wide use, the author feels that it is inferior in performance and general desirability to several of the alternative methods of frequency modulation described in following sections.

16.9 Frequency modulation by resistance variation

The vacuum tube is intrinsically a resistive rather than a reactive device. Therefore, the reactance-tube arrangement suffers rather

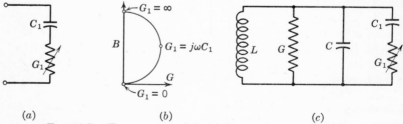

(a)   (b)   (c)

FIG. 16.7. Frequency modulation by conductance variation.

serious practical limitations. For this reason, several workers have devised alternative systems for obtaining frequency modulation. In general these schemes depend upon the fact that a loss-free network producing a 45° phase shift translates increments of load resistance or conductance into increments of input susceptance. Probably the simplest circuit for converting a variable conductance into a variable susceptance is shown in Fig. 16.7. The associated plot shows the variation of the admittance as the conductance is varied from zero to infinity. As is well known, the locus is a semicircle, and in the region of the point $G_1 = j\omega C_1$ an increment in G_1 results in a positive increment in B and no change in G. To establish the numerical relationship, we write the admittance equation

$$Y = G + jB = \frac{1}{1/G_1 + 1/j\omega C_1} = \frac{j\omega C_1 G_1}{G_1 + j\omega C_1}. \qquad (16.10)$$

To determine the effect of an increment in G_1 from the assumed condition, we substitute

$$G_1 = \omega C_1(1 + \delta), \qquad (16.11)$$

to obtain

$$Y = \frac{j\omega C_1(1 + \delta)}{1 + \delta + j1} = \omega C_1 \frac{(1 + \delta)(1 + j1 + j\delta)}{2 + 2\delta + \delta^2}. \qquad (16.12)$$

Expanding and neglecting terms in δ^2, we have

$$Y = \tfrac{1}{2}\omega C_1(1 + j1 + j\delta), \qquad (16.13)$$

which shows that G is unaffected and the fractional increment in B is equal to the fractional increment in G_1.

The extent to which the conductance G_1 may be varied from the reference value may be limited by either the variation of resulting conductance or by departure of the resulting susceptance from proportionality. Both limits may be examined by means of eq. 16.12, which can be separated and expanded in series to yield

$$G = \frac{\omega C_1}{2 + \delta^2/2} \qquad (16.14)$$

and

$$B = \frac{\omega C_1(1 + \delta)}{2 + \delta^2/2}. \qquad (16.15)$$

It is seen that both are decreased from their maximum value by the same factor in the denominator. The allowable variation thus depends upon the particular requirements to be met; however, the value $\delta = 0.1$ leads to an error of only 0.25 per cent, which is almost always tolerable.

A variety of other network configurations also have the property of changing a conductance increment into a susceptance increment.

Since it is impractical to investigate all the possibilities, we naturally seek a general proposition which applies to all. The needed relationship is provided by Bode,[34] who proves that the admittance or impedance of any physical network describes a circle (or straight line) in the complex plane if a single element is varied at a fixed frequency. The locus of Fig. 16.7b is an example of this theorem.

It is readily seen that the circle can be centered on the imaginary axis only if the network is nondissipative, except for G_1. On this basis, by a development similar to that following eq. 16.10, it may be shown that in the region of the operating point the change in reactive volt-amperes at the input is always equal to the change in resistive volt-amperes at the output. Moreover, the change in the input susceptance is numerically equal to the nominal input conductance multiplied by the fractional change in the load conductance. Therefore, a large change in input susceptance is unavoidably associated with a large constant input loading, that is, low Q.

The situation may be clarified by reference to Fig. 16.7c. The appropriate equations are

$$\omega_0^2 = \frac{1}{L(C + C_1/2)} \tag{16.16}$$

and

$$Q = \frac{1}{\omega_0 L(G + G_1/2)} = \frac{\omega_0(2C + C_1)}{2G + G_1}. \tag{16.17}$$

Assuming that G_1 may deviate from its nominal value by some small fraction δ without producing excessive amplitude modulation or nonlinearity of frequency response, we may obtain the frequency deviation by writing

$$\xi^2\omega_0^2 = \frac{1}{LC + (1 + \delta)LC_1/2}. \tag{16.18}$$

Employing eq. 16.16, we have

$$1 - \xi^2 = 1 - \frac{2LC + LC_1}{2LC + (1 + \delta)LC_1}. \tag{16.19}$$

Factoring and using $\xi \doteq 1$ yield

$$1 - \xi = \frac{\delta LC_1}{4LC + 2(1 + \delta)LC_1} \doteq \frac{\delta}{2 + 4C/C_1}. \tag{16.20}$$

Moreover, if G is negligible, the selectivity of the system reduces to

$$Q = 1 + 2C/C_1; \tag{16.21}$$

therefore,

$$1 - \xi = \delta/2Q. \tag{16.22}$$

Thus if $\delta = 0.1$ and $Q = 50$, the greatest possible fractional frequency deviation is ± 0.001.

Any physical dissipation in the tank circuit will lower still further the working selectivity and hence the general frequency stability. In view of these considerations, this method of generating frequency-modulated waves does not appear particularly attractive. Perhaps its greatest advantage is that the phase-shifting network may readily be made to give an impedance transformation so that a given tube can be utilized most efficiently, as in the circuit of Montgomery.[214]

It may be well to point out that finding a circuit in which the frequency deviation is proportional to a conductance change is much easier than the complementary problem of finding an electronic device in which a conductance change is proportional to an applied voltage. Nearly all the circuit complexity found in practical frequency modulators is associated with the latter problem, which has been discussed in some detail by Reich.[259]

16.10 Frequency modulation of resistance-capacitance oscillators

Because the frequency of a resistance-capacitance oscillator depends upon the value of two or more resistances in the circuit and because a vacuum tube may be made to act as a variable resistance, it is rela-

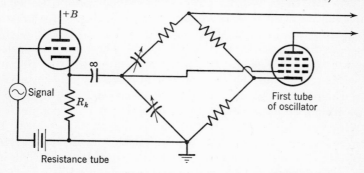

FIG. 16.8.   Frequency modulation of Wien bridge oscillator.

tively easy to modulate the frequency of such oscillators. Chang,[58] who appears to have done the first work in this field, used the Wien bridge arrangement and varied the grid-to-ground resistance by means of a variable transconductance tube, referred to as the resistance tube. The essential features of his arrangement are shown in Fig. 16.8.

Provided that the resistance tube has a large amplification factor, and the physical cathode resistor is large, the effective cathode resistance is equal to the reciprocal of the transconductance. In turn, the operating frequency is proportional to the square root of the transconductance. Over a moderate range, the frequency deviation is substantially proportional to the deviation of the transconductance from its mean value, which in turn is proportional to the modulating signal in a supercontrol tube such as the 6SK7. Chang presents experimental curves showing reasonably linear frequency deviations of about ±400 kc at center frequencies of 3 and 8 Mc.

The principal disadvantage of this arrangement is that the loop gain, and hence the amplitude of oscillation, varies greatly over the modulation cycle. The use of a thermistor in such oscillators is unwise because the thermal time constant is likely to be too great to follow the modulation. The difficulty may be avoided by using a second resistance tube suitably proportioned and located so as to preserve the loop gain, but the arrangement is rather complicated. Likewise the output may be passed through a limiter and filter to obtain a uniform output, but additional components are required, and the method fails if a frequency ratio in excess of 2:1 is involved.

A considerably simpler approach to the problem was taken by Artz,[17] who used an oscillator of the phase shift rather than the Wien bridge type. This is desirable because, as shown in Chapter 8, circuits which employ 180° phase shift are incapable of producing relaxation oscillations, whereas those based on the Wien bridge readily do so. The circuit diagram of such an oscillator, using a pentagrid for the resistance tube, is shown in Fig. 16.9.

The essential fact is that, in a suitable network, the variation of a single resistance varies the frequency associated with a 180° phase shift without varying the loop gain. Fortunately, the rate of frequency change is a maximum for the resistance at which the loop gain reaches its maximum. And a 2:1 frequency ratio, accompanied by only a one-decibel change in loop transmission, is produced by a resistance change of about 5:1. Under suitable conditions the resulting amplitude modulation is much less than one decibel. The interested reader is referred to Artz's paper for design details.*

Ames[6] has produced frequency-modulated signals in which the maximum-to-minimum frequency ratio is in excess of 100:1. His method is closely related to Artz' method, and the wide frequency ratio is obtained by simultaneously varying the resistance in all four

---

*The operation may also be explained by considering the oscillating loop to have two alternate paths, one through C, one variable through the 6SJ7.

sections of the phase shift network.   The total number of tubes used
is large, because a dual triode is used in each of the four sections.

The "seven league" oscillator of Anderson[7] described in Chapter
8 is capable of even wider frequency modulation than that of Ames,
and requires fewer tubes.   It is only necessary to vary the effective
transconductance of the two tubes fed from the ganged potentiometer.
However, the frequency varies logarithmically with the transmission
through this path; therefore, linear frequency modulation will be
produced only if a suitable exponential characteristic is obtained in
the transfer characteristic of the tubes used.   Although the circuit can produce design difficulty when wide frequency ratios are

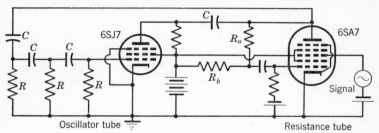

Fig. 16.9.   Frequency-modulated phase shift oscillator.

attempted, it appears very favorable for more moderate frequency
excursions, because the loop gain of the oscillation path may be made
very nearly uniform over a considerable frequency band.   Therefore,
the output may be made substantially uniform and free from harmonics.

Additional work on the frequency modulation of resistance-capacitance oscillators has been done by McGaughan and Leslie.[198]   They
produced frequency deviations as great as ± 50 per cent, with very
little distortion or amplitude modulation; but the circuits used are
somewhat complicated.

The frequency of relaxation oscillators such as multivibrators may
also be modulated over a considerable range and in quite a linear
manner.   This is most simply achieved by returning the grid leaks to a
suitable positive voltage in series with the modulating signal.   This
works very well when the modulating frequency is quite low compared
to the operating frequency, but may lead to difficulty with synchronization if the modulating frequency is comparable to the operating
frequency.   Experimental results are reported by Sturtevant.[300]

16.11 Frequency modulation by a variable phase shift

The common characteristic of the circuits so far described is that
separate tubes provide the real and the imaginary volt-amperes to the

tuned circuit. Therefore, all such circuits are essentially nonsymmetrical. De Lange[74] has recognized the possibility of distributing the burden so that two tubes contribute equally. His experimental circuit yields ± 3 Mc deviation about a center frequency of 65 Mc. Amplitude modulation is small, and the second and third harmonic outputs are, respectively, 32 and 37 db below the fundamental.

A simplified schematic of the arrangement is shown in Fig. 16.10. The limiter in the interstage circuit, a pair of 1N28 silicon crystal

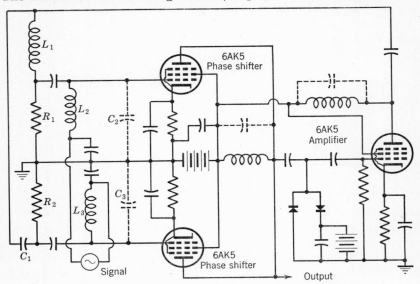

FIG. 16.10. Symmetrical frequency-modulated oscillator.

diodes, serves to limit the amplitude of oscillation and minimize amplitude modulation. The 6AK5 amplifier produces a phase reversal and needed gain; however, both of these functions could be performed by a transformer if the center and deviation frequencies were somewhat lower.

The essential feature of the operation is shown by the phasor diagram of Fig. 16.11. The amplifier produces a phase shift of 180° at the center frequency, where the phase shifting networks R_1L_1 and R_2C_1 are adjusted to produce equal and opposite phase shifts; thus the total loop phase shift is zero provided the two 6AK5 tubes are biased equally. When the bias is unbalanced by the modulating signal, the outputs of the two tubes are unequal, and the loop phase shift is disturbed. The resulting frequency shift is in such a direction as to restore zero phase.

Results comparable to those of De Lange but at a somewhat lower frequency have been achieved by Bruck,[43] who uses a dual triode in the symmetrical circuit shown in Fig. 16.12.   The operation depends upon the phase shift introduced by the coupled circuits, which operate as a frequency discriminator, as discussed in the following chapter.   In the absence of a modulating signal, the two grids receive equal alternating voltages displaced about 90° in phase, so that two pulses of cathode current are delivered per cycle.   The grid leaks are relatively

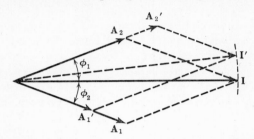

Fig. 16.11.   Phasor diagram of variable phase shifter.

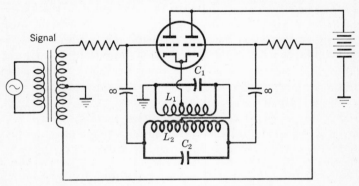

Fig. 16.12.   Frequency-modulated oscillator of Bruck.

large so that the grids are not driven appreciably positive.   When a signal is applied, the pulses due to one tube tend to decrease and those due to the other tend to increase; the loop phase shift is disturbed and the frequency changes.   The discriminator acts, not only as a phase shifting network, but also as a sort of negative-feedback device, because a frequency shift results in such a change of the relative magnitude of the alternating voltages as to tend to equalize the conduction of the two tubes.   Therefore, the linearity of modulation depends largely upon the characteristics of the discriminator, which can be made quite linear.   In addition to simplicity and economy of parts, the method has the advantage that the average frequency depends principally upon the properties of the tuned circuits, which can be made quite stable.

Velocity modulation oscillators may be frequency modulated by varying the accelerating or reflector voltages. The resulting change of phase shift due to transit time results in frequency modulation, which may be made quite linear and free from amplitude variation.

Magnetrons may be frequency-modulated by addition of controlled electron beams between the vanes and parallel to the axis of the system. Such electron beams add a pure variable susceptance to the resonator, hence produce substantially pure and linear frequency modulation. Magnetrons and other oscillators may also be frequency-modulated by means of an external electronic susceptance based on electron beam techniques and operating on the principle of the reactance tube. The interested reader is referred to the work of Kilgore, Shulman, and Kurshan.[168]

16.12 The reactance-tube oscillator

It has often been observed that a tube intended as a reactance tube may oscillate if the phase shifting network is incorrectly adjusted. This is readily explained because the tube will produce an effective negative conductance if the grid voltage is more than 90° out of phase with the plate voltage. Following this idea, Chang and Rideout[59] have devised a very simple single-tube frequency-modulated oscillator which should be useful in many applications.

The analysis is based upon a generalized reactance tube, with an impedance $\mathbf{Z}_1$ between grid and plate and $\mathbf{Z}_2$ between grid and cathode. The plate-to-cathode admittance is readily shown to be

$$\mathbf{Y} = \frac{1}{\mathbf{Z}_1 + \mathbf{Z}_2} + \frac{1}{r_p} + \frac{g_m \mathbf{Z}_2}{\mathbf{Z}_1 + \mathbf{Z}_2}. \tag{16.23}$$

Omitting the first term to obtain the contribution of the tube, and writing

$$\frac{\mathbf{Z}_2}{\mathbf{Z}_1 + \mathbf{Z}_2} = Ae^{j\theta} = A \cos \theta + jA \sin \theta, \tag{16.24}$$

we have

$$\mathbf{Y}_t = \frac{1}{r_p} - g_m A \cos \theta + jg_m A \sin \theta = \frac{1}{R_t} + \frac{j}{X_t}. \tag{16.25}$$

The terms R_t and X_t represent the tube on the basis of two impedances in parallel. The resistance R_t will be negative if r_p is relatively large and if $\cos \theta$ is negative, which requires that $\mathbf{Z}_1$ and $\mathbf{Z}_2$ have reactances of opposite sign.

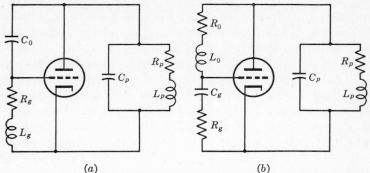

FIG. 16.13. Two forms of the reactance-tube oscillator.

Two forms of the reactance-tube oscillator are shown in Fig. 16.13. The equations that apply to the circuit of form a are

$$f = \frac{1}{2\sqrt{L_p C_p (1 + a)}} \left[1 + \frac{g_m C_0 (L_p R_g + L_g R_p)}{C_p L_p (1 + a)} \right]^{-\frac{1}{2}} \quad (16.26)$$

and

$$g_m = \frac{R_p C_p (L_p - L_g) + C_p L_p{}^2/C_0 r_p - C_p{}^2 L_p R_p/C_0}{L_p L_g}, \quad (16.27)$$

where

$$a = (C_0/C_p)(1 + L_g/L_p). \quad (16.28)$$

Similar equations applying to the circuit of Fig. 16.13b are

$$f = \frac{\sqrt{1 + b}}{2\pi \sqrt{L_p C_p}} \left[1 + \frac{g_m L_p R_g}{L_0 (1 + b)} \right]^{\frac{1}{2}} \quad (16.29)$$

and

$$g_m = \frac{(L_0 + L_p)(R_p C_g/L_p - C_g/C_p r_p)}{L_p} + \frac{(C_p + C_g)(R_g + R_0)}{L_c}, \quad (16.30)$$

where

$$b = (L_p/L_0)(1 + C_p/C_g). \quad (16.31)$$

Both sets of equations show that the frequency depends upon the effective transconductance, and that the variation is substantially linear for moderate frequency deviations. However, in the first case the frequency decreases with an increase of transconductance, whereas in the second case it increases.   The problem, therefore, is to obtain a variation in transconductance without producing an undesirable change in amplitude.   Moreover, as previously noted, in typical class C oscillators the effective transconductance adjusts itself to the value which satisfies the loop-gain equation; and the application of an external bias is ineffective.

In the present circuit the tube operates in a nearly linear manner with an externally applied negative bias.   By a proper choice of the operating point, a variation of the control grid bias affects the transconductance and plate resistance oppositely and in such a ratio as to satisfy eqs. 16.27 and 16.30.   Thus, the operating frequency is a substantially linear function of the voltage applied to a negatively biased grid.   Experimental oscillators using the 6L6G beam tube gave substantially constant output and nearly linear frequency modulation of ± 2 per cent about a midfrequency of 1.5 Mc.   The actual circuits differ from those shown only by the addition of feed chokes and blocking condensers for application of the direct and modulating voltage.

It is interesting to note that the locked oscillator of Bradley[37] (Fig. 13.14), although designed for another purpose, is also a one-tube frequency-modulated oscillator.   This circuit may be explained in terms of the reactance tube concept, or thought of in the same light as the oscillators of De Lange or Chang and Rideout.   The single-tube frequency-modulated oscillator of Johnson[158] is very similar to that of Bradley, though it appears to have been developed from a somewhat different viewpoint.

16.13 Superregeneration

The principle of superregeneration was introduced by E. H. Armstrong[16] in 1922, but was not generally understood until much later. Its application has been greatly retarded by this lack of information. The subject is discussed here, because the method is based upon the initiation of oscillation in the presence of noise and a small signal.   The principle may be used to obtain both detection and amplification and is applicable to signals modulated in a variety of ways.   Moreover, a given circuit configuration may operate in quite different ways, depending upon the relative values of the parameters.

Probably the simplest application of superregeneration is as an amplifier in what is called the linear mode. The fundamental functions are indicated in Fig. 16.14.   The external conductance g, representative of the action of the vacuum tube, is periodically varied from positive to negative by the action of the quench source.   It is assumed that the conductance g is changed suddenly, but that no appreciable shock excitation results.   Under these circumstances, oscillations build up exponentially from the level which existed in the resonator at the time of turn-on.   The initial level depends upon the signal, here represented by a constant-current source, and any noise which may be present.   If the conductance is not maintained negative for too long an interval, the system will remain linear, and the maximum oscillation level reached will be directly proportional to the input signal.   The nature of this variation is indicated in Fig. 16.15.

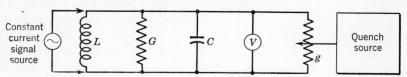

Fig. 16.14.   Essential functions of a superregenerative amplifier.

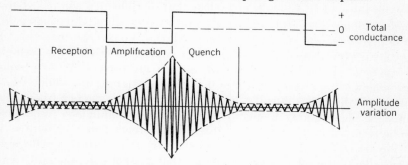

Fig. 16.15.   Amplitude variation in linear mode as an amplifier.

From this picture it is immediately clear that the total conductance must have a positive average value; otherwise the decay during the quench interval would be insufficient to balance the build-up during the amplification interval, and the average amplitude would increase until saturation due to nonlinearity set in.   In practice, the self-oscillation should be allowed to decay below the noise level during each quench cycle.   Otherwise the voltage which governs the next build-up includes both the incoming signal and portions of the previous oscillation.   Such a situation is referred to as *hangover*, and is undesirable because it degrades the sensitivity of the system as well as produces undesirable undulations in the selectivity characteristic.

16.14 Selectivity of the superregenerative amplifier

Subject to the assumption that the previous oscillation has decayed below the noise level and that the conductance varies in a square-wave manner, the selectivity of the system shown in Fig. 16.14 is substantially equal to the selectivity of the total system during the quench interval. In particular, if G is zero over this interval, the selectivity is simply the selectivity of the passive tuned circuit. To show this we may imagine the frequency of the signal to be varied from the natural frequency of the resonator, in which case the voltage effective in starting the oscillation decreases according to the selectivity of the passive system.

If the amplitude of the input signal is varied slowly with time, the peaks of the resulting envelopes of oscillation will vary accordingly. Therefore, the system serves as a linear amplifier of unmodulated or amplitude-modulated waves.

As the frequency of the signal modulation is increased, the successive samples of the modulated input signal, obtained by the quench process, differ more and more in amplitude. Provided the other parts of the system respond adequately, it is clear that no difficulty will be experienced as long as several samples are taken over each modulation cycle. It is plausible, and can be demonstrated, that no serious distortion of any kind occurs until the modulation frequency is half of the quench frequency. Filters in one form or another are used to remove high-frequency components, thus producing a smooth output. This situation rarely leads to difficulty in practice, because the quench frequency must be considerably higher than the highest modulation frequency to be received in order to avoid direct interference from this source.

We are now in a position to see how a variation of the quench wave form affects the selectivity. Suppose that the total conductance has the form shown in Fig. 16.16. The reduction of the conductance of the tuned circuit during the reception interval is desirable because it leads to a high selectivity and a larger starting voltage from a given signal. The large negative conductance during the amplification period is desirable because it leads to a rapid expansion of the signal, thus giving more time for quenching and amplification. Finally, the large positive conductance leads to rapid and complete quenching. In practice, it is very difficult to approximate this wave form, and it is often undesirable to do so because of the excessive selectivity produced.

The performance of other conductance variations was investigated by H. A. Wheeler and reported by Hazeltine[131] et al. in a very informative paper. The interesting feature of this work is that the overall selectivity depends to some extent upon the conductance during the amplification interval as well as upon that during the reception. In practical systems the net conductance always passes through zero at a finite rate, and the selectivity is most affected by the interval when the

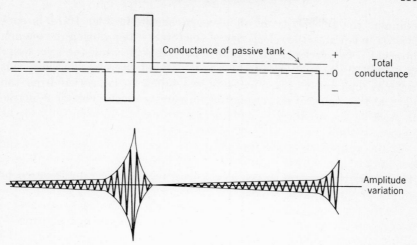

Fig. 16.16.   Preferred form of conductance variation.

conductance is small.   In particular, if the conductance varies linearly
with time from a large positive to a large negative value the selectivity
curve has the form

$$A = A_0 e^{-\left|\frac{\omega^2 C}{dG/dt}\right|}, \tag{16.32}$$

where A_0 is the midband amplification, A is the amplification at an
angular frequency differing from the midband by ω, and C and G are,
respectively, the total capacitance and conductance of the resonator as
shown in Fig. 16.14.

16.15 Noise in the superregenerative amplifier

Under favorable circumstances, the signal-to-noise ratio of a superregenerative receiver is very good, because the needed selectivity is
produced directly in the input circuit.   Moreover, the system is
inherently insensitive to isolated noise impulses, such as those produced by automobile ignition systems, because it is not affected unless
the pulse occurs near the end of the reception period, and because the
system does not saturate.   However, as pointed out by Bradley,[38]
the signal-to-noise ratio is seriously degraded if the quench wave form
does not have the property of holding the total conductance low or zero
for a considerable portion of the cycle, as shown in Fig. 16.16.

16.16 The logarithmic mode

If the amplification interval is extended without modifying the
build-up rate, the system will overload during each cycle as shown in

Fig. 16.17. However, the saturation level will be reached sooner, and therefore the average output will be increased, if the signal is increased. It can be shown that the area enclosed by the oscillation envelope increases as the logarithm of the instantaneous input. This leads to marked distortion of an amplitude-modulated wave, particularly near the troughs of modulation where the instantaneous amplitude is small. It is therefore not ordinarily desirable.

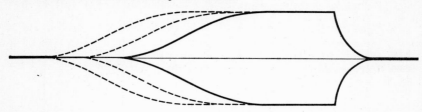

FIG. 16.17.   Oscillation envelopes for three signal levels applied to a superregenerative system in the logarithmic mode.

A circuit which operates as a superregenerative amplifier will also serve as a demodulator if any portion of the circuit acts as a rectifier. This nearly always happens in a practical circuit, although not always in an efficient manner. Limiting usually occurs by grid rectification, so the average grid current may be used as an output. The average plate current usually shows a corresponding variation at a higher power level.

The preceding discussion has assumed that the quenching signal is supplied from a separate source, preferably a relaxation oscillator yielding a suitable wave shape. However, the quenching action can also be obtained by causing the superregenerative oscillator to operate intermittently as discussed in Chapter 10. This method has the advantage that the system passes through the condition of zero net conductance rather slowly so that the selectivity is good. It has the disadvantage that the quench frequency is quite sensitive to the level of the input signal and that it is difficult to design a circuit which performs all the necessary functions simultaneously and well.

The reader is referred to Stockman[297] for a good discussion of applications of superregeneration, and to Kalmus[161] for several operating circuits. Additional information concerning the theory of operation is given by Frink,[104] Glucksman,[115] and Riebman.[263]

PROBLEMS

16.1. An oscillator has a passive Q of 100 and is to be frequency-modulated ± 1 per cent. How many reactive volt-amperes are required if the power output is 10 mw?

16.2. If a circuit is to transmit 100 words per minute, what minimum bandwidth is required? Consistent with Fig. 16.3, what time constants are allowable?

16.3. Discuss the basic problem of a start-stop oscillator and show how Chance's circuit solves it.

16.4. Sketch a circuit for plate-modulating a tuned-plate triode oscillator and discuss power and element relationships.

16.5. Show how screen-grid modulation may be applied to a beam tetrode and discuss the linearity and efficiency which may be obtained.

16.6. Discuss the design of the frequency modulated oscillator of Artz (Section 16.10).

16.7. Draw a circuit for producing frequency-modulated square waves with a multivibrator, and discuss the use of filters to obtain sinusoidal output waves.

16.8. Discuss the operation of De Lange's oscillator.

16.9. Discuss the operation of Bruck's oscillator.

16.10. Justify by physical reasoning the general form of eq. 16.32.

17

AUTOMATIC FREQUENCY CONTROL

17.1 Purpose of automatic frequency control

Under ordinary circumstances, it is customary to employ a resonator in conjunction with an amplifier or negative resistance device to produce oscillations. Under certain circumstances, however, it is desirable to employ an *automatic frequency control* system in which a relatively unstable oscillator is constrained to operate at the desired frequency by means of a feedback system. The essential features of such a system include the *oscillator* which generates a signal, the *discriminator* which produces a response that depends upon the deviation from the desired frequency, and a *correction mechanism* which causes the deviation to decrease.

Automatic frequency control was devised by Travis[313] to simplify the design and tuning of high-frequency radio receivers in which a high degree of selectivity is achieved by the superheterodyne method. The full selectivity available by this method is obtained only if the local oscillator is, and remains, accurately tuned to a frequency which differs from that of the transmitter by the intermediate frequency of the receiver. Such accurate tuning can be achieved more cheaply and easily by means of automatic frequency control than by careful manual adjustment of a highly stable beat oscillator. Also, automatic frequency control has the additional advantage that the desired frequency difference is maintained, even if the transmitter frequency varies somewhat. In communication systems the transmitter frequency rarely varies to an appreciable extent, but in radar systems this is not always true; and automatic frequency control has been found an effective solution to the problem of keeping the radar system properly tuned.[261]

Automatic frequency control is used in many frequency-modulation transmitters. In this application the instantaneous frequency is varied about the average value by means of a reactance tube or otherwise, as described in Chapter 16. The average frequency, however, is held constant with respect to a stable resonator or oscillator by means of automatic frequency control.[232,311]   In practice, this is often accomplished by slowly varying the bias of the reactance tube so that both slow and fast variations of frequency are controlled by the same electrode.

In the microwave region, automatic frequency control is employed for a somewhat different reason. At these frequencies, oscillators and highly stable resonators exist separately, but it is difficult to combine them; and satisfactory four-terminal amplifiers are unavailable. Under these circumstances it is often more convenient to refer the frequency to a cavity indirectly by automatic frequency control rather than directly by methods discussed in the previous chapters.

In induction heating and other industrial applications it is often expedient to generate the required output directly in a high-power oscillator which is held within the allowable frequency tolerance by means of an automatic frequency control system. The advantage of this arrangement is that a minimum number of high-frequency, high-power components is required.

17.2 Discriminators

Discriminator circuits have received extensive development in connection with receivers for frequency-modulated signals.[100,103] The simplest possible discriminator is a tuned circuit operated slightly away from its natural frequency. If such a circuit is subjected to a signal of constant amplitude but variable frequency, the output depends upon

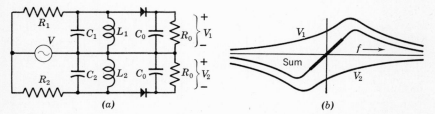

FIG. 17.1. Frequency discriminator based on two circuits tuned to different frequencies: (a) circuit and (b) typical response.

the frequency. In radio receivers we ordinarily use a *limiter*, in which the output is independent of the input amplitude, to provide a substantially constant signal to the discriminator; but in automatic frequency control oscillators this limiting function is usually inherently present.

A basic form of symmetrical frequency discriminator is shown in Fig. 17.1. It is seen that the output voltage is zero at a frequency lying between the natural frequencies of the two tuned circuits, and varies almost linearly with frequency in this region. It again decreases toward zero at frequencies remote from the useful range. Although capable of excellent performance, this arrangement is rarely used, because it is difficult to maintain the required relationships between the selectivity and the tuning of the resonant circuits, and because the output is not grounded at either end.

To avoid these difficulties, we may employ the arrangement indicated in Fig. 17.2, in which the transformers are assumed to be lossless. At the center frequency L_1 and C_1 are resonant so that the current flowing in this mesh is in phase with $\mathbf{V}$. Therefore the voltages $\mathbf{V}_1$ and $\mathbf{V}_2$ are in quadrature with $\mathbf{V}$, and hence with $\mathbf{V}_a$, as shown in Fig. 17.2b. Assuming that the rectifiers are ideal and the load resistors

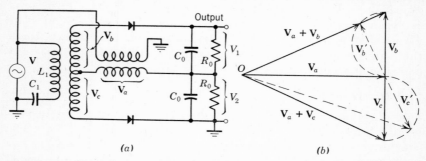

(a)   (b)

FIG. 17.2. Frequency discriminator based upon tuned circuit and phase quadrature: (a) circuit and (b) phasor diagram.

are sufficiently large, the voltages V_1 and V_2 are equal and opposite, and no net output is produced. At a frequency slightly different from that of resonance there is a phase shift in the tuned circuit, and the phasor diagram takes the form indicated by the dotted lines. Under these circumstances the rectified voltages are unequal, and a net output is produced. By appropriate choice of the primary selectivity and the transformer turns ratio it is possible to obtain a highly linear discriminator characteristic of the form shown in Fig. 17.1b.

The circuit just described is the prototype of most practical discriminators, but is capable of still further simplification, as indicated in Fig. 17.3. Two similar circuits are tuned to the same frequency, and are magnetically coupled as shown. In this arrangement the voltages *induced* in the center-tapped coil remain *in phase* with the driving voltage V, and the relative shifts corresponding to Fig. 17.2b are produced by the selectivity of this secondary circuit. The selectivity of the primary coil does not contribute essentially to the operation, but does affect the linearity of the resulting characteristic. Arguimbau[15] has shown that identical results may be had from the circuits represented in Figs. 17.1 and 17.3, and there is reason to believe that very similar results are obtained from the circuit of Fig. 17.2. Extensive use has shown that the arrangement of Fig. 17.3 is readily manufactured, highly reliable, and capable of excellent performance. Additional discussion of discriminators is given by Sturley.[299]

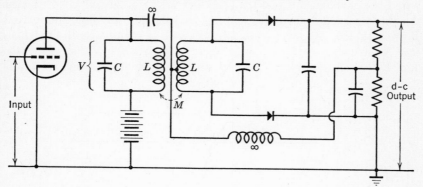

FIG. 17.3.   A practical and widely used discriminator circuit.

Crain[67] has shown that a response very similar to that of Fig. 17.1b may be obtained from a suitable RC network, which has very reasonable element values for frequencies in the audio range. The ratio detector of Seeley and Avins[276] employs a circuit somewhat similar to that of Fig. 17.3, to obtain the combined actions of detector and limiter in receivers of frequency-modulated signals. It does not, however, discriminate against *slow* amplitude changes, so it has no special advantages for the present application.

17.3 Microwave discriminators

In the microwave region it is impractical to employ ordinary lumped-circuit techniques. However, wave guides and cavity or molecular resonators may be employed to produce results equivalent to those just described. An arrangement due to Rideout[262] and illustrated in Fig. 17.4 is a good example of such a microwave discriminator. The operation corresponds to that represented in Fig. 17.2. The resonant cavity replaces the tuned circuit, the hybrid junction[318] or "magic tee" replaces the pair of transformers for voltage addition, and the phase shifter in the auxiliary wave guide facilitates establishment of the desired phase relationship.

The cavity shown is rectangular, and has dimensions appropriate to the TE_{112} mode, but other shapes and modes may be used. It is highly desirable that its apertures be of approximately equal size and coincide with the walls of the two associated sections of wave guide. The transmission of the auxiliary path is insensitive to frequency and is adjusted to have a magnitude equal to or somewhat greater than that through the cavity. The desired performance is most conveniently obtained by proportioning the hybrid junction so as to provide an impedance match between the auxiliary guide and the two crystal rectifiers. The transmission through the auxiliary wave guide is then controlled by the nature and size of the aperture between

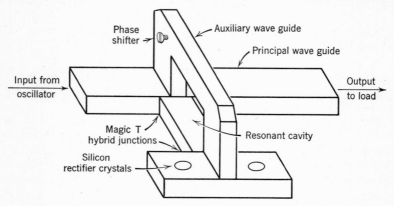

FIG. 17.4. Microwave frequency discriminator of Rideout.

it and the principal wave guide. The crucial feature is that the signal delivered to the rectifiers through the cavity at its natural frequency is in time quadrature with that through the auxiliary path.

Pound[243] has devised a microwave discriminator which employs a cavity with a single aperture and operates in a manner substantially different from that of the Rideout discriminator. Two hybrid junctions of the "magic tee" form are used, as shown in Fig. 17.5. The wave-guide arrangement is indicated schematically rather than pictorially, using the convention that opposite arms of each junction are conjugate. Therefore, half of the input power goes to the useful load, and half is propagated toward the right to the second junction, where it again divides. At frequencies remote from its natural frequency, the cavity appears as a short circuit at its coupling aperture, and with the path lengths shown the signals returned to this second junction are 90° out of phase. Under these circumstances equal signals are propagated right and left at the second junction. The 3-db attenuator is provided so that the signal output of crystal detector 2 is equal to that provided by detector 1, which receives only half of the power propagated to the left, the other half being returned to the source.

The same behavior occurs at the natural frequency of the cavity, where the aperture again appears as a virtual short circuit. At frequencies slightly removed from the natural frequency, however, the

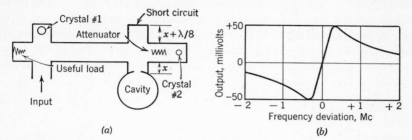

(a)   (b)

FIG. 17.5. Microwave frequency discriminator using two magic tee junctions: (a) arrangement and (b) performance.

cavity has an appreciable susceptance, and the phase relationship and power division at the second junction are upset. The outputs from the two detectors are no longer equal, and the difference voltage takes the characteristic form shown in the associated curve. The values are representative of the results which can be expected from a power input of a few milliwatts with a cavity having a Q of about 10,000 at a frequency of 10,000 Mc.

17.4 Automatic frequency control systems

An automatic frequency control system results when a discriminator is associated with an oscillator in such a way that the oscillator frequency is controlled by the discriminator response. The mechanism of control may take many forms, but ordinarily it is either mechanical or electrical. In a typical mechanical arrangement a variable condenser is tuned by a small motor which responds to an amplified signal supplied by the discriminator. Such systems respond relatively slowly but are usually arranged so that, in the event of failure in the control system, the condenser remains at its previous position; thus the frequency drifts off only very slowly. This property is very desirable in situations where the reference signal is transmitted by radio or wire, and is therefore subject to occasional interruption, because the system merely "waits" until new frequency correction information is received. Systems involving mechanical correction of frequency are well adapted to frequency-modulation transmitters and to industrial applications in which the load and other frequency-determining factors are not subject to sudden changes. The system described by Morrison[216] is an excellent example of this class.

In most applications, however, a rapid frequency correction is desirable. This is particularly true where microwave oscillators are involved, because they are subject to rapid and erratic frequency deviations. In all such cases an electrical method of control is suitable. In velocity modulation oscillators the necessary frequency-correcting mechanism already exists, in that the frequency is quite sensitive to some applied voltage. In other oscillators a correcting mechanism must ordinarily be added. The three principal mechanisms, nonlinear

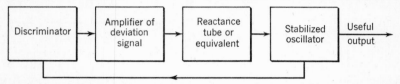

Fig. 17.6. Typical automatic frequency control system. The voltage gain of the amplifier is A; the response of the reactance tube is B mhos per volt; the control factor of the oscillator is C cycles per mho; and the discriminator response is D volts per cycle deviation.

coil, nonlinear condenser, and reactance tube, have already been described in Chapter 16 and will not be discussed further. It is, however, appropriate to note that microwave triode oscillators are not readily frequency-modulated, and that the electron-beam methods described for modulating magnetrons may prove to be the best available mechanisms for this purpose.

The arrangement of a typical automatic frequency control system is shown in block diagram in Fig. 17.6. The discriminator produces a signal which indicates the direction and magnitude of the deviation from the desired frequency. This signal, although usually a direct voltage, may also be an alternating voltage in which the direction of the deviation is conveyed by the relative phase. The associated amplifier serves only to increase the accuracy with which the frequency is controlled. A reactance tube is indicated as the mechanism which causes the oscillator to tend toward the desired frequency, but the system will operate in the same general way if any of the other mechanisms is substituted.

17.5 Analysis of automatic frequency control

It is seen from Fig. 17.6 that an automatic frequency control arrangement constitutes one form of single-loop feedback system. Analysis is facilitated if we assume that the discriminator has the simple output characteristic of Fig. 17.1 and that a reactance tube is used, but the results apply with minor changes to other arrangements. The behavior of the system is most conveniently studied by opening the path at the output of the discriminator.

Let us assume that a *small* voltage E is supplied to the deviation signal amplifier and that the resulting signal AE is applied to the reactance tube. The resulting change of susceptance (or reactance) may be represented by ABE; it affects the oscillation frequency by an amount $ABCE$. Finally the discriminator produces a response voltage V given by

$$V = ABCDE. \qquad (17.1)$$

Evidently, the product $ABCD$ represents the loop transmission, and corresponds to the factor $\mu\beta$ discussed in Chapter 5. Therefore, we conclude that the inherent frequency stability is enhanced by the factor $1 - ABCD$. Likewise, the system will generate spontaneous frequency modulation by undesired oscillation if the stabilizing loop does not satisfy the Nyquist condition.

Pound[243] has tested a system operating at about 9000 Mc which differs from Fig. 17.6 only in that the discriminator is a microwave bridge of the type shown in Fig. 17.5, and the reactance tube is unnecessary because the reflex oscillator used has a frequency-sensitive repeller. In his system the d-c amplifier has an effective gain of $A = 600$; the frequency sensitivity of the tube corresponds to a product $BC = 1$ Mc per volt; and the discriminator has a response of $D = 1$ volt per Mc. Thus, the stabilizing factor, as given by eq. 17.1, is 600. If, for example, a temperature change causes the inherent frequency of the oscillator to change by 600 kc, the operating frequency changes by only one kilocycle. Moreover; the response has a time constant of the order of one millisecond; thus rapid as well as slow frequency deviations are corrected.

If the automatic frequency control system has no nonlinearity except that of the limiter, the output frequency will vary in the manner indicated in Fig. 17.7, as the natural frequency of the oscillator is varied manually. It is seen that the frequency changes very slowly in the central region, but that the tuning rate is greatly increased at more remote frequencies. Under the conditions shown a considerable amount of hysteresis exists, and the frequency tends to "snap in" as the correct tuning is approached. For the same reason the frequency "snaps out" as the tuning direction is reversed.

The form of hysteresis just described is usually tolerable and is sometimes desirable. In cases when it is undesirable, however, it may be avoided by use of a discriminator having a monotonic response as shown in Fig. 17.8a. Such a response may be obtained by combination of two (or more) discriminators such that the slope of the second is positive and greater than the negative slope of the first throughout the region of interest. The extra complication of the discriminator circuit may readily be justifiable in a system which must meet exacting requirements.

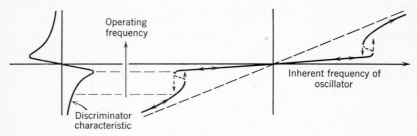

FIG. 17.7. Construction yielding response of automatic frequency control system as inherent frequency of oscillator is varied. The discriminator response is represented in terms of actual frequency correction produced.

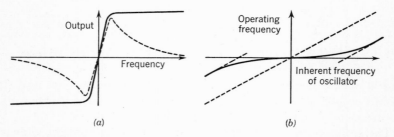

FIG. 17.8. Effect of modified discriminator: (a) discriminator response and (b) tuning characteristic.

17.6 Use of alternating current for the stabilizing signal

The system described in the previous sections has two important practical limitations. Rectifiers, particularly microwave crystals, are considerably more noisy at low frequencies than in a corresponding band at higher frequencies; and d-c amplifiers are much less stable and convenient than equivalent tuned amplifiers. Both difficulties are alleviated by use of alternating current at a suitable *intermediate frequency*.

A system of this sort, having certain advantages over that originally devised by Pound, has been developed by Tuller et al.[317] and is presented in Fig. 17.9. The signal delivered from the directional coupler to the "magic tee" of the discriminator divides between the cavity and a crystal driven by an auxiliary 30-Mc oscillator. The sidebands produced by this modulation process, supplemented by the phase-shifted signal from the cavity, again divide in the "magic tee," half being lost in the termination of the directional coupler and half meeting in the detector crystal to re-establish a 30-Mc signal in which the phase depends upon the relation of the output frequency to the cavity tuning. This new signal is amplified by well-known techniques,[142]

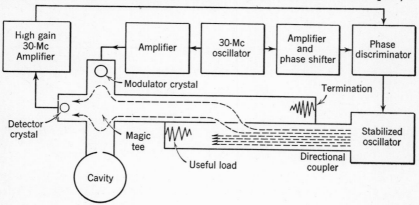

FIG. 17.9. Microwave frequency stabilization system of Tuller, Gallaway, and Zaffarano.

and is recombined with the amplified, phase-shifted signal from the 30-Mc oscillator to produce a rectified voltage which depends upon the frequency delivered to the master cavity.

The action of the modulating crystal may also be thought of as due to a variable reflection coefficient. If the modulating crystal and the cavity are suitably coupled to their wave guides, they present matched impedances to the magic tee if the 30-Mc signal is absent and if the output frequency corresponds to the natural frequency of the cavity. When the 30-Mc signal is applied, the resistance of the modulating crystal is periodically increased and decreased about the matching value, and a signal of the form shown in Fig. 17.10a is delivered to the rectifying crystal, which is also matched to the wave guide source for maximum response. The crucial fact is that the phase of the high-frequency signal reverses at each point where the envelope passes through zero. The signal delivered to the rectifying crystal by the cavity is directly proportional to the degree of detuning, but reverses in phase as the frequency passes through resonance. It is shown in

Fig. 17.10b. Thus the combined wave has a 30-Mc component in the envelope such that rectification produces a signal which, by magnitude and phase, indicates the degree of detuning of the cavity. It also contains a strong 60-Mc component which is removed by filtering.

The phase-sensitive detector may correspond to Fig. 17.2 or may simply be a multiple-grid tube in which the signals are injected on separate control electrodes. If, for example, the oscillator signal is applied to the suppressor of a pentode, the average plate current will be proportionately increased or decreased by an in-phase or counter-phase voltage on the first grid.

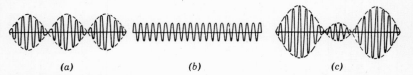

(a)   (b)   (c)

FIG. 17.10. Signals in alternating-current stabilizing system: (a) output due to modulation of crystal, (b) output due to detuning of cavity, and (c) sum of two outputs.

The arrangement described has the great advantage that the only critical paths, to and opposite the cavity, may be made of equal length. Therefore, the system operates without readjustment save of the cavity and the reflex oscillator over the full range of the latter's tuning. The particular system tested operated over the entire 8500 to 9600 Mc range of the 2K25 oscillator used. The directional coupler serves to deliver nearly all the oscillator output to the useful load and also masks the cavity discriminator from the oscillator to an extent which is sufficient to ensure that undesirable direct pulling does not occur.

The degree of frequency stabilization which may be achieved in this way is very high. Numerical data are lacking, but it appears that stabilizing factors in the order of 10^5 may be attained in practical systems. By this means it is possible to produce frequencies of the order of 9000 Mc which have a total bandwidth of less than 25 cycles due to noise and residual hum. It is to be noted that the stability of the output frequency is independent of that of the 30-Mc auxiliary oscillator so long as the latter does not contribute appreciable phase error through the selectivity of the intermediate frequency amplifier.

17.7 The time coincidence method

It is possible to achieve automatic frequency control by a feedback method which involves phase or time coincidence in a manner which

differs considerably from that of the systems described so far.   Figure
17.11 shows the block diagram of such a system, which has been used
successfully by Hershberger[139] in connection with the ammonia
resonator.[11]   An auxiliary (search) oscillator is frequency-modulated
in a saw-tooth manner, and part of this signal is passed through the
ammonia cell.   Because the rate at which the frequency is varied is low
compared to the rejection band of the ammonia chamber, the effect
may be considered from a quasi-stationary viewpoint; and it is seen
that the signal delivered to the phase detector will drop to a minimum

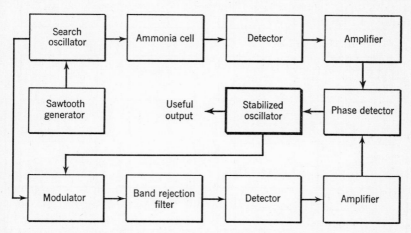

FIG. 17.11.   Block diagram of automatic frequency control system based on time
coincidence.

at the instant when the auxiliary oscillator reaches the natural frequency of the ammonia.   The beat frequency produced by mixing the
signals of the auxiliary and main oscillators is frequency-modulated
in the same manner as that delivered to the ammonia cell; therefore,
by giving the networks of the band rejection filter a response similar
to that of the ammonia, it is possible to deliver similar signals to the
two inputs of the phase detector.   The phase detector consists of
circuits such that the polarity and magnitude of the output voltage
depends upon the relative timing of the signals received from the two
inputs.   Therefore, the master oscillator is stabilized at a frequency
which differs from that of the ammonia resonance by the relatively low
frequency at which the characteristic of the band-rejection filter is
centered.

The sensitivity which can be achieved in this way is probably
somewhat inferior to that which can be produced by the method

described in the previous section. However, very creditable performance is possible. Values of $D = 70$ millivolts per Mc and of $BC = 2$ Mc per volt are typical of results which have been attained. If an amplification factor of $A = 1400$ is supplied in the form of a d-c amplifier, the overall stabilizing factor becomes 100.

A desirable modification of the time coincidence method employs a quartz crystal oscillator with frequency multipliers to replace the

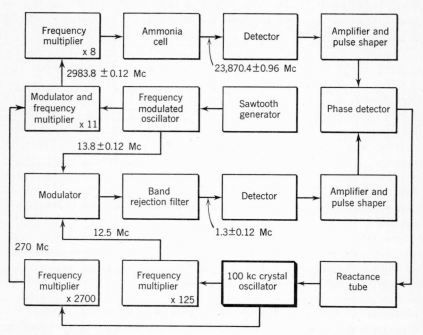

FIG. 17.12. Block diagram of improved time coincidence automatic frequency control system.

stabilized reflex oscillator. This arrangement, which is shown in block diagram in Fig. 17.12, has the advantage of excellent short-term stability as well as the absolute long-term stability inherent in the ammonia resonance. The crystal oscillator is so proportioned that the frequency can be adjusted over a narrow range by the signal applied to the reactance tube.

In the present case a relatively low-frequency oscillator is subjected to the saw-tooth frequency modulation, and the network which simulates the response of the ammonia cell operates at a frequency of only about 1.3 Mc where it is easy to control the response. The frequency multipliers are so arranged as to produce a frequency-modulated signal which sweeps through the ammonia cell about one hundred times per second. The pulses generated in this way are compared in the phase detector circuit with similar pulses produced by the sweep of the corresponding low frequency through the band-rejection filter; and the resulting output is used to modify the frequency of the master oscillator. The stabilizing factor which can be produced in this way is not significantly better than that of the simpler time coincidence method, but the superior inherent stability of the basic oscillator leads to improved performance over both long and short periods.

The time coincidence method appears awkward and cumbersome, and one is led to ask why it is used. The answer depends upon the peculiar properties of the wave-guide type of ammonia resonator. Because the molecular resonance of ammonia acts as a rejector rather than selector of the natural frequency, one finds it necessary to balance its transmission against that of some nonselective system. Unfortunately a shifting reference exists, because the nonresonant loss and phase shift of the ammonia path vary with the length of the wave guide and the pressure of the gas. Efforts to employ the steep phase shift characteristics of the ammonia resonance in structures such as that of Fig. 17.4 are difficult because the reference condition is too unstable.

Smith[290] and his co-workers have succeeded in escaping some of these difficulties by employing balanced low-Q cavities in a discriminator similar to that of Fig. 17.5. Because one cavity is filled with ammonia while the other is filled with air, the absorption characteristic of the ammonia may be retained while the effects of mechanical expansion and variable gas pressure are largely balanced.

In an experimental system the cavities consisted of rectangular wave guides approximately ½ by 1 cm in section and 2 meters long. The system corresponded to Fig. 17.5a, and a discriminator response very similar to Fig. 17.5b was observed. The discriminator gave a response of $D = 32$ millivolts per Mc, and a d-c amplifier gain of $A = 2000$ was achieved. With the oscillator used, the control response corresponded to a product $BC = 2$ Mc per volt. The stabilization factor was thus 128.

Smith recognized that a larger stabilization factor could be attained by use of alternating current for the control method, and that more compact cavities might give superior results. It appears that further advantages could be secured through the use of the symmetrical arrangement due to Tuller as illustrated in Fig. 17.9, and by substitution of a crystal oscillator with frequency multipliers for the klystron.

17.8 Frequency synthesis by automatic frequency control

An ingeneous application of automatic frequency control in an aircraft radio receiver has been described by Hedeman.[133]   The fundamental problem is to produce a large number (120) of accurately controlled frequencies (± 70 ppm) by means of a small number of quartz crystals. The required frequencies can be obtained by simple modulation processes involving sums and differences, but the elimination of undesirable modulation products is prohibitively difficult.   Therefore, it was decided to use a variable-frequency oscillator, constrained to operate at the desired frequency by means of an automatic frequency

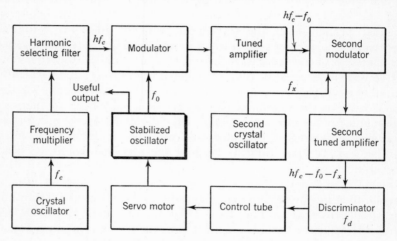

FIG. 17.13.   Frequency synthesis system.

control system which was insensitive to the undesired modulation products.   The block diagram of the system is shown in Fig. 17.13.

The discriminator operates at a frequency near one megacycle using the circuit of Fig. 17.3, and is constructed with exceptional care so as to minimize drift of the center frequency.   The variable oscillator, which operates over a band 24 Mc wide in the 100-Mc region, is controlled by means of a variable condenser which is supplemented by a reactance tube (not shown) for fine tuning.   A total of 120 frequencies uniformly spaced by 200 kc over a 24-Mc band is obtained by means of ten quartz crystals, the choice of up to seven harmonics of each crystal frequency, and the use of two discriminators.   It is emphasized that the use of automatic frequency control does not contribute to either the basic frequency stability or to the number of frequencies obtained; however, it *does* facilitate generation of a wave completely free from spurious frequency components which would lead to undesirable extraneous responses in the associated radio receiver.

PROBLEMS

17.1. Discuss the applications of automatic frequency control in terms of actual systems.

17.2. Why is the limiter needed in automatic frequency control systems for radio receivers but not for oscillators?

17.3. The primary Q in Fig. 17.2 is 200, $V_a = 10$, and $V_b = V_c = 5$ rms volts. Calculate the output in the region of the center frequency which is one megacycle.

17.4. Discuss the relative advantages of mechanical and electronic frequency-correcting devices.

17.5. Show that eq. 17.1 is correct and explain its application.

17.6. Show how to apply eq. 17.1 to the system of Fig. 17.9, taking into account the modulating properties of the crystals, etc.

17.7. Obtain an equation corresponding to 17.1 for the time-coincidence method of automatic frequency control.

17.8. Discuss the design of a synthesis system similar to that of Fig. 17.13.

18

LONG-LINE AND
MULTIPLE-RESONANCE EFFECTS

18.1 Introduction

The foregoing discussions have, with a few exceptions, assumed that the resonator has a single response. It is ordinarily desirable to maintain this condition because it greatly simplifies the behavior of the system. In many important cases, however, it is impossible to produce a suitable resonator having a single response over a frequency band. We must, therefore, consider the behavior of these more complicated systems with a view to taking advantage of any attractive features and to avoiding the more troublesome ones.

Multiple-resonance effects are readily produced at low frequencies by means of coupled circuits or circuits involving several coils and condensers. Any finite number n of antiresonant (or resonant) frequencies can be produced by using n distinct inductances in suitable combination with n capacitances in a lumped circuit. Mutual inductance is not necessary but is often convenient for this purpose. An infinite number of responses, ordinarily at frequencies related in an orderly but nonharmonic series, is associated with any form of distributed system or periodic structure. Quartz crystals, cavity resonators, and electrical transmission lines are the most important distributed systems which have application to oscillators.

Particularly interesting and complex effects are observed when the system includes lumped elements connected by low-loss electrically long transmission lines. An important example of such a system is a microwave magnetron coupled to an antenna by means of a considerable length of wave guide.[286] The example cited is still further complicated by the fact that the magnetron is pulsed rather than operated continuously. It is therefore necessary to study the transient as well as the steady state response of these systems.

The discussion in the following sections is expressed in terms of admittances rather than impedances because they apply naturally to parallel resonant circuits, which are shown to be essential for stable operation with voltage-controlled negative resistance devices. Thus the use of admittance is desirable because nearly all electronic devices are of this parallel type.

18.2 The complex frequency plane

The phenomena under consideration are most conveniently treated in terms of the complex frequency plane,[147] which was introduced in Chapter 2. These ideas are reviewed and extended with reference to Fig. 18.1a, which shows the roots of a lightly damped passive circuit which is singly resonant at ω_1. It is recalled that the vertical axis is

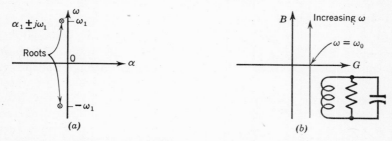

FIG. 18.1. (a) The complex frequency plane where the variable is $p = \alpha + j\omega$. (b) The complex admittance plane where the variable is $Y = G + jB$.

the axis of real frequencies, and that all steady-state measurements involve real frequencies. If the network in question has a parallel resonant configuration, we find that the admittance reaches a minimum and the susceptance is zero for a frequency equal to ω_0 as shown in Fig. 18.1b. This is the familiar behavior at antiresonance and governs the steady-state performance of an oscillator controlled by this resonator.

During build-up and decay of oscillation we are concerned with waves which increase or decrease exponentially with respect to time. Such transients are of relatively short duration, and we find it possible to evade their treatment in most situations. Here, however, they are of primary interest. In a basic sense these transients are not short; a typical oscillator describes several hundred complete cycles while the amplitude is building up to its normal value from the level of thermal noise.

Our clue to the situation lies in the transient decay of the passive antiresonant circuit when open-circuited and given an initial disturbance. As we have seen the wave produced has a frequency ω_1 and a damping factor α_1, as plotted in Fig. 18.1a. This natural frequency ω_1 is nearly but not quite equal to the steady-state frequency of unity power factor designated ω_0. *The important fact is that the circuit has zero admittance to a wave having the complex frequency $\alpha_1 + j\omega_1$. This is true because voltage exists across the circuit in the absence of an external current.*

From this basic observation we draw the correct generalization that the conductance of the circuit is decreased if we shift to the left and is increased if we shift to the right in the p plane. The validity of this statement is substantiated when we reflect that a point in the right half of the plane corresponds to a wave which is expanding in amplitude

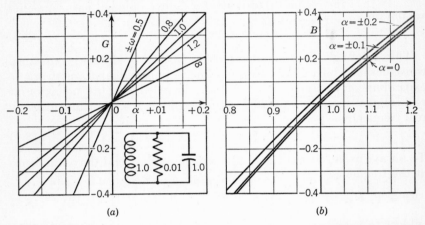

(a)   (b)

FIG. 18.2.   Variation of G and B with $p = \alpha + j\omega$ in a parallel resonant circuit.   The admittance is $Y = G + jB = 0.01 + \alpha + j\omega + (\alpha - j\omega)/(\alpha^2 + \omega^2)$.
$(Q = 100.)$

with time.   To create such a wave it is necessary to supply energy for storage in the reactive elements as well as that for cycle-by-cycle dissipation.   *Thus, we may think of a given circuit as being heavily damped to an expanding wave and lightly damped to a decaying wave.* To demonstrate the latter point we have only to add a separate conductance to the antiresonant circuit previously considered.   Again, assuming an initial disturbance and decaying transient of the entire system, the original circuit must be viewed as the generator or source which drives the added conductance.   Additional insight is gained from Fig. 18.2, which shows the conductance and the susceptance of a high-Q antiresonant circuit as a function of p.   It is seen that G is nearly proportional to α and that B is nearly proportional to $(\omega - \omega_0)$ in the region of interest.

An important characteristic of the functions which describe the behavior of physical networks is that they are *analytic*.   For example, the admittance of the antiresonant circuit is an analytic function of the complex frequency.   Analytic functions have the important property that the derivative is uniquely defined and is independent of the direction in which it is taken, as shown by Sokolnikoff.[291]   Associated with a unique derivative are the Cauchy-Riemann equations, which for our purposes may be written

$$\partial G/\partial \alpha = \partial B/\partial \omega \quad \text{and} \quad \partial B/\partial \alpha = -\partial G/\partial \omega. \qquad (18.1)$$

Substituting

$$Y = G + jB, \qquad (18.2)$$

we obtain

$$\partial Y/\partial \alpha = -j\,\partial Y/\partial \omega. \qquad (18.3)$$

This seemingly abstract relationship justifies a simple geometrical construction which gives the approximate impedance of a network to expanding or decaying waves from a knowledge of its behavior at real frequencies.   In a parallel resonant circuit the admittance at any real frequency ω is

$$Y = G + j\omega C + 1/j\omega L. \qquad (18.4)$$

To a wave expanding at the rate of α nepers per second the admittance at the frequency ω is

$$Y_1 = Y + \alpha(\partial Y/\partial \alpha) = G + j\omega C + 1/j\omega L + \alpha(C + 1/\omega^2 L), \quad (18.5)$$

subject to the restriction that α is not too large.   It is seen that the susceptance is unchanged while the effective conductance is increased by an amount proportional to α, as indicated in Fig. 18.2.

In a general case the admittance change due to an increment in α is numerically equal to the admittance change due to an increment in ω and is directed 90° to the right thereof.   *Thus, given the real-frequency admittance plot of any network, we need only divide off the curve in convenient uniform small increments in frequency and rotate these segments 90° in order to determine the admittance to an expanding wave.   Natural units of radians per second and nepers per second are used.*

18.3 A doubly resonant system

The essential features of multiple resonance are illustrated by the negative resistance oscillator of Fig. 18.3.   Two parallel-loaded antiresonant circuits in series are connected to a voltage-controlled negative resistance provided by a transitron.   It will be assumed that the antiresonant circuits are not coupled and that they have comparable values of impedance, selectivity, and natural frequency.   The behavior of this composite tank is explored most conveniently by adding the impedances of the separate circuits, as shown. The susceptance of the overall circuit is obtained by inversion and is indicated in polar and rectangular form in Fig. 18.4. It is seen that the susceptance (or reactance) is zero at three separate real frequencies, and that the conductance is considerably higher at the central frequency ω_3 than at the others. Superimposed upon these diagrams is the negative of the inherently negative conductance contributed by the tube. Consistent with the usual situation, it is assumed that the effective value of this conductance decreases with increase of the amplitude of oscillation.

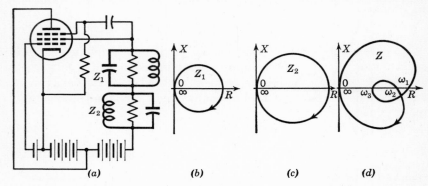

FIG. 18.3. Transitron oscillator with two degrees of freedom (a) circuit, (b) impedance of circuit one, (c) impedance of circuit two, and (d) total resonator impedance.

This is indicated by the heavy arrow in Fig. 18.4a. The problem is to determine what frequency or frequencies will be produced by this system.

Let us suppose that the system is energized without an appreciable starting transient so that oscillation will build up from the level of thermal noise. For a considerable period the system is essentially linear because the oscillations are still small, and it is thus possible to apply the principle of superposition. On this basis we may calculate the transient behavior of the composite system and find that the two pairs of conjugate roots now lie in the right rather than the left half plane. Therefore, two separate waves having frequencies close to ω_1 and ω_2 and expanding with time are produced.*

When the amplitudes approach the limiting level the effects of non-linearity become important. The analysis of this situation becomes

* This is true provided the net negative conductance is relatively small as will be discussed more fully in a later paragraph.

quite complex and will not be given here.   In general, however, the
average negative conductance is reduced by overload, and the two
separate oscillations compete for the reduced energy which is available.
Van der Pol[319] has shown that, provided the negative conductance is
representable by a linear and a cubic term, one or the other of these
frequencies will be suppressed.   Within reasonably wide limits of the
circuit variables it is possible for either frequency to gain control and
suppress the other.   Ordinarily, the oscillation which is first to reach
a large amplitude will persist.

From our study of noise we know that the initial level of these two
oscillations will depend upon the instant at which the system was

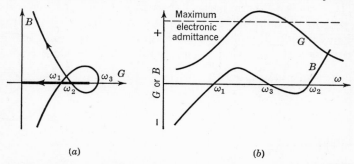

(a)   (b)

FIG. 18.4.   Admittance of total resonator: (a) complex admittance plane and (b)
variation with frequency.

energized, so that upon repetition of the experiment we would expect a
randomness, corresponding to jitter, as to which frequency is first to
reach a large amplitude and so suppress the other.   By careful adjustment of the circuit parameters it is possible to achieve a condition in
which the two frequencies are equally probable, and the occurrence
corresponds to the flipping of a coin.   However, a relatively small disturbance of the adjustment leads to a great change in the probability,
so that one or the other frequency practically ceases to appear.
A substantially larger disturbance of the adjustment is necessary
before the favored frequency is able to suppress the other when once
established (for example, by short-circuiting the favored antiresonant
branch).

Because experimental results generally conform to the results
obtained by van der Pol's simplified analysis, his assumptions were
lost sight of, and it was generally believed that no nonlinear oscillator
of this type could simultaneously produce sustained oscillations at two
frequencies.   However, analytical work by Skinner[285] shows that the
simultaneous production of two unrelated frequencies is possible,

provided the negative resistance device has a relatively complicated shape involving at least a fifth-order term in the power series expression.   The correctness of this analysis was experimentally confirmed with a transition oscillator equivalent to Fig. 18.3a.   A similar effect in microwave reflex oscillators has been observed by Huggins.[146]   The possibility of producing such oscillations is of considerable theoretical interest and may find some practical applications as well.

18.4 Tuning hysteresis in a doubly resonant system

The coupled circuit of Fig. 18.5 is capable of yielding the same essential characteristics as that of Fig. 18.3, and is much more common in practice.   It is chosen for the present discussion because it illustrates the effect in a much more natural manner.   It is readily shown that the admittance facing the tube will have the form of the solid line in Fig. 18.5, provided the coupling is considerably greater than critical and

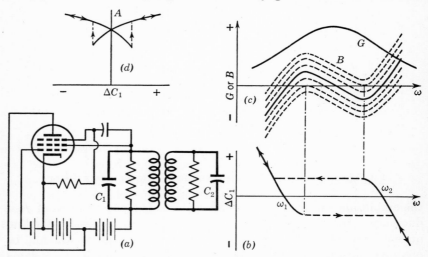

FIG. 18.5.   Oscillation hysteresis in a doubly resonant oscillator using coupled circuits: (a) circuit, (b) tuning hysteresis, (c) resonator susceptance, and (d) amplitude characteristics.

the primary is suitably tuned.   Under these conditions the oscillation will occur at ω_1 or ω_2 with equal probability if the circuit is repeatedly switched off and on.   Let us see what happens when the tuning is disturbed.

Variation of the primary tuning by means of a capacitance variation is considered first.   Subject to the idealization made in the circuit representation, the only effect is that the primary susceptance is raised or lowered by an amount proportional to the capacitance increment and the frequency. Therefore, an increase in capacitance will raise the susceptance curve and tilt it somewhat to the left, as shown in Fig. 18.5c, greatly favoring the lower frequency. If the system is initially oscillating at the higher frequency, it will continue to do so[*] until the susceptance curve is raised sufficiently to have only one intersection with the horizontal axis. At this time the oscillation will abruptly change to the lower frequency, as shown in Fig. 18.5b, and

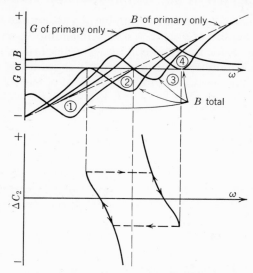

FIG. 18.6. Oscillation hysteresis with respect to secondary tuning.

the amplitude will increase somewhat because of the decrease of conductance. If the tuning is restored to its initial condition, the frequency will increase only slightly, and a sudden jump will not be observed until the tuning again reaches the point of producing a single intersection between the real axis and the susceptance curve. Under the conditions assumed, there is a considerable interval of frequencies which cannot be obtained by primary tuning. Moreover, the amplitude changes considerably with tuning because of variation of the conductance facing the tube, as shown in Fig. 18.5d.

Detailed information as to the cycle-by-cycle behavior during the transition is not available. However, it is certain that the changeover is not instantaneous, because a considerable shift of stored energy is

[*] Provided the conductance does not vary too greatly in the range of interest. No simple statement of the critical value is available.

involved.   Fortunately, the matter is of limited interest because hysteresis is undesirable and is avoided as far as possible.

Hysteresis is also observed when the secondary is tuned.   However, the analysis is somewhat more complicated because the conductance as well as the susceptance is affected when the secondary condenser is varied.   The manner of these variations is shown in Fig. 18.6.   If we start with the secondary tuned to a relatively low frequency (curve 1), the oscillation frequency is first raised (curves 2 and 3) and then slightly lowered as the secondary capacitance is decreased.   When the critical point (curve 4) is passed, the frequency suddenly decreases to somewhat less that the original value.   Further decrease of the secondary capacitance raises the frequency toward the original value; however, with a finite range of secondary tuning there is a narrow band of frequencies near the center of the range which cannot be produced.

18.5 Stable and unstable operating points

In Chapter 3 it was stated on intuitive grounds that parallel resonant systems are required for oscillation with voltage-controlled negative resistances and that series resonant systems are appropriate to current-controlled negative resistances.   It is evidently necessary to extend these concepts somewhat in order to treat multiply-resonant systems, in which both resonance and antiresonance occur within relatively small frequency intervals.

The issue was avoided in Fig. 18.4 by choosing the parameters so that the negative conductance was sufficient to produce oscillation at either of the antiresonant frequencies but was insufficient at the resonant frequency.   However, practical situations exist in which the resonant and antiresonant admittance are nearly equal and are both smaller than the maximum negative conductance available from the electronic device.   It is therefore necessary to determine the conditions under which stable sustained oscillations can exist.

The answer is implicit in Fig. 18.4 and may be stated in two ways, corresponding to the two admittance representations used.   Ford and Korman[97] have given one criterion in terms of the frequency variable; *a system is potentially capable of stable oscillation with a voltage-controlled negative conductance (or resistance) provided $B = 0$ and $\partial B/\partial \omega > 0$, where B is the net susceptance facing the negative conductance device. Stable oscillation is impossible under the same conditions if $\partial B/\partial \omega < 0$.* Similarly, with a current-controlled negative conductance (or resistance) stable oscillation is possible only if $B = 0$ and $\partial B/\partial \omega < 0$.

The alternative criterion, expressed in terms of the admittance plane, is due to J. R. Pierce and is not believed to have been previously published: *Stable oscillation can occur only if the admittance curve of the resonator crosses the negative of the conductance curve of the electronic device in such a way that the admittance increment produced by a positive increment of frequency in the resonator appears right-handed with respect to the increment of conductance produced by an increase in the level of oscillation.* In terms of Fig. 18.4 stable oscillations can occur at ω_1 or ω_2, but would be impossible at ω_3 even if the negative electronic admittance were larger. It is seen that the latter statement applies to both resonant and antiresonant behavior and to both current and voltage-controlled electronic devices. Moreover, it is equivalent to the criterion presented in the preceding paragraph.

To prove the validity of these criteria we turn to the concept of complex frequencies and analytic network functions developed in the first section of this chapter. We may represent any form of oscillator by a nonlinear negative conductance Y_e (the electronic device) in parallel with a linear but frequency-sensitive admittance Y_c (the circuit). The condition for oscillation is of course

$$Y_e + Y_c = 0. \tag{18.6}$$

To test the stability of an oscillation satisfying eq. 18.6 we assume that the amplitude A and the frequency ω of operation are modified by increments dA and $d\omega$, respectively. The oscillation is stable only if the assumed increments decrease with time. The principle of equivalent linearization is used implicitly by the assumption that the admittance of the electronic device is a pure real quantity, independent of frequency but dependent upon the amplitude of oscillation.

It should be noted that eq. 18.6 is satisfied, not only during sustained oscillation, but at *all* times. For example, Y_e is relatively large during the build-up interval in a simple parallel tuned oscillator. Equilibrium exists, nevertheless, because the effective positive conductance of the tuned circuit increases while the wave is expanding and energy is being stored.

In terms of the assumed increments, eq. 18.6 takes the form

$$Y_e + \frac{\partial Y_e}{\partial A}\, dA + Y_c + \frac{\partial Y_c}{\partial \omega}\, d\omega + \frac{\partial Y_c}{\partial \alpha}\, d\alpha = 0, \tag{18.7}$$

which with the substraction of eq. 18.6 yields

$$\frac{\partial Y_e}{\partial A}\, dA + \frac{\partial G}{\partial \omega}\, d\omega + j\frac{\partial B}{\partial \omega}\, d\omega + \frac{\partial G}{\partial \alpha}\, d\alpha + j\frac{\partial B}{\partial \alpha}\, d\alpha = 0. \tag{18.8}$$

The imaginary part, together with eq. 18.1, gives

$$\frac{\partial B}{\partial \omega} d\omega = \frac{\partial G}{\partial \omega} d\alpha, \tag{18.9}$$

which, when substituted in the real part of eq. 18.8, yields

$$\frac{\partial B}{\partial \omega} \frac{\partial Y_e}{\partial A} dA + \left(\frac{\partial G}{\partial \omega}\right)^2 d\alpha + \left(\frac{dB}{\partial \omega}\right)^2 d\alpha = 0 \tag{18.10}$$

or

$$-\frac{dA}{d\alpha} = \frac{(\partial G/\partial \omega)^2 + (\partial B/\partial \omega)^2}{(\partial B/\partial \omega)(\partial Y_e/\partial A)}. \tag{18.11}$$

Stability requires that $dA/d\alpha$ be negative, so that an increase in amplitude is associated with a decaying wave, and vice versa. That is, the left member of eq. 18.11 must be inherently positive, as is the numerator of the right. *Therefore, stability requires that $\partial B/\partial \omega$ and $\partial Y_e/\partial A$ be either both positive or both negative. Since Y_e is inherently negative, this means that the magnitude of Y_e must decrease with increase of A for stability if $\partial B/\partial \omega$ is positive, and vice versa.* Thus the stated criteria are established.

The requirement just developed is entirely consistent with elementary reasoning. If, with an antiresonant system, the negative conductance increases with amplitude the expansion rate then increases rather than decreases with amplitude, and no limiting process occurs. Presently the negative conductance is so large as to correspond to relaxation oscillation and the stored energy is converted into a one-way transient. Depending upon the properties of the system, the oscillation then may cease entirely or may continue in an entirely different mode.

18.6 Load connected through a transmission line

In microwave oscillators and in certain dielectric heating installations, the load is connected to the oscillator by means of a transmission line of appreciable length. It is therefore appropriate to investigate the behavior of such systems. It is convenient to begin the discussion by assuming that the load is a pure conductance and later to generalize the results, rather than to begin with a general treatment. The arrangement in question is shown in Fig. 18.7, in which the transmission line is of physical length l, has a characteristic admittance Y_0, and is assumed to be loss-free. The following discussion closely follows that given on page 524 of the article by Pierce and Shepherd.[241] Lythall[195] reaches essentially the same conclusions by a similar procedure.

If the characteristic admittance of the line is equal to that of the load, the line has no effect, and the case degenerates to the ordinary one. In general, however, there is a considerable mismatch, and the input admittance of the line varies in a regular manner with frequency according to the familiar transmission line equations. The situation is illustrated in the admittance plot of Fig. 18.8a, which assumes that the load conductance is twice that of the line. In order to combine these plots it is necessary to specify a relationship between the length

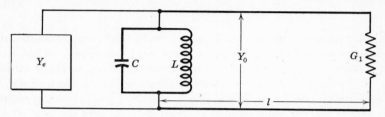

Fig. 18.7.   Oscillator loaded through a transmission line.

of the line and the susceptance of the tuned circuits. One useful parameter is the Q value which the resonator would have if the line were matched. That is,

$$Q = \omega_0 C/Y_0 = 1/\omega_0 L Y_0. \qquad (18.12)$$

A second desirable parameter is the length l expressed in terms of a corresponding number of wavelengths at the frequency ω_0.

Figure 18.8b illustrates the situation which exists when $Q = 100$ and a line 50 wavelengths long is terminated in twice its characteristic conductance, so that the voltage-standing-wave-ratio is two. It is seen that the response is similar to that of Fig. 18.4a and that oscillation hysteresis will occur if we attempt to tune the circuit by means of L or C. In particular, those frequencies for which $\partial B/\partial \omega$ is negative simply cannot be produced under these conditions if we make the usual assumption that Y_e is voltage-controlled. The situation differs from that of the coupled circuit principally in that the phenomenon repeats itself at uniform frequency intervals as the line corresponds to successive even and odd multiples of a half wavelength. The variation with tuning corresponds very closely to a simple sliding of the diagram up or down relative to the axis.

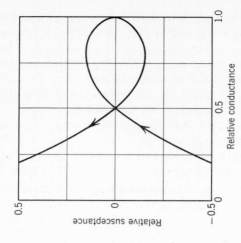

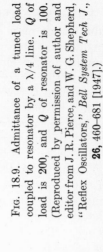

Fig. 18.9. Admittance of a tuned load coupled to resonator by a λ/4 line. Q of load is 200, and Q of resonator is 100. (Reproduced by permission of author and editor from J. R. Pierce, and W. G. Shepherd, "Reflex Oscillators," *Bell System Tech J.*, **26**, 460–681 [1947].)

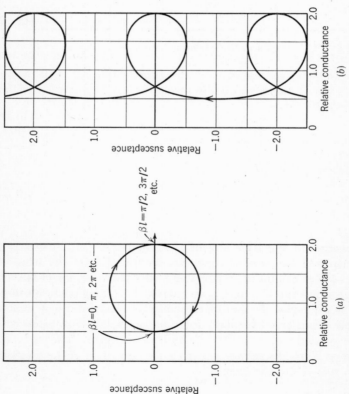

Fig. 18.8. Admittance diagram of system of Fig. 18.7: (*a*) line and load and (*b*) line, load, and resonator. (Reproduced by permission of author and editor from J. R. Pierce and W. G. Shepherd, "Reflex Oscillators," *Bell System Tech. J.*, **26**, 460–681 [1947].)

Either one or three intersections between the real axis and the circuit admittance may exist.* However, one of the three intersections is unstable, so that at most two frequencies may be favored for a given tuning; and, as mentioned previously, the two will exist simultaneously only if the electronic device possesses quite unusual properties. If the system Q were lower, the loops would be more nearly circular and would be much closer together. Under these conditions there may be four or more frequencies which satisfy the conditions of oscillation; such situations are of academic interest only.

It is clear that loops in the admittance characteristic will be removed by a sort of stretching process if the Q is raised sufficiently. The same result is obtained if the load is sufficiently accurately matched to the line, since in the limit the effect of the line vanishes. Let us therefore determine the conditions required for stability, that is, the absence of loops. The first step in this process is to write for the input admittance of a lossless line of length l the expression

$$Y_1 = Y_0 \frac{(Y_r/Y_0)\cos \beta l + j \sin \beta l}{\cos \beta L + j(Y_r/Y_0)\sin \beta l}. \tag{18.13}$$

Introducing for the voltage standing wave ratio on the line the real variable σ defined by

$$\sigma = Y_r/Y_0, \tag{18.14}$$

and substituting

$$\beta l = \omega l/v = x, \tag{18.15}$$

we may differentiate with respect to ω, obtaining

$$\begin{aligned} \frac{dY_1}{d\omega} &= Y_0 \frac{l(\cos x + j\sigma \sin x)(j \cos x - \sigma \sin x)}{v(\cos x + j\sigma \sin x)^2} \\ &\quad - Y_0 \frac{l(\sigma \cos x + j \sin x)(j\sigma \cos x - \sin x)}{v(\cos x + j\sigma \sin x)^2} \end{aligned} \tag{18.16}$$

From inspection of Fig. 18.8 we see that loops will be avoided (and a sharp cusp will be formed) if in the above equation the negative maximum of the imaginary part is less than the positive susceptance derivative for the tuned circuit. Moreover, this condition will occur when the real part of Y_1 is a maximum, that is, when $\sin x$ is zero. Making this substitution greatly simplifies the expression to the useful form

$$\partial B_1/\partial \omega = Y_0 l(1 - \sigma^2)/v. \tag{18.17}$$

* Two intersections exist when the loop is tangent to the real axis, but this case is of little interest.

In the operating region the derivative of the susceptance of the tuned circuit is simply

$$\partial B/\partial \omega = 2C. \tag{18.18}$$

Stability is ensured if the sum of eqs. 18.17 and 18.18 is positive, which occurs if

$$2C > Y_0 l(\sigma^2 - 1)/v. \tag{18.19}$$

We may now use eq. 18.12 and recall that $\sin x$ is zero only if

$$x = n\pi \tag{18.20}$$

to show that the criterion for stability of oscillation becomes

$$Q > n\pi(\sigma^2 - 1)/2, \tag{18.21}$$

where n is an integer representing the number of half wavelengths in the line.

In microwave oscillators loaded through wave guides the situation is restricted somewhat more severely because the phase changes more rapidly with frequency in wave guides than it does in ordinary lines. In this case the criterion becomes

$$Q > \frac{n\pi}{2} \frac{(\sigma^2 - 1)}{(1 - f_0{}^2/f^2)}, \tag{18.22}$$

where f is the operating frequency and f_0 is the frequency of cutoff in the guide.

18.7 Tuned load at end of a transmission line

Ordinarily, the load coupled to an oscillator by a transmission line is more or less sharply tuned. It is therefore appropriate to extend the analysis of the previous section to include an inductance L_1 and a capacitance C_1 in parallel with the load, which for simplicity is assumed to match the line. Intuitively, we should expect the simplest behavior if the load susceptances are small, the oscillator susceptances high, and the line relatively short. The analysis is complicated by the fact that the standing wave ratio of the line increases rapidly as the frequency departs from the natural frequency of L_1 and C_1. Therefore, the admittance presented to the resonator varies through extreme limits and may readily produce instability. An example calculated by Pierce and Shepherd[241] is presented in Fig. 18.9.

The loop shown is evidently the only one which can cross the real axis. It is therefore of some interest to determine the conditions under which this loop degenerates into a cusp. The procedure is similar to one used previously. Assuming that the load and resonator are tuned to the same frequency, we may write the admittance of the load at a frequency $\omega_0 + d\omega$ as

$$Y_L = Y_0 + j2C_1\, d\omega = Y_0(1 + j2C_1\, d\omega/Y_0). \qquad (18.23)$$

The substitution of the load Q,

$$Q_L = \omega_0 C_1/Y_0, \qquad (18.24)$$

permits writing the input admittance of the line in the form

$$Y_1 = Y_0\, \frac{(1 + j2Q_L\, d\omega/\omega_0)\cos\beta l + j\sin\beta l}{\cos\beta l + j(1 + j2Q_L\, d\omega/\omega_0)\sin\beta l}. \qquad (18.25)$$

Because the behavior is most favorable when the line length is an odd number m of quarter wavelengths at the operating frequency, we may substitute at the frequency $\omega_0 + d\omega$ the values

$$\cos\beta l \doteq \tfrac{1}{2}m\pi\, d\omega/\omega_0 \text{ and } \sin\beta l \doteq 1. \qquad (18.26)$$

The input admittance thus becomes

$$Y_1 = Y_0\, \frac{m\pi\, d\omega/\omega_0 + j2(1 - m\pi Q_L\, d\omega/\omega_0)}{m\pi\, d\omega/\omega_0 - 4Q_L\, d\omega/\omega_0 + j2}. \qquad (18.27)$$

The susceptance, obtained by rationalizing and neglecting second-order terms, is

$$B_1 = Y_0\, \frac{2m\pi\, d\omega/\omega_0 - 8Q_L\, d\omega/\omega_0 - 2m\pi\, d\omega/\omega_0}{(m\pi - 4Q_L)^2(d\omega/\omega_0)^2 + 4} = -2Y_0 Q_L\, d\omega/\omega_0. \qquad (18.28)$$

Loops will be avoided if the sum of this term and $2C\, d\omega$ is positive. Using this condition and defining $Q = \omega_0 C/Y_0$, we have for stability the simple relationship $Q > Q_L$.

In the course of the development, the parameter m representing the number of quarter wavelengths of the line disappeared. This is proper, because m does not affect the criterion for a cusp at the operating frequency; however, the possibility of other crossings must be investigated separately.

It would appear that some general criterion must exist for the absence of loops in the admittance characteristic of this system. Unfortunately, none has been found, although Wheeler[341] has contributed some useful results towards this end.

18.8 Oscillation build-up with transmission line

Very interesting and rather complicated phenomena are observed when pulse modulation is applied to an oscillator loaded through a long transmission line. Several viewpoints are useful, but that of direct time delay is probably simplest. It is a fundamental property of transmission lines, and indeed of all sorts of delay systems, that no information as to the far end termination can be secured in a time shorter than the round-trip travel time. Therefore, *if a pulsed oscillator is connected to its load by a line having a time delay t_0, the behavior during the initial period of $2t_0$ is completely independent of the load admittance.* At the end of this interval the reflection of the initiation of oscillation is returned to the resonator in accordance with the reflection coefficient of the load and the attenuation, if any, of the line. The returned signal may conveniently be thought of as a synchronizing voltage from a source having the line impedance.

Because the first signal to reach the load is expanding with time, the load circuit will appear to have a power factor nearer unity than it does to a continuous wave. Thus, the signal which is first returned to the oscillator is small and expands in a somewhat complicated manner with time. The reaction produced by this wave depends upon its amplitude and phase with respect to that currently being generated; and progressive changes of amplitude and frequency are likely to result from this interaction. Ultimately, of course, the frequency and amplitude must satisfy the balance of conductance and susceptance on a steady-state basis as represented by Fig. 18.4.

An alternative viewpoint, as presented by Pierce and Shepherd,[241] serves to supplement that of reflection. Consistent with the first section of this chapter, the admittance of a given network to an expanding wave differs in a simple known manner from the ordinary value associated with a continuous wave. This is illustrated in Fig. 18.10, which shows the behavior of a looped admittance curve to waves having several different rates of expansion. The construction depends upon eq. 18.3 and is readily applied to any admittance curve for which the frequency scale is given. The important result is that loops tend to disappear from the admittance plot as α increases.

Following this viewpoint, if the build-up rate is sufficient to suppress the loop in the admittance characteristic, the oscillation builds up as a simple single-frequency exponential until the amplitude is sufficient to produce nonlinearity and reduce the build-up rate to the point at which a cusp appears in the admittance characteristic. The oscillation may now continue along one or the other branch of the admittance curve, depending upon dissymmetry of the characteristic and upon a random factor, which may include the phase of oscillation at the time overload occurs.

This viewpoint agrees very well with that of reflection in connection with long lines.   It is equally applicable to doubly tuned lumped circuits, but an apparent contradiction needs to be resolved.   In an earlier discussion it was stated that two frequencies are present during the early stages of oscillation, and that their relative amplitude, based on thermal or other noise, contributes to the manner in which the final frequency is determined.   This is true only if the build-up rate is small enough that a loop remains in the admittance curve.   If the conditions are such as to remove this loop the complex roots merge and a single frequency is generated.

A remarkable situation exists when the round-trip delay time of the line to the load is greater than the duration of the oscillator pulse. Under these circumstances the *amplitude and frequency are absolutely*

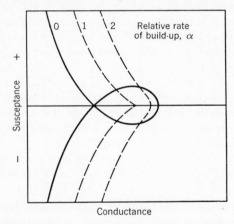

Fig. 18.10.   Suppression of loops by rapid expansion of oscillations.

independent of the load impedance, regardless of how slowly or how rapidly the oscillations build up or of any other considerations.   Moreover, in microwave radar systems it is at least nearly practical to take advantage of this fact.   Any substantial advance in the art, either toward shorter pulses or lower attenuation for a given line delay, would render the method quite practical.

This phenomenon may also be explained in terms of the complex frequency concept.   The input admittance of the line, which is necessarily quite long, will be represented by a complicated curve having very many loops in the admittance plane.   In the region of the operating frequency, however, these loops will be substantially circular and described at a uniform rate as the frequency varies.   Under these circumstances a very small expansion rate α will shrink these circles to the central point which corresponds to the characteristic admittance of the line itself.   Thus we see that there is no contradiction between the alternative viewpoints.

18.9 Rate of build-up

The admittance plot offers a convenient means of estimating the rate at which oscillations expand and the manner in which limiting occurs. This construction, which is also due to Pierce and Shepherd,[241] is shown in Fig. 18.11.   In the example illustrated the build-up rate for small oscillations is 3.4, and the curve of Fig. 18.11b has the form $A = A_0 e^{3.4\tau}$ to the left of $\tau = 2$.   At this time the relative amplitude is one (for the value of A_0 assumed) and reference to curve a shows that the exponent should be decreased to $\alpha = 2.8$.   The curve between $A = 1$ and $A = 2$ is therefore drawn with this reduced expansion rate.   A

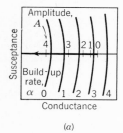
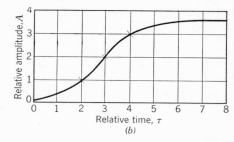

Fig. 18.11.   Graphical calculation of the rate of oscillation build up: (a) admittance plane and (b) build-up curve.

repetition of this process permits us to approximate the actual build-up curve to any desired degree of exactness, provided sufficiently small increments of time or amplitude are chosen.

The construction just described may be thought of as an example of the method of isoclines.   It has been illustrated in terms of a singly resonant system, but also applies to multiply resonant systems, provided we give separate treatment to oscillation in each of the possible modes.

18.10 Pulling

The term pulling has been used in a variety of connections with respect to oscillators.   However, it is most widely used to express the frequency change produced in microwave oscillators by a variation in the load impedance.   As used here, it applies to oscillators of all kinds and frequencies.   In oscillators which are loaded by means of a long transmission line it is possible to simplify the problem somewhat by specifying the frequency change in terms of the voltage standing wave ratio on the line. In particular, the "pulling figure" of a micro-wave oscillator is defined as the maximum frequency excursion produced by a voltage standing wave ratio of 1.50, which is varied arbitrarily in phase angle. In general, it is necessary to specify pulling somewhat more explicitly in terms of the separate fractional frequency deviations resulting from resistive and reactive variations in the load. Pulling is closely related to frequency stability and to the possibility of multiple frequencies. At the boundary between single and multiple response the frequency stability is zero and the pulling figure infinite. This is the desired condition in locked oscillators, but otherwise very undesirable.

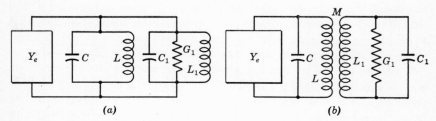

FIG. 18.12. Pulling in lumped resonant systems: (a) singly resonant system and (b) coupled circuits.

Pulling may be studied with reference to Fig. 18.12a, which represents a system with lumped constants. The susceptances of C_1 and L_1 are assumed to be part of the load and thus distinct from the resonator $L - C$, although all are directly in parallel. Such separation, although rather artificial in this case, becomes quite real when the load is isolated from the resonator by a transmission line or by the action of mutual inductance. Assuming that the load is tuned to the operating frequency, we may write

$$\omega_1{}^2 = 1/L_1C_1 = \omega_0{}^2 = 1/LC, \tag{18.29}$$

$$Q_L = \omega_0C_1/G_1 = 1/\omega_0L_1G_1, \tag{18.30}$$

and

$$Q = \omega_0C/G_1 = 1/\omega_0LG_1. \tag{18.31}$$

On the basis of equivalent linearization, the operating frequency is entirely independent of G_1, although the amplitude is affected in a manner which depends upon the saturation characteristics of the electronic device. In turn, the amplitude is entirely independent of the load susceptances, whereas the frequency is directly affected. An increment dC_1 in the load capacitance produces a frequency increment

$d\omega$ given by

$$\frac{d\omega}{\omega_0} = -\frac{dC_1}{2(C + C_1)}. \tag{18.32}$$

This may be converted to the form

$$\frac{d\omega}{\omega_0} = -\frac{Q_L}{2(Q + Q_L)} \cdot \frac{dC_1}{C_1}. \tag{18.33}$$

Similarly a variation in the load inductance produces a frequency deviation

$$\frac{d\omega}{\omega_0} = -\frac{Q_L}{2(Q + Q_L)} \cdot \frac{dL_1}{L_1}. \tag{18.34}$$

From these expressions it is clear that a small value of Q_L and a large value of Q are desirable in the interest of minimizing pulling.

A special case of pulling has already been studied in Chapter 16 in connection with frequency modulation. By using a 45° network it is possible to establish conditions in which the frequency is unaffected by an increment in load susceptance but is markedly affected by the load conductance. For the intended purpose this arrangement is entirely suitable, but it has no particular merits for general application. The effects of pulling in coupled circuits may be studied by reference to Fig. 18.12b. However, the analysis is quite complex, and no generally useful formulas are available.

PROBLEMS

18.1. A series LRC circuit has a Q of 200 at its resonant frequency $\omega = 10^5$. Calculate its impedance to the following complex (p) frequencies: $0 + j10^5$, $0 + j1.01 \times 10^5$, $10^3 + j10^5$, $10^3 + j1.01 \times 10^5$.

18.2. In Fig. 18.3a the two circuits have equal values of impedance and a selectivity of 100. Their natural frequencies are, respectively, $\omega = 99$ and 101. Calculate the impedance plot corresponding to 18.3d for real frequencies and for a wave having $\alpha = 1$.

18.3. In Fig. 18.5a each of the tuned circuits each has a Q of 50, and the coupling coefficient is 0.04. Calculate the relative frequency variation which will result from tuning the primary circuit.

18.4. In Fig. 18.7 the loading parameter is $Q = 25$, $\sigma = 2$, and $n = 12.1$ at the natural frequency of the resonator. Calculate the locus corresponding to Fig. 18.8b.

18.5. Verify Fig. 18.9, adding a frequency scale to your curve; then demonstrate how the loop is eliminated if the wave is expanding with time.

18.6. A simple antiresonant circuit having a Q of 200 at $\omega = 10^5$ is associated with a negative conductance which at low levels is five times sufficient to produce oscillation. Assuming that the effective negative conductance varies inversely with the level, calculate the oscillation build-up as in Section 18.9.

BIBLIOGRAPHY

1. Abraham, H., and E. Block, "Sur la mésure en valuer absolue des périodes des oscillations électriques de haute fréquence," *Compt. rend.*, **168**, 1105–1108 (1919).

2. Adler, R., "Locking Phenomena in Oscillators," *Proc. I.R.E.*, **34**, 351–357 (1946).

3. Adler, R., "A New System of Frequency Modulation," *Proc. I.R.E.*, **35**, 25–31 (1947).

4. Aigrain, P. R., and E. M. Williams, "Theory of Amplitude Stabilized Oscillators," *Proc. I.R.E.*, **36**, 16–19 (1948).

5. Aigrain, P. R., and E. M. Williams, "Pseudosynchronization in Amplitude Stabilized Oscillators," *Proc. I.R.E*, **36**, 800–801 (1948).

6. Ames, M. E., "Wide Range Deviable Oscillator," *Electronics*, **22**, 96–100 (May 1949).

7. Anderson, F. B., "Seven-League Oscillator," *Proc. I.R.E.*, **39**, 881–890 (1951).

8. Anderson, J. E., "Frequency Characteristics of Piezoelectric Oscillators," *Electronics*, **11**, 22–24 (August 1938).

9. Andrew, V. J., "The Adjustment of the Multivibrator for Frequency Division," *Proc. I.R.E.*, **19**, 1911–1917 (1931).

10. Anon., "Improved Material for Magnetic Amplifiers," *Electronics*, **21**, 128 (August 1948).

11. Anon., "Stable Time and Frequency Standard," *Electronics*, **22**, 82–84 (April 1949).

12. Appleton, E. V., "The Automatic Synchronization of Triode Oscillators," *Proc. Camb. Phil. Soc.*, **21**, 231–248 (1922–1923).

13. Appleton, E. V., and B. van der Pol, "On the Form of Free Triode Vibrations," *Phil. Mag.*, **42**, 201–220 (1921).

14. Arguimbau, L. B., "An Oscillator Having a Linear Operating Characteristic," *Proc. I.R.E.*, **21**, 14–28 (1933).

15. Arguimbau, L. B., *Vacuum-tube Circuits*, John Wiley, New York (1948).

16. Armstrong E. H., "Some Recent Developments of Regenerative Circuits," *Proc. I.R.E.*, **10**, 244–260 (1922).

17. Artz, M., "Frequency Modulation of Resistance-Capacitance Oscillators," *Proc. I.R.E.*, **32**, 409–414 (1944).

18. Babat, G., and M. Losinsky, "Power Oscillators," *Wireless Eng.*, **17**, 16–18 (1940).

19. Bakker, C. J. and C. J. Boers, "On the Influence of the Nonlinearity of the Characteristics on the Frequency of Dynatron and Triode Oscillators," *Physica*, **3**, 649–665 (1936).

20. Bardeen, J., and W. H. Brattain, "The Transistor, a Semi-Conductor Triode," *Phys. Rev.*, **74**, 230 (1948).

21. Bartelink, E. H. B "A Wide-Band Square-Wave Generator," *Trans. A.I.E.E.*, **60**, 371–376 (1941).

22. Bartlett, R. M., "*N*-Phase Resistance-Capacitance Oscillators," *Proc. I.R.E.*, **33**, 541–545 (1945).
23. Bass, S. L., and T. A. Kauppi, "Silicones—A New Class of High Polymers of Interest to the Radio Industry," *Proc. I.R.E.*, **33**, 441–447 (1945).
24. Batcher, R. R., "Thermistors in Electronic Circuits," *Electronic Inds.*, **4**, 76–80 (January 1945).
25. Bauer, B., "Design Notes on the Resistance-Capacity Oscillator Circuit," *Hewlett-Packard J.* (November and December 1949).
26. Beck, F. J., and J. M. Kelly, "Magnetization in Perpendicularly Superposed Direct and Alternating Fields," *J. Appl. Physics*, **19**, 551–562 (1948).
27. Becker, J. A., C. B. Green, and G. L. Pearson, "Properties and Uses of Thermistors—Thermally Sensitive Resistors," *Trans. A.I.E.E.*, **65**, 711–725 (1946).
28. Beers, G. L., "A Frequency-Dividing Locked-in-Oscillator Frequency-Modulation Receiver," *Proc. I.R.E.*, **22**, 730–737 (1944).
29. Benjamin, R., "Blocking Oscillators," Part IIIA, *J. I.E.E.*, **93**, 1159–1175 (1946).
30. Bennett, W. R., "A General Review of Linear Varying Parameter and Non-linear Circuit Analysis," *Proc. I.R.E.*, **38**, 259–263 (1950).
31. Berberich, L. J., C. V. Fields, and R. E. Marbury, "Characteristics of Chlorinated Impregnants in Direct-Current Paper Capacitors," *Proc. I.R.E.*, **33**, 389–397 (1945).
32. Bertram, S., "The Degenerative Positive-Bias Multivibrator," *Proc. I.R.E.*, **36**, 277–280 (1948).
33. Black, H. S., "Stabilized Feedback Amplifiers," *Bell System Tech. J.*, **13**, 1–18 (1934); also *Elec. Eng.*, **53**, 114 (1934).
34. Bode, H. W., *Network Analysis and Feedback Amplifier Design*, D. Van Nostrand, New York (1945).
35. Boella, M., "Performance of Piezo-Oscillators and the Influence of the Decrement of the Quartz on the Frequency of Oscillations," *Proc. I.R.E.*, **19**, 1252 (1931).
36. Bothwell, F. E., "Nyquist Diagrams and the Routh-Hurwitz Stability Criterion," *Proc. I.R.E.*, **38**, 1345–1348 (1950).
37. Bradley, W. E., "Single Stage F-M Detector," *Electronics*, **19**, 88–91 (October 1946).
38. Bradley, W. E., "Superregenerative Detection Theory," *Electronics*, **21**, 96–98 (September 1948).
39. Brotherton, M., *Capacitors*, D. Van Nostrand, New York (1946).
40. Brown, G. H., "Efficiency of Induction Heating Coils," *Electronics*, **17**, 124–129 (August 1944).
41. Brown, G. H., C. N. Hoyler, and R. A. Bierwith, *Theory and Application of Radio Frequency Heating*, D. Van Nostrand, New York (1947).
42. Brown, R. H., "Harmonic Amplifier Design," *Proc. I.R.E.*, **35**, 771–777 (1947).
43. Bruck, G. S., "Simplified Frequency Modulation," *Proc. I.R.E.*, **34**, 458 (1946).
44. Brunetti, C., "The Clarification of Average Negative Resistance with Extension of Its Use," *Proc. I.R.E.*, **25**, 1593–1616 (1937).
45. Brunetti, C., "The Transitron Oscillator," *Proc. I.R.E.*, **27**, 88–94 (1939).
46. Brunetti, C., and L. Greenough, "Some Characteristics of a Stable Negative Resistance," *Proc. I.R.E.*, **30**, 542–546 (1942).

47. Buehler, E., and A. C. Walker, "Growing Quartz Crystals," *Sci. Monthly*, **69**, 148–155 (1949).

48. Builder, G., "A Stabilized Frequency Divider," *Proc. I.R.E.*, **29**, 177–181 (1941).

49. Burgess, R. E., "Oscillator Power Relations," *Wireless Eng.*, **23**, 237–240 (1946).

50. Bushby, R. W., "Thermal Frequency Drift Compensation," *Proc. I.R.E.*, **30**, 546–553 (1942).

51. Butler, F., "Series Resonant Crystal Oscillators," *Wireless Eng.*, **23**, 1 (1946).

52. Cady, W. G., *Piezoelectricity*, McGraw-Hill, New York (1946).

53. Carnahan, C. W., and H. P. Kalmus, "Synchronized Oscillators as F-M Receiver Limiters," *Electronics*, **17**, 108–111 (August 1944).

54. Chaffee, E. L., and C. N. Kimball, "A Method of Determining the Operating Characteristics of a Power Oscillator," *J. Franklin Inst.*, **221**, 237 (1936).

55. Chaffee, J. G., "The Application of Negative Feedback to Frequency-Modulation Systems," *Bell System Tech. J.*, **18**, 404–437 (1939); also *Proc. I.R.E.*, **27**, 317–331 (1939).

56. Chance, B., "Some Precision Circuit Techniques Used in Wave Form Generation and Time Measurement," *Rev. Sci. Instruments*, **17**, 396–415 (1946).

57. Chance, B., et al., *Waveforms*, McGraw Hill, New York (1949).

58. Chang, C. K., "A Frequency-Modulated Resistance-Capacitance Oscillator," *Proc. I.R.E.*, **31**, 22–25 (1943).

59. Chang, H., and V. C. Rideout, "The Reactance Tube Oscillator," *Proc. I.R.E.*, **37**, 1330–1331 (1949); also 1096 (1950).

60. Chireix, H., et al., U. S. Patent 2,076,264.

61. Christopher, A. J., and J. A. Kater, "Mica Capacitors for Carrier Telephone Systems," *Elec. Eng.* (*Transactions Sect.*), **65**, 670–673 (1946).

62. Chu, E. L., "Notes on the Stability of Linear Networks," *Proc. I.R.E.*, **32**, 630–637 (1944).

63. Clapp, J. K., "An Inductance-Capacitance Oscillator of Unusual Frequency Stability," *Proc. I.R.E.*, **36**, 356–358; also 1261 (1948).

64. Close, R. N., and M. T. Lebenbaum, "Design of Phantastron Time-Delay Circuits," *Electronics*, **21**, 100–107 (April 1948).

65. Cocking, W. T., "Linear Saw-Tooth Oscillator," *Wireless World*, **52**, 176–178 (June 1946).

66. Coursey, R., *Electrical Condensers*, Pitman, London (1927).

67. Crain, H. M., "Low-Frequency Discriminator," *Electronics*, **22**, 96–97 (June 1949).

68. Crossley, A., "Piezo-Electric Crystal-Controlled Transmitters," *Proc. I.R.E.*, **15**, 9–36 (1927).

69. Dailey, H. J., "Rules for Prolonging Tube Life," *Electronics*, **16**, 76–78 (April 1943).

70. David, E. E., Jr., *Locking Phenomena in Microwave Oscillators*, Technical Report 63, April 8, 1948, Research Laboratory of Electronics, Massachusetts Institute of Technology.

71. David, E. E., Jr., *Some Aspects of RF Phase Control in Microwave Oscillators*, Technical Report 100, June 11,1949, Research Laboratory of Electronics, Massachusetts Institute of Technology.

72. Davis, K. H., "Multivibrator Step-Down by Fractional Ratios," *Bell Lab. Record*, **26**, 114 (March 1948).

73. Day, J. R., "Serrasoid F-M Modulator," *Electronics*, **21**, 72–76 (October 1948).

74. De Lange, O. E., "A Variable Phase-Shift Frequency-Modulated Oscillator," *Proc. I.R.E.*, **37**, 1328–1330 (1949).

75. De Laup, S., "Sine Waves in R-C Oscillators," *Electronics*, **14**, 34–36 (January 1941).

76. Doherty, R. E., and E. G. Keller, *Mathematics of Modern Engineering*, John Wiley, New York (1936).

77. Donal, J. S., and R. R. Bush, "A Spiral-Beam Method for the Amplitude Modulation of Magnetrons," *Proc. I.R.E.*, **37**, 375–382 (1949).

78. Dow, J. B., "A Recent Development in Vacuum-Tube Oscillator Circuits," *Proc. I.R.E.*, **19**, 2095–2108 (1931).

79. Dudley, B., "Introduction to Transients," *Electronics*, **17**, 132 (August 1944).

80. Easton, A., "Pulse-Modulated Oscillator," *Electronics*, **20**, 124–129 (March 1947).

81. Eccles, W. H., and F. W. Jordan, "Trigger Relay," *Radio Rev.*, **1**, 143 (October 1919).

82. Edson, W. A., "Intermittent Behavior in Oscillators," *Bell System Tech. J.*, **24**, 1–22 (1945).

83. Edson, W. A., et al., *The Keying Properties of Quartz Crystal Oscillators*, Final Report on Signal Corps Contract W36-039-sc-32100, Georgia Institute of Technology, State Engineering Experiment Station, Atlanta, Ga. (December 1947).

84. Edson, W. A., et al., *High Frequency Crystal-Controlled Oscillator Circuits*, Final Report on Signal Corps Contract W36-039-sc-36841, Georgia Institute of Technology, State Engineering Experiment Station, Atlanta, Ga. (December 1950).

85. Edwards, C. M., "A Precision Decade Oscillator for 20 Cycles to 200 Kilocycles," *Proc. I.R.E.*, **39**, 277–278 (1951).

86. Eltgroth, G. V., "Frequency Stability of Tuned Circuits," *Electronics*, **17**, 118 (February 1944).

87. Espley, D. C., "Harmonic Production and Cross Modulation in Thermionic Valves with Resistive Loads," *Proc. I.R.E.*, **22**, 781–790 (1934).

88. Everitt, W. L., "Optimum Operating Conditions for Class C Amplifiers," *Proc. I.R.E.*, **22**, 152–176 (1934).

89. Everitt, W. L., *Communication Engineering*, McGraw Hill, New York (2nd ed., 1937).

90. Fair, I. E., "Piezo Electric Crystals in Oscillator Circuits," *Bell System Tech. J.*, **24**, 161–216 (1945).

91. Fallou, J., "Sur un demultiplicateur de fréquence statique," *Rev. gén. eléc.* **19**, 987–991 (1926).

92. Federal Telephone and Radio Corp., *Reference Data for Radio Engineers*, New York (2nd ed., 1946).

93. Feinberg, R., "Symmetrical and Asymmetrical Multivibrators," *Wireless Eng.*, **26**, 153–158 and 326–330 (1949).

94. Fleming, L., "Thermistor-Regulated Low-Frequency Oscillator," *Electronics*, **19**, 97–99 (October 1946).

95. Fleming-Williams, B. C., "A Single-Valve Time-Base Circuit," *Wireless Eng.*, **17**, 161–163 (1940).

96. Floyd, G. H., "Vacuum Capacitors," *Proc. I.R.E.*, **32**, 463–470 (1944).

97. Ford, J. R., and N. I. Korman, "Stability and Frequency Pulling of Loaded Unstabilized Oscillators," *Proc. I.R.E.*, **34**, 794–799 (1946).

98. Fortescue, R. L., "Quasi-Stable Frequency Dividing Circuits," *J. I.E.E.*, **84**, 693–698 (1939).

99. Foster, D. E., and A. E. Newton, "Measurements of Iron Cores at Radio Frequencies," *Proc. I.R.E.*, **29**, 266–276 (1941).

100. Foster, D. E., and S. W. Seeley, "Automatic Tuning, Simplified Circuits and Design Practice," *Proc. I.R.E.*, **25**, 289–313 (1937).

101. Foster, R. M., "A Reactance Theorem," *Bell System Tech. J.*, **3**, 259–269 (1924).

102. Franklin, C. S., British Patents 335,526 and 369,575.

103. Freeman, R. L., "Improvements in AFC Circuits," *Electronics*, **9**, 20–23 (November 1936).

104. Frink, F. W., "The Basic Principles of Superregenerative Reception," *Proc. I.R.E.*, **26**, 76–107 (1938).

105. Frommer, J. C., "A Graphical Method to Find the Optimal Operating Conditions of Triodes as Class C Telegraph Transmitters," *Proc. I.R.E.*, **30**, 519–525 (1942).

106. Furst, U. R., "Harmonic Analysis of Overbiased Amplifiers," *Electronics*, **17**, 143–144 (March 1944).

107. Fyler, G. W., "Parasites and Instability in Radio Transmitters," *Proc. I.R.E.*, **23**, 985–1012 (1935).

108. Gager, F. M., and J. B. Russell, Jr., "A Quantitative Study of the Dynatron," *Proc. I.R.E.*, **23**, 1536–1566 (1935).

109. Gardner, M. F., and J. L. Barnes, *Transients in Linear Systems*, v. I, John Wiley, New York (1942).

110. George, W. D., M. C. Selby, and R. Scolnik, "Precision Measurement of Electrical Characteristics of Quartz-Crystal Units," *Proc. I.R.E.*, **36**, 1122–1131 (1948).

111. Ginzton, E. L., and L. M. Hollingsworth, "Phase-Shift Oscillators," *Proc. I.R.E.*, **29**, 43–49 (1941); also corrections, **32**, 641 (1944).

112. Gladwin, A. S., "Oscillation Amplitude in Simple Valve Oscillators," *Wireless Eng.*, **26**, 159–170 and 201–209 (1949).

113. Glasoe, G. N., and J. V. Lebacqz, *Pulse Generators*, McGraw-Hill, New York (1948).

114. Glegg, K., "Cathode-Coupled Multivibrator Operation," *Proc. I.R.E.*, **38**, 655–675 (1950).

115. Glucksman, H. A., "Superregeneration—An Analysis of the Linear Mode," *Proc. I.R.E.*, **37**, 500–504 (1949).

116. Gordon, J. F., "A New Angular-Velocity-Modulation System Employing Pulse Techniques," *Proc. I.R.E.*, **34**, 328–334 (1946).

117. Gouriet, G. G., "High Stability Oscillator," *Wireless Eng.*, **27**, 105–112 (1950).

118. Griffiths, W. H. F., "Recent Improvements in Air Cored Inductances," *Wireless Eng.*, **19**, 8–19 and 56–63 (1942).

119. Griffiths, W. H. F., "The Temperature Compensation of Condensers," *Wireless Eng.*, **19**, 101–111 and 148–157 (1942).

120. Groszkowski, J., "Frequency Division," *Proc. I.R.E.*, **18**, 1960–1970 (1930).

121. Groszkowski, J., "The Interdependence of Frequency Variation and Harmonic Content, and the Problem of Constant-Frequency Oscillators," *Proc. I.R.E.*, **21**, 958–981 (1933).

122. Groszkowski, J., "Oscillators with Automatic Control of the Threshold of Regeneration," *Proc. I.R.E.*, **22**, 145–151 (1934).

123. Groszkowski, J., "The Temperature Coefficient of Inductance," *Proc. I.R.E.*, **25**, 448–464 (1937).

124. Guillemin, E. A., *Communication Networks*, v. I, John Wiley, New York (1931).

125. Guillemin, E. A., and P. T. Rumsey, "Frequency Multiplication by Shock Excitation," *Proc. I.R.E.*, **17**, 629–651 (1929).

126. Gunn, R., "A New Frequency-Stabilized Oscillator System," *Proc. I.R.E.*, **18**, 1560–1574 (1930).

127. Harries, J. H. O., "Apertures in Cavities," *Electronics*, **19**, 132–135 (December 1946).

128. Harris, W. A., "Space-Charge Limited Current Fluctuations in Vacuum-Tube Amplifiers and Input Systems," *R.C.A. Rev.*, **5**, 505–524 (1941).

129. Harrison, A. E., and N. W. Mather, "Graphical Analysis of Tuned Coupled Circuits," *Proc. I.R.E.*, **37**, 1015–1020 (1949).

130. Hartley, R. V. L., "Oscillations in Systems with Non-linear Reactance," *Bell System Tech. J.*, **15**, 424–440 (1936).

131. Hazeltine, A., D. Richman, and B. D. Laughlin, "Superregenerator Design," *Electronics*, **21**, 95–102 (September 1948).

132. Healy, C. P., and J. C. Niven, "Mould and Humidity in Radio and Signals Equipment," *Proc. I.R.E.*, **33**, 300–306 (1945).

133. Hedeman, W. R., "Few Crystals Control Many Channels," *Electronics*, **21**, 118–121 (March 1948).

134. Heegner, K., "Gekoppelte Selbsterregte Elektrische Kreise and Kristellozillatoren," *E.N.T.*, **15**, 364 (1938).

135. Heising, R. A., "The Audion Oscillator," *Phys. Rev.*, **16**, 216–237 (1920).

136. Heising, R. A., "Stability in High Frequency Oscillators," *Proc. I.R.E.*, **31**, 595–600 (1943).

137. Heising, R. A., *Quartz Crystals for Electrical Circuits*, D. Van Nostrand, New York (1946).

138. Herold, E. W., "Negative Resistance and Devices for Obtaining It," *Proc. I.R.E.*, **23**, 1201–1223 (1935).

139. Hershberger, W. D., and L. E. Norton, "Frequency Stabilization with Microwave Spectral Lines," *R.C.A. Rev.*, **9**, 38–49 (1948).

140. Hinton, W. R., "The Design of R-C Oscillator Phase-Shifting Networks," *Electronic Eng.*, **22**, 13–17 (1950).

141. Holubow, H., "DC Saturable Reactors for Control Purposes," *Electronic Ind.*, **4**, 76–79 (March 1943).

142. Hopper, A. L., and S. E. Miller, "Considerations in the Design of a Radar Intermediate-Frequency Amplifier," *Proc. I.R.E.*, **35**, 1208–1220 (1947).

143. Horton, J. W., United States Patent 1,690,299.

144. Horton, J. W., "Vacuum-Tube Oscillators," *Bell System Tech. J.*, **3**, 508–524 (1924).

145. Howe, G. W. O., "Natural and Resonant Frequencies of Coupled Circuits," *Wireless Eng.*, **18**, 221–223 (1941).

146. Huggins, W. H., "Multifrequency Bunching in Reflex Klystrons," *Proc. I.R.E.*, **35**, 1518 (1947).

147. Huggins, W. H., "The Potential Analogue in Network Synthesis and Analysis," Publication E 5066, Air Force Cambridge Research Laboratories, Cambridge, Mass. (March 1951).

148. Hull, A. W., "The Dynatron, a Vacuum Tube Possessing Negative Resistance," *Proc. I.R.E.*, **6**, 5–36 (1918).

149. Hund, A., *Frequency Modulation*, McGraw-Hill, New York (1942).

150. Hund, A., "Reactance Tubes in Frequency Modulation Applications," *Electronics*, **15**, 68 (October 1942).

151. Huntoon, R. D., and A. Weiss, "Synchronization of Oscillators," *Proc. I.R.E.*, **35**, 1415–1423 (1947).

152. Hussey, L. W., and L. R. Wrathall, "Oscillations in an Electromechanical System," *Bell System Tech. J.*, **15**, 441–445 (1936).

153. Ide, J. M., "Magnetostrictive Alloys with Low Temperature Coefficients of Frequency," *Proc. I.R.E.*, **22**, 177–190 (1934).

154. Ives, R. L., "The Relay Oscillator and Related Devices," *J. Franklin Inst.*, **242**, 243–277 (1946).

155. Jaderholm, H. W., "Iron Powder Cores and Coils," *Proc. I.R.E.*, **33**, 904 (1945).

156. Jefferson, H., "Stabilization of Feedback Oscillators," *Wireless Eng.*, **22**, 384–389 (1945).

157. Johnson, J. B., "Thermal Agitation of Electricity in Conductors," *Phys. Rev.*, **32**, 97–109 (1928).

158. Johnson, K. C., "Single-Valve Frequency-Modulated Oscillator," *Wireless World*, **55**, 122–123 and 168–170 (1949).

159. Johnson, R. W., "Extending the Frequency Range of the Phase-Shift Oscillator," *Proc. I.R.E.*, **33**, 597–602 (1945).

160. Johnson, W. C., *Mathematical and Physical Principles of Engineering Analysis*, McGraw-Hill, New York (1944).

161. Kalmus, H. P., "Some Notes on Superregeneration with Particular Emphasis on Its Possibilities for Frequency Modulation," *Proc. I.R.E.*, **32**, 591–600 (1944).

162. Kantor, M., "Theory and Design of Progressive and Ordinary Universal Windings," *Proc. I.R.E.*, **35**, 1563–1570 (1947).

163. Karplus, E., "Wide-Range Tuned Circuits and Oscillators for High Frequencies," *Proc. I.R.E.*, **33**, 426–441 (1945).

164. Keithley, J. F., "Low-Frequency Oscillator," *Electronics*, **21**, 108–109 September 1948).

165. Keller, E. G., "Analytical Methods of Solving Discrete Nonlinear Problems in Electrical Engineering," *Trans. A.I.E.E.*, **60**, 1194–1200 (1941).

166. Kellogg, J. B. M., and S. Millman, "Molecular Beam Magnetic Resonance Method," *Rev. Mod. Phys.*, **18**, 323–352 (1946).

167. Kiebert, M. V., and A. F. Inglis, "Multivibrator Circuits," *Proc. I.R.E.*, **33**, 534–539 (1945).

168. Kilgore, G. R., C. I. Shulman, and J. Kurshan, "A Frequency Modulated Magnetron for Super-High Frequencies," *Proc. I.R.E.*, **35**, 657–664 (1947).

169. E. W. Kimbark, *Electrical Transmission of Power and Signals*, John Wiley, New York (1949).

170. Kinn, T. P., "Vacuum-Tube Radio-Frequency-Generator Characteristics and Application to Induction Heating Problems," *Proc. I.R.E.*, **33**, 640–657 (1945).

171. Kingston, R. H., "Resonant Circuits with Time-Varying Parameters," *Proc. I.R.E.*, **37**, 1478–1481 (1949).

172. Kinzer, J. P., and I. G. Wilson, "Some Results on Cylindrical Cavity Resonators," *Bell System Tech. J.*, **26**, 410–445 (1947).

173. Kirby, T., "Twin Oscillator," *Electronics*, **22**, 170 (October 1949).
174. Klingaman, G. W., and G. H. Williams, "Shielding of Dielectric Heating Installations," *Electronics*, **18**, 106–109 (May 1945).
175. Kobayashi, M., U. S. Patent 1,913, 449.
176. Koga, I., "Characteristics of Piezo-Electric Quartz Oscillators," *Proc. I.R.E.*, **18**, 1935–1959 (1930).
177. Kryloff, N., and N. Bogoliuboff, *Introduction to Non-Linear Mechanics*, Princeton University Press (1943).
178. Kunz, K. S., "Bilinear Transformations Applied to the Tuning of the Output Network of a Transmitter," *Proc. I.R.E.*, **37**, 1211–1217 (1949).
179. Kurtz, E. B., and G. F. Corcoran, *Introduction to Electric Transients*, John Wiley, New York (1935).
180. Ladner, A. W., and C. R. Stoner, *Short-Wave Wireless Communication*, John Wiley, New York (5th ed., 1950).
181. Lampkin, G. F., "An Improvement in Constant Frequency Oscillators," *Proc. I.R.E.*, **27**, 199–201 (1939).
182. Lane, C. E., "Duplex Crystals," *Bell Lab. Record*, **24**, 59–62 (1946).
183. Last, E., "Blocking Oscillator," *Electronics*, **18**, 184 (October 1945).
184. Lawson, H. W., "Precision Tuning Fork With Vacuum-Tube Drive," *Gen. Radio Expt.*, **20**, 1–5 (September 1945).
185. Lea, N., "Notes on the Stability of L-C Oscillators," *J. I.E.E.*, **92**, 261–274 (1945).
186. le Corbeiller, Ph., "The Nonlinear Theory of the Maintenance of Oscillations," *J. I.E.E.*, **79**, 361–368 (1936).
187. Lee, R., "Radio Telegraph Keying Transients," *Proc. I.R.E.*, **22**, 213–215 (1934).
188. Leonard, S. C., "Measurement of Minute Changes of Capacitance and Inductance," *Electronics*, **11**, 18 (March 1938).
189. Liénard, A., "Étude des oscillations entretenus," *Rev. gén. élec.*, **23**, 901–946 (1928).
190. Linder, E. G., "Attenuation of Electromagnetic Fields in Pipes Smaller Than the Critical Size," *Proc. I.R.E.*, **30**, 554–556 (1942).
191. Llewellyn, F. B., "A Study of Noise in Vacuum Tubes and Attached Circuits," *Proc. I.R.E.*, **18**, 243–265 (1930).
192. Llewellyn, F. B., "Constant-Frequency Oscillators," *Proc. I.R.E.*, **19**, 2063–2094 (1931).
193. Loraine Products Corp., Loraine, Ohio, *Bulletin* 153.
194. Lyons, H., "Microwave Frequency Dividers," *J. Appl. Phys.*, **21**, 59–60 (1950).
195. Lythall, W. B., "Frequency Instability of Pulsed Transmitters with Long Wave Guides," *J. I.E.E.*, **93** (part IIIA), 1081–1089 (1946).
196. McCreary, H. J., "The Magnetic Cross Valve and Its Application to Subfrequency Power Generation," *Proc. Natl. Elec. Conf.*, **5**, 450–466 (1949).
197. McDade, J. R., "The Phantastron Control Circuit," *Elec. Eng.*, **67**, 974–977 (1948).
198. McGaughan, H. S., and C. B. Leslie, "A Resistance-Tuned Frequency-Modulated Oscillator for Audio Frequency Applications," *Proc. I.R.E.*, **35**, 974–978 (1947).
199. McLean, W. R., "The Reactance Theorem for a Resonator," *Proc. I.R.E.*, **33**, 539–541 (1945).

200. Maa, D. Y., "A General Reactance Theorem for Electrical, Mechanical, and Acoustical Systems," *Proc. I.R.E.*, **31**, 365–371 (1943).

201. Mallett, E., "Frequency Stabilization of Valve Oscillators," *J. I.E.E.*, **68**, 2063–2094 (1930); also *Wireless Sect.*, **5**, 124 (1930).

202. Malling, L. M., "Triode Linear Saw-tooth-Current Oscillator," *Proc. I.R.E.*, **32**, 753–757 (1944).

203. Maloff, I. G. and D. W. Epstein, *Electron Optics in Television*, McGraw-Hill, New York (1938).

204. Marcum, J., and T. P. Kinn, "Heating with Microwaves," *Electronics*, **20**, 82–85 (March 1947).

205. Marks, B. H., "Ceramic Dielectric Materials," *Electronics*, **21**, 116–120 (August 1948).

206. Mason, W. P., and I. E. Fair, "A New Direct Crystal-Controlled Oscillator for Ultra-Short Wave Frequencies," *Proc. I.R.E.*, **30**, 464–472 (1942).

207. Mather, N. W., "Multivibrator Circuits," *Electronics*, **19**, 136–138 (October 1946).

208. Maxwell, J. C., "On Governors," *Proc. Roy Soc.*, **16**, 270–283 (1868).

209. Meacham, L. A., "The Bridge Stabilized Oscillator," *Bell System Tech. J.*, **17**, 574–590 (1938); also *Proc. I.R.E.*, **26**, 1278–1294 (1938).

210. Miller, R. L., "Fractional-Frequency Generators Utilizing Regenerative Modulation," *Proc. I.R.E.*, **27**, 446–456 (1939).

211. Minorsky, N., *Introduction to Nonlinear Mechanics*, J. W. Edwards, Ann Arbor, Mich. (1947).

212. Mittelman, E., "Load Matching in Electronic Heating," *Electronics*, **18**, 110–115 (February 1945).

213. Modrak, P., "Small Temperature Coefficient of Frequency Quartz Plates," *Wireless Eng.*, **16**, 6–15 (1939).

214. Montgomery, B. E., "An Inductively Coupled Frequency Modulator," *Proc. I.R.E.*, **29**, 559–563 (1941).

215. Moore, J. B., "Design of Stable Heterodyne Oscillators," *Electronics*, **18**, 116–118 (October 1945).

216. Morrison, J. T., "A New Broadcast Transmitter Circuit Design for Frequency Modulation," *Proc. I.R.E.*, **28**, 444–449 (1940).

217. Moullin, E. B., "Effect of Curvature of the Characteristic on Frequency of Dynatron Generators," *J. I.E.E.*, **73**, 186 (1933).

218. Moullin, E. B., *Spontaneous Fluctuations of Voltage*, Oxford, London (1938).

219. Muller, W., "Transitron Oscillator for High Stability," *Electronic Inds.*, **4**, 110 (December 1945).

220. Newitt, J. H., "R-C Oscillator Performance," *Electronics*, **17**, 126 (March 1944).

221. Nolle, A. W., "Adjustment Speed of Automatic Control Systems," *Proc. I.R.E.*, **36**, 911–916 (1948).

222. Norrman, E., "A Precision Tuning Fork Frequency Standard," *Proc. I.R.E.*, **20**, 1715–1731 (1932).

223. Norrman, E., "Tuning Fork Stabilization," *Electronics*, **13**, 15–17 (January 1940).

224. Norrman, E., "The Inductance-Capacitance Oscillator as a Frequency Divider," *Proc. I.R.E.*, **34**, 799–803 (1946).

225. North, H. Q., "Properties of Welded Contact Germanium Rectifiers," *J. Appl. Phys.*, **17**, 912–923 (1946).

226. Norton, R. L., "Crystal Controlled Diathermy," *Electronics*, **19**, 113–115 (October 1946).

227. Nyquist, H., "Thermal Agitation of Electric Charge in Conductors," *Phys. Rev.*, **32**, 110–113 (1928).

228. Nyquist, H., "Regeneration Theory," *Bell System Tech. J.*, **11**, 126–147 (1932).

229. O'Brien, E. J., "A Coupled-Circuit Frequency Modulator," *Proc. I.R.E.*, **32**, 348–350 (1944).

230. Offner, F. F., "The Effect of Q on Power-Amplifier Efficiency," *Proc. I.R.E.*, **34**, 896–897 (1946).

231. Osborn, P. H., "A Study of Class B and Class C Amplifier Tank Circuits," *Proc. I.R.E.*, **20**, 813–834 (1932).

232. Ostlund, E. M., A. R. Vallerino, and M. Silver, "Center-Frequency-Stabilized Frequency Modulation Systems," *Proc. I.R.E.*, **35**, 1144–1147 (1947).

233. Page, R. M., "An Investigation of the Phenomena of Frequency Multiplication, as Used in Tube Transmitters," *Proc. I.R.E.*, **17**, 1649–1655 (1929).

234. Page, R. M., and W. E. Curtis, "The van der Pol Four-Electrode Relaxation Oscillator," *Proc. I.R.E.*, **18**, 1921–1929 (1930).

235. Peirce, B. O., *A Short Table of Integrals*, Ginn & Co., Boston (2nd rev. ed., 1910).

236. Peterson, E., "Impedance of a Non-Linear Circuit Element," *Trans. A.I.E.E.*, **46**, 528 (1923).

237. Peterson, E., J. G. Kreer, and L. A. Ware, "Regeneration Theory and Experiment," *Proc. I.R.E.*, **22**, 1191–1210 (1934).

238. Peterson, E., J. M. Manley, and L. R. Wrathall, "Magnetic Generation of a Group of Harmonics," *Bell System Tech. J.*, **16**, 436–455 (1937).

239. Pierce, G. W., "Magnetrostriction Oscillators," *Proc. I.R.E.*, **17**, 42–88 (1929).

240. Pierce, J. R., "Noise in Resistances and Electron Streams," *Bell System Tech. J.*, **27**, 158–174 (1948).

241. Pierce, J. R., and W. G. Shepherd, "Reflex Oscillators," *Bell System Tech. J.*, **26**, 460–681 (1947).

242. Post, E. J., and H. F. Pit, "Alternate Ways in the Analysis of a Feedback Oscillator and Its Applications," *Proc. I.R.E.*, **39**, 169–174 (1951).

243. Pound, R. V., "Frequency Stabilization of Microwave Oscillators," *Proc. I.R.E.*, **35**, 1405–1415 (1947).

244. Prichard, A. C., M. A. A. Druesne, and D. G. McCaa, "Increase in Q Value and Reduction in Aging of Quartz Crystal Blanks," *Proc. I.R.E.*, **38**, 314 (1950).

245. Prince, D. C., "Vacuum Tubes as Power Oscillators," *Proc. I.R.E.*, **11**, 275–315, 405–435, and 527–550 (1923).

246. Proshauer, R., and H. E. Smith, "Fungus and Moisture Protection," *Electronics*, **18**, 119–123 (May 1945).

247. Puckle, O. S., "A Time Base Employing Hard Valves," *J. Television Soc. London*, **2**, 147 (1936).

248. Puckle, O. S., *Time Bases*, John Wiley, New York (2nd ed., 1951).

249. Pullen, K. A., "The Cathode-Coupled Amplifier," *Proc. I.R.E.*, **24**, 402–405 (1946).

250. Rambo, S. I., "AFC for RF Heating," *Electronics*, **19**, 120–122 (April 1946).

251. Rayleigh, Lord, *Theory of Sound*, v. 1, Macmillan, London (1926).

252. R.C.A. Application Note 53.

253. Record, F. A., and J. L. Stiles, "An Analytical Demonstration of Hartley Oscillator Action," *Proc. I.R.E.*, **31**, 281–287 (1943).

254. Reddick, H. W., and F. H. Miller, *Advanced Mathematics for Engineers*, John Wiley, New York (2nd ed., 1947).

255. Regener, V. H., "Decade Counting Circuits," *Rev. Sci. Instruments*, **17**, 185–189 (1946).

256. Regener, V. H., "Reversible Decade Counting Circuits," *Rev. Sci. Instruments*, **17**, 375–376 (1946).

257. Reich, H. J., *Theory and Applications of Electron Tubes*, McGraw-Hill, New York (1939).

258. Reich, H. J., "Trigger Circuits," *Electronics*, **12**, 14–17 (August 1939).

259. Reich, H. J., "The Use of Vacuum Tubes as Variable Impedance Elements," *Proc. I.R.E.*, **30**, 288–293 (1942).

260. Rice, S. O., "Mathematical Analysis of Random Noise," *Bell System Tech. J.*, **23**, 282–332 (1944) and **24**, 46–156 (1945).

261. Ridenour, L. N., *Radar System Engineering*, McGraw-Hill, New York (1947).

262. Rideout, V. C., "Automatic Frequency Control of Microwave Oscillators," *Proc. I.R.E.*, **35**, 767–771 (1947).

263. Riebman, Leon, "Theory of the Superregenerative Amplifier," *Proc. I.R.E.*, **37**, 29–33 (1949).

264. Roberds, W. D., "Problems in the Design of High-Frequency Heating Equipment," *Proc. I.R.E.*, **34**, 489–500 (1946).

265. Roberts, S., "Dielectric and Piezoelectric Properties of Barium Titanate," *Phys. Rev.*, **71**, (2nd ser.), 890 (1947).

266. Sarbacher, R. I., "Graphical Determination of Power Amplifier Performance," *Electronics*, **15**, 52 (December 1942).

267. Sarbacher, R. I., "Power-Tube Performance in Class C Amplifiers and Frequency Multipliers as Influenced by Harmonic Voltage," *Proc. I.R.E.*, **31**, 607–625 (1943).

268. Sarbacher, R. I., and W. A. Edson, *Hyper and Ultra-High Frequency Engineering*, John Wiley, New York (1943).

269. Schaffner, H., *Range of Synchronization of Subharmonic External Resonance*, Report from E. E. Research Laboratory, University of Illinois (1949).

270. Schelkunoff, S. A., "Representation of Impedance Functions in Terms of Resonant Frequencies," *Proc. I.R.E.*, **32**, 83–90 (1944).

271. Schmidt, C. R., "Frequency Division with Phase-Shift Oscillators," *Electronics*, **23**, 111–113 (June 1950).

272. Schottky, W., "Spontaneous Current Fluctuations in Electron Streams," *Ann. Physik*, **57**, 541–547 (1918).

273. Scroggie, M. G., "Applications of the Dynatron," *Wireless Eng.*, **10**, 527–540 (1933).

274. Seddon, J. C., "Square Wave Keying of Oscillators," *Electronics*, **23**, 162 (February 1950).

275. Seeley, S. W., and E. I. Anderson, "U-H-F Oscillator Frequency-Stability Considerations," *R.C.A. Rev.*, **5**, 77–88 (1940).

276. Seeley, S. W., and J. Avins, "The Ratio Detector," *R.C.A. Rev.*, **8**, 201–236 (1947).

277. Selgin, P. J., *Electrical Transmission in the Steady State*, McGraw-Hill, New York (1946).

278. Shannon, C. E., "Communication in the Presence of Noise," *Proc. I.R.E.*, **37,** 10–21 (1949).

279. Sharpless, T. K., "High Speed N-Scale Counters," *Electronics*, **21,** 122–125 (March 1948).

280. Shea, T. E., *Transmission Networks and Wave Filters*, D. Van Nostrand, New York (1929).

281. Shenk, E. R., "The Multivibrator, Applied Theory and Design," *Electronics*, **17,** 136–141, 140–145, 138–142 (January, February, March 1944).

282. Shepherd, W. G., and R. O. Wise, "Variable-Frequency Bridge-Type Frequency-Stabilized Oscillators," *Proc. I.R.E.*, **31,** 256– 269 (1943).

283. Simon, A. W., "On the Theory of the Progressive Universal Winding," *Proc. I.R.E.*, **33,** 868–871 (1945).

284. Sing, C., "Series Sawtooth Oscillator," *Electronics*, **23,** 178 (August 1950).

285. Skinner, L. V., *Criteria for Stability in Circuits Containing Non-Linear Resistance*, Doctor's Thesis, University of Illinois (1948).

286. Slater, J. C., "Microwave Electronics," *Rev. Mod. Phys.*, **18,** 441–512 (1946).

287. Sloane, R. W., and E. G. James, "Transit Time Effects in Diodes in Pictorial Form," *J. I.E.E.*, **79,** 291–296 (1936).

288. Slonziewski, T., "High-Accuracy Heterodyne Oscillators," *Bell System Tech. J.*, **19,** 407 (1940).

289. Smith, P. H., "Optimum Coax Diameters," *Electronics*, **23,** 111 (February 1950).

290. Smith, W. V., J. L. G. de Guevedo, R. L. Carter, and W. S. Bennett, "Frequency Stabilization of Microwave Oscillators by Spectrum Lines," *J. Appl. Phys.*, **18,** 1112 (1947), and **19,** 831 (1948).

291. Sokolnikoff, I. S., and E. S., *Higher Mathematics for Engineers and Physicists*, McGraw-Hill, New York (1948).

292. Soucy, C. I., "Temperature Coefficients in Electronic Circuits," *Electronics*, **21,** 117–121 (January 1948).

293. Spitzer, C. F., "Sustained Subharmonic Response of Non-Linear Series Circuits," *J. Appl. Phys.*, **16,** 105–110 (1945).

294. Spring, W. S., "Characteristics of Deltamax," *Electronics*, **22,** 152 (June 1949).

295. Stansel, F. R., "A Secondary Frequency Standard Using Regenerative Frequency-Dividing Circuits," *Proc. I.R.E.*, **30,** 157–162 (1942).

296. Sterky, H., "Frequency Multiplication and Division," *Proc. I.R.E.*, **25,** 1153–1174 (1937).

297. Stockman, H., "Superregenerative Circuit Applications," *Electronics*, **21,** 1153–1174 (1937).

298. Stone, J. E., "An Ultra-Low Frequency Oscillator," *Electronics*, **23,** 94–95 (Jan. 1950).

299. Sturley, K. R., "The Phase Discriminator," *Wireless Eng.*, **21,** 72–78 (1944).

300. Sturtevant, M., "A Voltage Controlled Multivibrator," *Electronics*, **22,** 144 (October 1949).

301. Sulzer, P. G., "The Tapered Phase-Shift Oscillator," *Proc. I.R.E.*, **36,** 1302–1305 (1948).

302. Summerhayes, H. R., "A 260 to 350 Megacycle Converter Unit," *Proc. I.R.E.*, **31,** 252 (1943).

303. Swan, A. G., "Radiation from R-F Heating Generators," *Electronics*, **19,** 162 (May 1946).

304. Teare, B. R., Jr., and E. R. Schatz, "Copper-Covered Steel Wire at Radio Frequencies," *Proc. I.R.E.*, **32**, 397–403 (1944).

305. Terman, F. E., "Resistance Stabilized Oscillators," *Electronics*, **6**, 190 (July 1933).

306. Terman, F. E., "Resonant Lines in Radio Circuits," *Elec. Eng.*, **53**, 1046 (1934).

307. Terman, F. E., *Radio Engineers Handbook*, McGraw-Hill, New York (1943).

308. Terry, E. M., "The Dependence of the Frequency of Quartz Piezo-Electric Oscillators upon Circuit Constants," *Proc. I.R.E.*, **16**, 1486 (1928).

309. Thomas, H. A., "The Dependence on Frequency of the Temperature Coefficient of Inductance of Coils," *J. I.E.E.*, **84**, 101–112 (1939).

310. Thomas, H. A., *Theory and Design of Valve Oscillators*, Chapman & Hall, London (2nd ed., 1951).

311. Thomas, H. P., and R. H. Williamson, "A Commerical 50-kilowatt Frequency-Modulation Broadcast Transmitting Station," *Proc. I.R.E.*, **29**, 537–545 (1941).

312. Thompson, B. J., D. O. North, and W. A. Harris, "Fluctuations in Space-Charge-Limited Currents at Moderately High Frequencies," *R.C.A. Rev.*, **6**, 114–124 (1941).

313. Travis, C., "Automatic Frequency Control," *Proc. I.R.E.*, **23**, 1125–1141 (1935).

314. Tucker, D. G., "The Generation of Groups of Harmonics," *Electronic Eng.*, **15**, 232–237 (1942).

315. Tucker, D. G., "The Synchronization of Oscillators," *Electronic Eng.*, **15**, 412–418 and 457–461 (1943); also **16**, 26–30 and 114–117 (1944).

316. Tucker, D. G., "Forced Oscillations in Oscillator Circuits and the Synchronization of Oscillators," *J. I.E.E.*, **92**, 226–233 (Part III), (1945).

317. Tuller, W. G., W. C. Galloway, and F. P. Zaffarano, "Recent Developments in Frequency Stabilization of Microwave Oscillators," *Proc. I.R.E.*, **36**, 794–800 (1948).

318. Tyrrell, W. A., "Hybrid Circuits for Microwaves," *Proc. I.R.E.*, **35**, 1294–1306 (1947).

319. van der Pol, B., "On Oscillation Hysteresis in a Triode Generator with Two Degrees of Freedom," *Phil. Mag.*, **43**, 700–719 (1922).

320. van der Pol, B., "On Relaxation Oscillations," *Phil. Mag.*, **2**, 978–992 (1926).

321. van der Pol, B., and M. J. O. Strutt, "On the Stability of the Solutions of Mathieu's Equation," *Phil. Mag.*, **5**, 18–38 (1928).

322. van der Pol B., "The Nonlinear Theory of Electric Oscillations," *Proc. I.R.E.*, **22**, 1051–1086 (1934).

323. van der Ziel, A., "On the Mixing Properties of Nonlinear Condensers," *J. Appl. Phy.*, **19**, 999–1006 (1948).

324. Van Dyke, K. S., "The Electric Network Equivalent of a Piezoelectric Resonator" (abst.), *Phys. Rev.*, **25**, 895 (1925).

325. Van Dyke, K. S., "A Determination of Some of the Properties of the Piezoelectric Quartz Resonator," *Proc. I.R.E.*, **23**, 386–392 (1935).

326. Van Dyke, K. S., "The Standardization of Quartz Crystal Units," *Proc. I.R.E.*, **33**, 15–20 (1945).

327. van Slooten, J., "The Stability of a Triode Oscillator with Grid-Condenser and Leak," *Wireless Eng.*, **16**, 16–19 (1939).

328. van Slooten, J., "Stability and Instability in Triode Oscillators," *Philips Tech. Rev.*, **7**, 40–45 and 171–177 (1942).

329. Vaughan, W. C., "Phase Shift Oscillator," *Wireless Eng.*, **26,** 391–399 (1949).
330. Vazsonyi, A., "A Generalization of Nyquist's Stability Criteria," *J. Appl. Phys.*, **20,** 863–867 (1949).
331. Vecchiacchi, F., "Oscillations in the Circuit of a Strongly Damped Triode," *Proc. I.R.E.*, **19,** 856–872 (1931).
332. Verman, L. C., "Negative Circuit Constants," *Proc. I.R.E.*, **19,** 676–681 (1931).
333. von Ardenne, M., "Distortion of Saw-Tooth Wave Forms," *Electronics*, **10,** 36–38 (November 1937).
334. von Hippel, A., R. G. Breckenridge, R. G. Chesley, and L. Tiza, *Ind. and Eng. Chem.*, **38,** 1097 (1946).
335. Wallace, R. L., and W. J. Pietenpol, "Some Properties and Applications of *n-p-n* Transistors," *Proc. I.R.E.*, **39,** 753–767 (1951).
336. Watanabe, Y., "The Piezoelectric Resonator in High-Frequency Oscillation Circuits," *Proc. I.R.E.*, **18,** 695–717 and 862–893 (1930).
337. Webb, H. W., and G. E. Becker, "Theory of the Multivibrator," *J. Appl. Phys.*, **15,** 825–834 (1944).
338. Whale, H. A., "Optimum Conditions for an R-C Oscillator," *Electronics*, **21,** 178 (February 1948).
339. Wheeler, H. A., "Formulas for the Skin Effect," *Proc. I.R.E.*, **30,** 412–424 (1942).
340. Wheeler, L. P., "Analysis of a Piezoelectric Oscillator Circuit," *Proc. I.R.E.*, **19,** 627 (1931).
341. Wheeler, M. S., "Frequency Contours for Microwave Oscillator with Resonant Load," *Proc. I.R.E.*, **37,** 1332–1336 (1949).
342. Whinnery, J. R., "Skin Effect Charts and Formulas," *Electronics*, **15,** 44–48 (Feb. 1942).
343. Williams, E., "A Valve Oscillator Theorem," *Wireless Eng.*, **20,** 489–491 (1943).
344. Williams, S. R., *Magnetic Phenomena*, McGraw-Hill, New York (1931).
345. Willoner, G., and F. Tihelka, "A Phase-Shift Oscillator with Wide-Range Tuning," *Proc. I.R.E.*, **36,** 1096–1100 (1948).
346. Wilson, I. G., C. W. Schramm, and J. P. Kinzer, "High-Q Resonant Cavities for Microwave Testing," *Bell System Tech. J.*, **25,** 408–434 (1946).
347. Wing, A. H., "On the Theory of Tubes with Two Control Grids," *Proc. I.R.E.*, **29,** 121–136 (1941).
348. Winlund, E. S., "Electronic Heating in the Furniture Industry," *Electronics*, **19,** 108–113 (May 1946).
349. Woodyard, J. R., "Application of the Auto-Synchronized Oscillator to Frequency Demodulation," *Proc. I.R.E.*, **25,** 610–619 (1937).
350. Wright, J. W., "The Piezoelectric Crystal Oscillator," *Proc. I.R.E.*, **17,** 127 (1929).
351. Young, C. H., "A Precise Decade Oscillator," *Bell Lab. Record*, **28,** 487–489 (1950).
352. Young, J. D., and H. M. Beck, "Design Equations for Reactance Tube Circuits," *Proc. I.R.E.*, **37,** 1078–1082 (1949).

NAME INDEX

SUBJECT INDEX